GEORGE ELIOT
Collected Poems (Pbk £9.95 $19.95, Hbk £18.95 $35)
Edited with an introduction by Lucien Jenkins

George Eliot's poetry has been unjustly neglecte
writing evocatively of rural childhood, as in the s
the issues of nationalism and racial prejudice in he
George Eliot is a wonderful and surprising poet. Thi
and makes many of her poems available for the first

RAINER MARIA RILKE
The Sonnets to Orpheus (Pbk £5.99 Not USA)
Translated by Leslie Norris and Alan Keele

Rilke's sonnet sequence, among the greatest works of modern literature, explores the
meaning of death and the value of art.
Leslie Norris has published many collections of poetry and short stories. Born in Wales,
he is Professor of Creative Writing at Brigham Young University.
Alan Keele is Professor of German Language and Literature at Brigham Young University.

GÜNTER EICH
Pigeons and Moles: Selected Writings (Pbk £7.99 Not USA)
Translated by Michael Hamburger

Pigeons and Moles introduces a sceptical, witty and anarchic poet to British readers, with
the first substantial selection from Eich's bitter and graceful poems, his acclaimed radio
plays and the controversial late prose poems.
He was the winner of the European Literature Prize for translation 1990.

WONG PHUI NAM
Ways of Exile (Pbk £5.99 $11.95)

Until now, this collection of poetic accomplishment has been limited to academic circles.
Out of the deepest resources of his heart and life, Mr Wong has forged an identity in the
interaction of cultures and ethnicity. This collection traces the development of the poet
from student days to early maturity in lyrical litany, honouring the Malaysian soul as
well as the geographical and spiritual ground of his country. We have here an important
Malaysian collection being added to World Literatures in English.

SHIRLEY GEOK-LIN LIM
Monsoon History (Pbk £6.99 $11.99)

Poems selected from *Modern Secrets* and *No Man's Grove* with the complete *Crossing
the Peninsula* winner of the Commonwealth Poetry Prize 1980.
Shirley Geok-lin Lim brings a uniqueness to her poetry which neither past nor
contemporary, Eastern nor Western writers can claim.
Professor Lim has also a legitimate claim within the Chinese-American canon. Like
Maxine Hong Kingston and Amy Tan, she represents an important voice in breaking the
long silence of an ethnic group, in articulating concerns of "place" and "gender".

Direct Orders U.K. post-free Fax: 44-171-404 4398

Editor: Christopher R. Johnson

Individual Contributors:

Kenneth Grant	© 1995
Colin Wilson	© 1995
George Hay	© 1995
Gerald Suster	© 1995
James Barter	© 1995
Kit Leee	© 1995
Ron Adams	© 1995
Ann Rivers	© 1995
Gareth Medway	© 1995
Sharon Beaumont	© 1995
Gavin Semple	© 1995
Christopher Johnson	© 1995
Paul Rosher (illustrations)	© 1995

Cover Painting © Steffi Grant

Published by
SKOOB BOOKS PUBLISHING LTD
11a - 17 Sicilian Avenue
Southampton Row
Holborn
London WC1A 2QH
England.

ISBN 1 871438 46 2

Distributors:

UK
Gazelle Book Services Ltd.
Falcon House
Queen Square
Lancaster LA1 1RN
Tel: 0524 68765
Fax: 0254 63232

USA
Atrium Publishers Group,
11270 Clayton Creek Road
P O Box 108
Lower Lake
CA 95457
Tel: (0101) 707 995 3906
Fax: (0101) 707 995 1814

SKOOB *ESOTERICA* ANTHOLOGY

CONTENTS

Skoob *Esoterica* Anthology is a forum for a diversity of viewpoints. The inclusion of contributions or reviews must not be taken to imply endorsement by the Editor or by Skoob Books Publishing Limited.

Black and White Illustrations by: Paul Rosher, Gridnac, Dunvegan, Isle of Skye, IV55 8GU.
Publisher: Ike Ong
Editor: Christopher R. Johnson

Ours sincere thanks to all our contributors, and to C.Y. Loh, Pearly Kok, James Barter, Mark Lovell, Gerald Suster, Gavin Semple.

PREFACE
by
Christopher R. Johnson
Editor

Skoob Occult Review is no more. Like many magical things it has not so much died, as undergone a transformation. It was conceived in less pressurised times, and was originally a 'labour of love' both for its generous contributors, and its editors. It attracted excellent contributors, and its successor publication continues to do so.

However, we are geared to publish books rather than magazines, and our contributors really deserve the permanence and attractiveness of being presented in book form, and certainly never more should they endure the fragmentation serialization brings!

So here is the first *Skoob Esoterica Anthology*. A book to keep and return to, rather than an A4 to get floppy and dog-eared.

The Kenneth Grant novella we kick off with alone runs to book length. It enshrines for those who can 'read between the lines' of 'fiction', much deep magical philosophy and first hand experience. It bears re-reading; after several times, I'm still finding new realizations!

More Kenneth Grant novellas will follow. Dion Fortune achieved a similar feat of living transmission of magical lore and life in her own novels. Lovecraft was also (in his case, with a certain reluctance for most of his life) recording perceptual truths that were indeed 'stranger than fiction'. For fiction is sometimes the most vivid, organic, suggestive, multi-layered way of embodying, communicating, and transmitting, sometimes almost inexhaustibly, the most subtle vital and seminal truths.

Possibilities, aspirations, ideals; the refinement and expansion of consciousness, such things are often involved, as will precipitate effects into the future. Sometimes, more darkly, predictive 'fictions' extrapolate from current circumstances adverse conditions in the near future which can scarcely be prevented, since the very possibility of accurate forecast (albeit the accuracy is comparatively rare) implies that a dreadful momentum is already in train.

However, there are other circumstances where rigorous argument is the best (most efficient) revealer of truth. An example would be where one wishes to anatomise the growth, development, and likely outcome of a pre-existing situation. Extrication from the errors which led to it is often what is hoped for. 'Conquest' has produced a carefully thought-through Essay contrasting Thelema's conceptual sanity with the 'black magical' subhuman bludgeoning of opinion rife amongst its far from life affirming media detractors; why and how these 'muddy mantras' arose, and what to do about the mentality which continues to spawn them. This Essay too, runs, with all its refinements of exposition, to the length of a short book. This, too, bears pondering more than once.

Our other contributors, in this rather Thelemic issue, demonstrate that we are not solely preoccupied with the ostensibly Thelemic. 'Green Grow the Rushes, Ho!' is something else!

But even when a particular orientation is represented (such as in this case Thelema!) there is no 'party line'. Distinguished authors Colin Wilson and Gerald Suster could hardly be said to agree about the import of Kenneth Grant's *Hecate's Fountain*!

The Book Reviews, I hope, will continue to provoke debate about the *ideas* and issues raised in the books selected, rather than merely being a brief thumbs up or thumbs down. This too reflects use of the book form rather than the magazine form; hopefully it is possible to be topical without being ephemeral. There will be no more subscriptions: the Anthology will be available from bookshops in the UK and USA and Australasia. In case of difficulty, though, we can supply it direct on the same postal and money terms as are found in advertisements for our other publications. I hope to bring out the Anthologies about twice a year. I thank our loyal Occult Review readers, quite a few of whom have kindly written to me during our period of silence; for helping to catalyse this new level of presentation by their enthusiasm, and I welcome new readers, as 'the adventure continues'.

Since so many people write to me about our publication plans, here is the news: Frank Letchford has taken back his *Magician of Southwark* to make some changes, so it no longer figures on our list. I'll forward any correspondence to Frank, as I do with letters sent to our published authors.

I've also been asked about an anthology of *Yeats' Esoteric Writings*. This too is now off the menu: We have got wind of an EEC directive which appears to change the copyright period after an author's death: this could involve expensive permissions we hadn't bargained for. However, *The Golden Dawn Anthology* is still in preparation, edited by John Bonner, whose commendably clear *Qabalah* is at the time of writing due shortly. From Kenneth Grant, I am currently editing *Beyond the Mauve Zone*, the next Trilogy volume - a voyage of discovery indeed! This new work should appear in the USA in the Spring of 1995, together with the reprinted *Outside the Circles of Time*. We will then have all of the Trilogy volumes he has written to date, in print. Gerald Suster's lucid investigation of Hitler's occult roots and ambitions, *Hitler: Black Magician* is currently in a late stage of preparation. Other publications appear in advertisements.

I welcome quality submissions for the Anthology; so get in touch if you feel you have something you'd like to offer, since we are planning future issues ahead. Articles on the esoteric side of Buddhism, Christianity, Islam, and Jewish mysticism, to name but a few, are things I would be happy to consider. And strong magical artwork, too.

To all of you; enjoy!

Late Extra. *Skoob Occult Review*, (now superseded by *Skoob Esoterica Anthologies*) was so named out of respect for the pioneers who started off *The Occult Review* in 1905, led by Ralph Shirley. Recently, with our usual serendipity, we got hold of a run of the very first volumes of *The Occult Review*, with their ornate Edwardian gold stamping. This happened just in time for us to reproduce for the first issue of all, from 1905, as a souvenir appendix to this first issue of *Skoob Esoterica Anthology*. So you'll be able to judge for yourselves how radically the style of presentation, and the nature and direction of research has changed after just ninety years, in the footsteps of those pioneers who helped to keep the flame of the Metaphysical Sciences burning, at a time when the Physical Sciences, as then commonly presented and understood, appeared to be at their most arrogant and blindly materialistic. But even in 1905, a new and sceptical generation of scientists were groping their way towards what then would have seemed some very Alice-in Wonderland ideas. Einstein's Relativity (Special Relativity, same year, 1905; General Relativity, 1916): Heisenberg's Uncertainty Principle: Shrödinger's enigmatically postulated Cat! All unseen, the Universe had wrested back its cloak of majesty and mystery from 'nothing-but-ists', and the way was already opening again for the restoration of a fruitful dialogue between the Physical, and the Metaphysical, Sciences.

AND THE WORD WAS OCCULT
Ron Adams

What does the word 'occult' suggest to you? If you are one of the newspaper reading, video- and television-latchkey general public, then it would conjure up visions of the Devil and all his works...Dark and dastardly goings-on in subterranean rooms, black robes and swirling incense smoke rising from an intricate burner at the periphery of a pentangled magic circle drawn on a stone floor, black pins transfixing a waxen image of an intended victim, and an aged crone, in a dark cave, muttering incantations over a bubbling cauldron, etc.

Try this experiment; find a quiet room with a comfortable chair and relax with your eyes closed. Imagine the word 'occult' drawn on a blackboard by an unseen hand and let your unconscious mind cast up its images. Prominent among the images will be the ones suggested above, with lots of other media-induced symbol association thrown in for good measure. Isn't it amazing how easily certain words or phrases can become triggers or anchors for contrived scenarios or atmosphere created by inaccurate information input?

The *Chamber's English Dictionary* definition of the word 'occult' is: Hidden; of a line, faint, or dotted, or to be rubbed out later (rare): secret, esoteric: unknown: not discovered without test or experiment (obs.): beyond the range of sense: transcending the bounds of natural knowledge: mysterious: magical: supernatural. Occultism the study of things hidden or mysterious - theosophy, etc.; Occult Sciences alchemy, astrology, magic, palmistry, etc. [L. occultus, p.a.p. of occulere, to hide - ob -, over, and the root of celare, to hide.]

Therefore by definition everything beyond the realms of conventional science is occult. Are we to assume, using the popular media distorted and superstition ridden definition of the word occult, that the acupuncturist's needles have been forged in hell's fire, or that his hand is guided by Lucifer? Does the astrologer draw his charts with a demon sitting on his shoulder? Did Madam Blavatsky consort with devils when she founded the Theosophical Society? Hardly, since the word theosophy comes from the Greek theosophus which means wise in things of God.

How many times have we seen the following headlines in the national press; "Mass murderer dabbled in the occult" or "Occult material found at home of rapist". What do they mean by "dabbled in the occult"? Did the deranged criminal have a secret room in his cellar where a pentagram was drawn on the floor and guttering black candles lit the whole depraved scene? Probably not, the evidence of 'occult dabbling' was likely to have been nothing more sinister than a ouija board and a few posters of buddhist mandalas. True, the ouija board can be dangerous in the hands of unstable people, but spiritualists have been using them for many years without any adverse effects. Thus, for the sake of sensationalism, and increased media 'appeal' and newspaper circulation the word 'occult' is once again employed to titillate the imagination of the reader. Unfortunately the public at large, because of such media conditioning, has lumped together such diverse subjects as witchcraft, satanism, fortune telling, under a blanket condemnation. They would no doubt be surprised to discover that their proponents often radically disagreed with one another, both methodologically and ethically.

And so it goes on; ignorance and superstition encouraged by the media have once again distorted a word, taken it over and made it synonymous with dark and swirling evil forces from our atavistic memories. This is linguistic imperialism!

But then many people, having a smattering of impressions gleaned from the books of Dennis Wheatley, have posed as occultists or 'masters of the occult'. These people have promoted misconceptions by wearing the 'required' uniform of black clothing, adorning themselves with cheap and grotesque silver jewellery and adopting a pseudo-mysterious ambience that is designed to intimidate the more superstitious elements among our easily-led society.

Logically by their shared 'obscurity' witchcraft, satanism, and clairvoyant practices are equally by dictionary definition part of the whole 'occult' spectrum. But then so is everything that is hidden or secret, without any ethical connotation. The best parallel that I can draw is one involving that part of the vibratory universe that covers the spectrum of sound. Exposure to the low frequencies (i.e. below 10 Hertz) can damage the central nervous system. However, at the higher frequencies we have the music of Mozart that is beneficial to the cardiovascular system. Another fact that one should be aware of is that yesterday's magic is today's science and part of our understanding of the working of the human brain and mind and the vast uncharted territories within ourselves.

In conclusion I would like to say; let us re-evaluate our comprehension of that oft misused word 'occult'. Let us realise that it is a 'blanket' term, and not a title for a narrow field of human depravity and atavistic fears and superstitious paranoia. By merely meaning 'hidden', it manages to include both the depths, and in *practice* more often the *heights* of human possibility.

"GREEN GROW THE RUSHES-HO"
Ann Rivers

The Rider-Waite Lovers card in the Tarot carries a suggestion of the Garden of Eden, not without its elemental serpent, which I have taken to represent the possessiveness inherent in the game of love. The illumination suggests a return to or recovery of lost innocence or earthly paradise. But the "rival" appearing in the Marseille cards points to a related activity which strengthens the connection between the child of six and the six of The Lovers. I have in mind reeling off verses of counting songs, in this instance the "three, three the rivals" stanza in the foremost of them, "Green Grow the Rushes-Ho". Between counting songs, games and dances such as "The Farmer in the Dell" (where the cheese like The Fool stands alone), "Green Grow the Rushes", and the Tarot there exists a mutuality bordering on cross-pollination. This bonding strengthens their appeal to young children. That six-year-olds, beginning school, should play musical and dancing games confirms the Tarot teacher, The Hierophant, in his opinion that art training should be encouraged at five.

Our counting obsession - technically speaking, a compulsion - takes attractive shape in the form of riddling songs and games like "This Is the House that Jack Built" and reaches its apogee in sophisticated songs like "The Twelve Days of Christmas". The obsessive element informs less elementary verse forms such as the villanelle, canzone, sestina, etc. in poetry. Like rhyme, a refrain makes them easier to memorize or remember. Normally we mouth these mnemonics without thinking, so much so one is brought up short in the event we do stop to analyze them. Some "Green Grow the Rushes" stanzas are self-explanatory. One such, "Twelve for the twelve Apostles" correlates to Arcanum 12, The Hanged Man. Its ruler Neptune governs the Piscean Age of Christ, our current World Age, and not a few of His Apostles made their quietus, if not at the hangman's hand, certainly in the Hanged Man's martyrdom. Not to be overlooked, grim as the hangman's shadow is Judas Iscariot, the 12th Disciple, who hanged himself.

Other verses are abstruse and arcane. Their occulted meaning is less susceptible to interpretation, or would be without the relevant Tarot key. What child of six, for example, could be expected to guess the identity of "Eleven for the eleven that went up to heaven"? The twelve Disciples minus Judas the suicide, who presumably could not enter heaven? Or could this stanza not commemorate an earlier event, also qualifying as an ascent? Many ancient heroes were catasterized - that is, translated to the stars - and a constellation of eleven such is well within the realm of the possible. I would submit as a candidate for the "Eleven for the eleven that went up to heaven" the stars in Libra, the constellation behind the Justice card, Arcanum 11. For it so happens that Libra, beyond its four principal stars also supports a spherical star cluster of - perhaps like the Pleiades - seven visible or invisible stars. "Ten for the Ten Commandments" is obvious as the "12s". But "Nine for the nine bright shiners" calls for the nine of the order of angels to explain it. I take

Hamlet's Mill to be authoritative in this matter, as it identifies the nine bright shiners as the nine planets - including the luminaries of the sun and the moon - recognized by astrology. The "brightness" of the spheres excludes the dark planet Pluto. The sum of nine is reflected in Arcanum nine, as is their light, in the lamp extended in The Hermit's hand. Pluto's absence from the catalogue is consistent with the ancient taboo on him. His name Hades the ancients avoided pronouncing, turning their heads aside at the mere mention of this planet-god.

"Eight for the April rainers" also darkens the clear sky needed for piecing out the words of the song. Clouds gathering at or about that hour, on the fateful day of the Crucifixion would justify the eight, only one short of the ninth hour, when Jesus yielded up the ghost.

The lyrics of the popular song "April Showers" are self-explanatory as "Into each life some rain must fall". Eliot extrapolated, citing April as "the cruellest month". This too is corroborated by the Passion, as Passion Week and the Crucifixion fall often as not in April, both of them being sufficient cause for the heavens to weep openly. In the matter of tears, April can mark the onset of hay fever which, as the pollen count rises brings on tears together with seizures of sneezing.

As can be seen, "Green Grow the Rushes" is largely a Christian ditty, but constructed as were the Christian churches themselves on a pagan base. The "rainers" of this verse may, consequently, be taken as an allusion to the Hyades, a star cluster in the Constellation Taurus. Their exact number is open to debate, but by all Classical standards their heliacal rising does precede rainy weather. Furthermore Taurus, the parent constellation, does rise with the sun in April.

The 8th verse has other pagan connections beside. It cannot escape association with the 8th house of the zodiac. From this dark house the dark inference would follow. The night of Pluto-Baal, the festival of Beltane falls on the last day of April, the 30th, May Eve, or Walpurgisnacht.

The more familiar star cluster in Taurus may be responsible for "Seven for the seven stars in the sky". In which case the stellar object in question would be the seven "sisters" of the Hyades, the seven visible Pleiades. But not necessarily, as there are seven stars as well in the Wain (the Great Bear). These circumpolar stars are remarkable for their steadfastness, so much so mariners swear by them as the compass of the night. No song concerning itself with the heavens - and despite its "earthing" in the rushes "Green Grow the Rushes" is about the heavenly firmament - would be likely to ignore them.

"Six for the six proud walkers" derives from geomantic land-survey. It is a residual account of how the lines of the earth were systematically paced off by walking over the land, in order to bring all the earth's pathways into alignment with the geography of the sky, uranography. (For this detail about sacred geometry I am indebted to "The Ley Hunter" Magazine, which claims they were six in number. Given the nature of their task they could justifiably call themselves proud.)

"Five for the cymbals at your gate" sustains the note sounded about giving music lessons to the five-year-old. All children, the younger the better, show a decided preference for percussive sound. If your ears can take it, give them triangles and blocks, cymbals and drums if you wish them, like the lark to approach near heaven's gate. The Psalms, or Psalter, songbook of the Bible, continually call for praising God with music, as infants innately sense. As soon as they are sufficiently coordinated they begin rhythmically to clap. Try "pat-a-cake" soon as you can.

"Four for the Gospel-makers" has a special relevance to the Tarot. The four Evangelists appear twice among the Major "Secrets", concealed behind their respective avatars in the Wheel of Fortune and The World. With "Three, three the rivals" we return to our point of departure, the three-in-six that is also the Empress-Venus informing The Lovers card. Interference from a third party on the loving couple of the Lovers card may commemorate the role of the mother-in-law. The other unwanted third party might be the Mother of the Gods, playing mother-in-law to us and them. Cybele, in a divinized heaven is called Rhea, the moon of Saturn. In the heaven of the Lovers the Cupid of the Marseille card is transformed into the Rider-Waite angel. By this transition high vocation or a divine calling may be implied, as the potential threat to union. Vocation, being a taskmistress, can be as threatening as "the other woman".

"Two, two the lily-white boys" conjures up visions of acolytes such as the Hierophants, postulants, modern-day Templars (De Molays), and suchlike candidates for initiation. But the factor of two in combination with the rushes growing in the title leads to surmise over the origin and purpose of counting songs in general and "Green Grow the Rushes" in particular.

There is a song about rushes, containing a verse describing two pure youths clad in green; rush-colour. Rushes in most children's minds will ineluctably be associated with Moses. The story of his dramatic discovery, by Pharaoh's daughter, in the bulrushes is as intended unforgettable. How this Sunday-school lesson was managed by his ambitious mother, a Levite, of the priestly tribe or caste, is not at issue here. But the contradiction between the account in Exodus and the song, the question raised of not one but two foundlings most decidedly is. Supposing their parent was equally ambitious for his brother Aaron, destined to become High Priest or Israelite Hierophant, is not helpful. But attention to detail, to the concealing growth of rushes in the River Nile, in Egypt is. For in that ancient land the child Horus, the reed-born was an object of religious adoration. Thus by twinning the Judaic and idolatrous elements the song lyrics cleverly mask their pagan content. Hence, as often happens in tradition, at the same time it succeeds in preserving it, under the guise of religious instruction of the young.

Like the Tarot, the song is most revealing where attempting to conceal. The non-dit in this case is that Moses was a magician of the first water. His branch or brand of magic survives today in the form of voodoo, which traversed Africa, wending its way across Egypt to Dahomey and thence to the Caribbean. Rushes, with their power to bind, are in the song spellbinding. They throw their pale rush-light over Moses as precursor to the Three Wise Men, all of them candidates for initiation, like the lily-white boys, in the Hermetic tradition taught in ancient Egypt.

"Ten for the Ten Commandments" is a straightforward biblical reference to Mosaic Law. The verse under consideration is the second reference to the Hebrew prophet. Twice the song invokes his magic, probably as a talisman, to call down all the stars of heaven to protect the singer, as a rule a child, atropaically.

Further to its talismanic properties is the suggestion of a counting song as a magic square. Magic squares are composed of numbers and worn as talismans, as was the breastplate of Aaron, studded albeit with jewels and not with numbers. Aaron stays in the picture when we consider, from the Tarot perspective, the magic wand. The rod of Moses, which could raise water from a stone or wiggle like a snake, eventually came into Aaron's possession. As Aaron's Rod it is a biblical example of that Hermetic twig of hazelwood we know as the magic wand, and which the Tarot claims for its suit of Wands.

The transition from songs to games is a natural one, especially in childhood. Their star-like appearance enlists jacks among the games of magical intent, descended from or aiming at the stars. The rules are elementary: From onesies and twosies the girl - for it is a girl's game - advances to 'round the world and shoot the moon', clear indications whither this counting game is tending. An apprentice might safely learn coordination from it, more so than the sorceror's broomstick (with or without its hidden allusion to the witch, the wand and the caduceus).

Rounds, or canons are a natural extension of counting songs, being as obsessive and as easily memorized. In conjunction with riddles and riddling songs, puzzles too may come into play at this stage. Jigsaw puzzles, to incalculate patience and jacks, to foster dexterity, are good games for a rainy day. Indoor games stress quiet, or as Browning spells it, Quiet. That stillness is a prerequisite for casting spells is attested to by the cobwebs festooning the alchemist's cell, laboratory or study.

Games in the context of The lovers card imply the oldest: loveplay, commonly alluded to in silence. That games come to the fore under the aegis of the Lovers is no accident. For the card is the Gemini correlate in the pack, and Geminians are the eternal children of the zodiac, likely as not to be the inventors of their own games, which, as in the case of love, they may play at all their lives.

Games intended to fix the child's ability to count find a natural outlet in dancing. For every dancer learning the two-step or the combinations of ballet, must learn to count. Group dances teach us to "mark time". It is a lesson to stand us in good stead, the lovers assure us, when it comes to partnering. I have heard the Morris Dancing of the witches in Warwickshire praised for its authenticity, but there is inferior magic in the Maypole and related circular dances too. In square dances "stars" are formed as ladies join hands in the centre of the "magic" square. In my prohibitive youth the taboo, not on dancing but on calling what we did dancing was honoured by referring to dances as "folk games" and dancing as "folk gaming". These quaint expressions shield the origins of the dance in folk magic.

In circular dances such as "The Farmer in the Dell" numbers grow by accretion, then dwindle as the spell is unbound. "The cheese stands alone" alludes to zero, a late concept in ciphering. It sets it apart like The Fool card, likewise so numbered, from the rest of the pack. Some exegetes reserve comment on the Zero-Fool till last. One is the number on its own in "Green Grow the Rushes". "One is one and all alone" cannot be misinterpreted as meaning anything but the Almighty. Or can it? where one considers the Tarot number one card, The Magus.

TENTACLES ACROSS TIME
by
Colin Wilson

This bewildering and fascinating book (*Hecate's Fountain*) makes me certain of something I had suspected for a long time: that Kenneth Grant is one of the strangest and most interesting characters alive today.

I first became aware of Grant's name when, together with John Symonds, he edited *The Confessions of Aleister Crowley* (1969). Apparently Grant had met Crowley in 1944, when Grant was twenty, and the Great Beast was sixty-nine and had only three years to live. (He hastened his own end by taking enough heroin per day to kill the average man.) After Crowley's death, Grant regarded himself as his spiritual heir and leader of the magical organisation called the OTO (*Ordo Templi Orientis*), which practised a form of sexual magic based on tantra.

It was not until 1972 that Grant launched himself into print with a book called *The Magical Revival* - by which time, the Beatles and various other pop stars had started a Crowley revival. Grant's book fascinated me because of its extraordinary thesis that the writer of 'weird tales', H P Lovecraft, had not simply invented his outlandish Cthulhu mythology, but had dredged it up from the depths of his own unconscious mind, which in turn had picked it up from the racial unconscious. I was inclined to suspect that Grant had simply invented his idea as a gimmick to appeal to a new audience of young Crowley and Lovecraft enthusiasts. But the book impressed me with its extraordinary knowledge of the history of magic. In the 1890s, W B Yeats had taken magic seriously, and had been a member of an organisation called the Golden Dawn; many other serious writers and thinkers of that period shared his attitude, including AE and Arthur Machen. For me, reading Grant created a wave of nostalgia for that 'tragic generation' of the *fin de siècle*, and even for Grant's dubious master, the Great Beast (who was also a member of the Golden Dawn).

In his next two books, *Aleister Crowley and the Hidden God* and *Cults of the Shadow*, it became clear that Grant was very serious indeed about his Lovecraft theory; he expounded it with a conviction that suggested that he had some quite extra-literary reason for believing it. By now I was hooked, and read them as eagerly as I had read Yeats's *Per Amica Silentia Lunae* and *Ideas of Good and Evil* - although, I must admit, without believing more than one word in ten.

Then, in the 1980s, Grant seemed to disappear. His last book, *Outside the Circles of Time* (1980) was as absorbing as ever - in fact, more so, since Grant seemed to be coming more skilful in mixing his potent cocktail of occultism, myth and Lovecraftian legend until it was positively lethal. But when I enquired at a bookshop about its announced sequel, *Hecate's Fountain*, I was told that it had never appeared - and that, moreover, the rest of Grant's books were now out of print.

Fortunately, that situation was remedied in the late 1980s when Grant found himself another publisher, Skoob Books, which began reprinting his early works (and a new work, the fascinating *Remembering Aleister Crowley.*) And now, at last, *Hecate's Fountain* has appeared.

Unlike some of Grant's earlier work, which could be read for its historical expositions of hermeticism, this one is so strange that it is bound to provoke extremely strong reactions in readers. It begins by describing an incident that, says Grant, actually occurred at one of the meetings of his own New Isis Lodge. The group was performing a magical ritual that revolved around a fragment of mummy casing that Grant had acquired via the Golden Dawn. Against the mummy casing there was a mirror in which the 'skryer' is supposed to see things as in a fortune teller's crystal ball. But on this occasion, all nine people present saw the same thing in the mirror, as if watching a television. It showed a naked woman who changed colour like a chameleon as a 'fungoidal tentacle' explored her body and produced 'multiple orgasms'. Later the lid of a box containing a small Egyptian manikin was accidentally knocked open, and the room was suddenly full of a wind that turned into a hurricane. The 'priestess' succeeded in forcing back the lid, whereupon the room became perfectly still...

There are many similar stories in *Hecate's Fountain*. And the Lovecraftian 'fungoidal tentacle' suggests an important unifying factor. What Grant is claiming is that the actual practice of magical ritual has made him aware of the reality of certain entities that exist outside space and time - in what he calls 'the mauve zone' - and which Lovecraft mistakenly believed he had conjured up out of his imagination. In *Hecate's Fountain*, Grant suddenly makes it clear why he has always been so insistent about their objective reality.

Many readers will dismiss all this as pure invention. Others will be impressed by Grant's consistency, and by the factual, almost dry tone in which he describes these experiences as if striving for precision.

My own attitude is certainly far less sceptical than it was when I reviewed *The Magical Revival* twenty years ago. During that time, my investigation of poltergeists convinced me that these are not manifestations of the unconscious minds of disturbed children, but genuine entities - spirits if you like - that take energy from emotionally upset human beings. The Rev Montague Summers once remarked critically that the 'spiritualism' of the nineteenth century was merely a revival of mediaeval witchcraft; oddly enough, he was quite correct. Magic (or 'magick', as the Beast preferred to spell it) works (or sometimes works) because some rather strange entities can be invoked if people really make the effort. (Thousands of idle partygoers have discovered this by sitting in a group round a smooth tabletop with their index fingers resting lightly on an upturned glass, which proceeds to shoot around like a demented bumble bee.) I myself am not sufficiently interested to pay much attention to spiritualism of magic - I prefer to devote my spare time to philosophy. But I have no doubt whatever that magic can work.

Kenneth Grant is now in a rather curious position. He is obsessively secretive about his personal life, refusing to release biographical details or even a photograph. An extremely courteous man, he apparently prefers to live the life of a scholar and a recluse. (I speak from information imparted by a mutual friend, for I have never met him or corresponded with him.) Perhaps he recalls how tabloid publicity almost destroyed Crowley. His earlier books gained him only a cult audience. But I suspect that the release of *Hecate's Fountain*, and the reissue of his earlier books, is going to bring him an increasingly wide - and voraciously curious - audience. Sooner or later, considering the unique and remarkable quality of his work, he was bound to become a 'public figure'. I shall watch with sardonic curiosity to see how that disinterested hermetic scholar copes with the problems of increased celebrity, and the loss of privacy it involves. For his own sake, I hope he does better than his master.

————

SKOOB *ESOTERICA* ANTHOLOGY: ADVERTISING RATES

MAXIMUM DIMENSIONS

Full Page; 18cm (height) X 12cm (width).

Half Page; 8.5cm (height) X 12cm (width)

One Third Page; 6cm (height) X 12cm (width)

One Quarter Page; 8.5cm (height) X 5.5cm (width)

We have an A5 (148mm x 210mm) two-column format. If you wish to place advertising which does not fit the maximum dimension examples we have given, due to the shape of your advertisment, please ring us for a quote. Clearly, if your advertisment will occupy a space a little under the maximum dimensions, then there is no problem.

PRICES

Full Page; £100
Except: front inside cover; £150, back inside cover; £120
Half Page; £60
Third Page; £45
Quarter Page; £30

PAYMENT

Payable to Skoob Books Publishing Ltd.

Sterling cheque, sterling International Money Order, or the following credit cards: Visa, Mastercard (Including Access), and American Express.

FAX NUMBER

071 - 404 4398

Christopher R. Johnson, editor

SKOOB BOOKS PUBLISHING

OUTER GATEWAYS   *Kenneth Grant*

A further exploration of *The Book of the Law*, *Outer Gateways* examines the influence of the 'alien' upon the 'human', and the attainment of undivided consciousness. The book culminates in a 'received text' of great beauty and authority, enhanced by a fascinating and lucid commentary.
ISBN 1 871438 12 8 Hbk £24.99 $39.95

Also from Kenneth Grant

REMEMBERING ALEISTER CROWLEY

Previously unpublished Crowley letters, written during Grant's 'discipleship', from world war two to Crowley's last years at Netherwood. An illuminating personal memoir, fascinating illustrations, large format.
1 871438 22 5 80pp (hbk) £24.99 $49.95

CULTS OF THE SHADOW

Reissue of the third volume in the trilogies with corrections. Explores techniques and traditions of the left hand path.
1 871438 67 5 hbk £18.99 $34.95

ALEISTER CROWLEY AND THE HIDDEN GOD

Reissue of the second volume of the trilogies. Relates Crowley's system of sexual magic to the tantric Rites of Kali and formulates a method of dream control for contacting non-human entities.
1 871438 36 5 hbk £18.99 $34.95

THE MAGICAL REVIVAL

New edition with corrections. Demonstrates that Thelema is as old as civilization. Points to the significance of Austin Osman Spare, H.P. Lovecraft and Dion Fortune in the transmission of the current associated with Crowley.
1 871438 37 3 272pp (hbk) £18.99 $34.95

HIDDEN LORE: THE CARFAX MONOGRAPHS
(With Steffi Grant)

Distillation of ancient and modern tributaries to the western occult tradition. Unexpected connections, with ten stunning telesmatic illustrations, nine by Steffi Grant, one by A.O. Spare. Constitutes a grimoire. A4 format, tipped-in plates.
1 871438 85 3 56pp (hbk, limited edn) £39 $75

NIGHTSIDE OF EDEN

Reveals the 'nightside' of the Jewish Qabalah's Tree of Life. Reissue of the fourth in the series, with corrections.
1 871438 72 1 hbk £19.99 $36.95

THE STELLAR LODE

by

Kenneth Grant

> *To the memory of*
> *Jacob Mendelssohn*
> *&*
> *The Beaumont Club*

1

The Curio Shop

A lustrous sun hung in the sky, creating out of the void a bright afternoon in early May. Two young women entered Louis Bruhm's curio shop in Chelsea. Ruth Chalmers was up from the country, and Flavia Keene had joined her for the pleasure of Spring shopping. A few days previously, Flavia had seen an admirer off to Nigeria - where he'd gone for professional reasons - and life had seemed suddenly empty. But Ruth made up for almost everything, and they had spent the first part of the day in pursuit of unnecessary odds and ends.

Having exhausted the possibilities of draping themselves in rare stuffs and costly fabrics, they had turned to the problem of adorning these with bangles, semi-precious stones and curious coins engraved with ancient profiles. Louis Bruhm's was Flavia's favourite resort when it came to matters like these; he had a 'nose' for choice baubles, and he mingled the ordinary with the extraordinary in such a manner that the resulting ornament was not merely fantastic or grotesque, eccentric or startling, but strangely magical in a sense which combined with impeccable taste the barbarisms of feminine fantasy.

As with her scents and stuffs, Flavia sought the most exquisite products, which, although they may not have possessed any character in themselves, were so grouped and arranged by her, and so cunningly blent, that the final result - the *impact* of the ensemble - struck a note of savagery and suavity vibrant with the hint of delicious mysteries. And these things were not manifested in the exotic and ostentatious fashion popular with many extravagant women but ambiguously suggested. Her perfumes were not entirely floral, nor entirely animal, they contained a metallic component which lent to the flowers a sombre saturnian quality, and to the animal essences a quality almost of moonlight.

Ruth Chalmers, slightly younger and rather less extreme than her dominant friend had nonetheless her own manner of choosing and wearing the things she finally purchased. Their jewelled fingers were now fluttering restlessly in the direction of the show-cases which formed a cunningly arranged labyrinth - geometrically precise - in Louis Bruhm's fabulous emporium. The absence of any human element but themselves enabled them to dispense with the veneer of polished calm which they usually assumed under the watchful eyes of the proprietor. They indulged in an

17

almost brutal plundering of the objects strewn haphazardly on the glittering surfaces of the large glass cases.

In a wedge of sunlight splashed across a corner of a cabinet heaped with ornaments which seemed to flash angrily at the rifling of their sanctuary, Ruth discovered a gleaming coin. The chink of its contact with other baubles disturbed by her, caused Flavia to turn in her friend's direction. As she did so she saw, shining in the dark alcove, a small sphere, like a skryer's crystal. The sun, striking the side of the cabinet which contained so many treasures, shot dazzling beams into the shadowy recess as Flavia approached it. Ruth dropped the coin as soon as her friend drew attention to the shining object, and they were both bending over it, utterly entranced, when Louis Bruhm himself appeared in the narrow doorway at the back of the shop.

'Ah ha! so you have spotted the prize of my collection, Miss Keene, Miss Chalmers; only such taste as you possess could have guided you so unerringly to such a rare treasure'.

Flavia turned, smiling blandly, oblivious of the unctuous flattery which Bruhm was lavishing upon them before naming the price, the astronomical price, which she knew he was bound to ask for so ravishing a treasure.

'Where did you find it?', she asked, casually.

'Ah ha!', he repeated; he always said 'ah ha!', like that, when skirting the province of uncertain and excessive charges; 'I neither know nor care'.

This evasion was purposeful, for, as Bruhm well knew, it always piqued and exasperated prospective buyers, but being such an old friend of Flavia's father he ran no risk of forfeiting this particular client. She waited in silence for his next remarks which would - she knew - apply themselves to his great delight in having the honour of a visit from Ruth and herself after so long a period of time. She had purchased several expensive items from him shortly before Christmas, with the sincere intention of making presents of them, but her perfect taste so unfailingly selected those very objects that pleased her the most, that, when the time came she could not bring herself to part with them. Her mother had had to scour the local shops in a last minute rush to get some costly but quite characterless bauble for Henrietta, Sylvia, Patricia and Betty.

But Louis Bruhm seemed strangely disinclined to release his usual flattering volleys. Ruth was looking at the sphere in a very absorbed manner, and it was the intent watchfulness with which Bruhm observed her friend's interest that caused Flavia to return her own gaze to the globe. There it nestled in its soft bed of violet satin, and it seemed to Flavia as if the rays of the sun set it smouldering in the deep cavern in which it appeared to be lying, like a nacreous shell caught suddenly by a powerful beam of sunlight as it clove the glaucous waters of a calm lake. Its almost conscious limpidity set against the dark impenetrable background seemed like the exudation of a dark flower just about to plash to the soft grass, shattering its fragile form and merging its glittering substance with the black earth.

Ruth felt a vague wave of irritation. The sphere was Flavia's prize; she had noticed it first; but Ruth suddenly wanted it above anything else she could imagine. The feeling was irrational and she suppressed it, and turned her attention to a selection of pendants, bracelets, antique rings and anklets which lay in heaped magnificence,

18

encircled by the serpentine chain from which depended the gold medallion she had recently admired.

Louis Bruhm seemed glad of the opportunity to chatter to Ruth in an inconsequential manner, and Flavia was equally glad because her attention had been once more ensnared by the bright globe. Having become accustomed to the gloom of the shop, as compared with the brilliance of the street, she was able to examine the object more closely. She saw that it was large and not perfectly round, being more inclined to the ovoid than the spherical. Its interior was opalescent, unlike that of a crystal which remains uniform in its limpid transparency, whereas when she had first set eyes on it, it had shone with pellucid lustre more pure than any she had noticed in ordinary crystals. Yet even as she watched, she sensed a disturbing movement, a subtle shifting of refractibility which seemed to occur outside the boundary of its bright surface. The alternations of light and shade suggested the tremulations of an invisible veil. She sensed the presence of an atmosphere, nothing more tangible, pervaded by uncanny movements, as if the faintest of breezes charged with particles of coloured light painted the merest suggestion of tone, now azure, now green, now downy as blown cloud, upon the globe's surface. It seemed to be enveloped from time to time in a luminous sheath, misty, vague, which had the effect of reducing and of magnifying by turns its molecular structure.

The sun now bathed it in its uncompromising brilliance, and the rays were shot back from the glazed cabinets ranged behind Flavia. Light penetrated the very essence of the sphere, so that one would have thought to see clear evidence of a vacuous and transparent heart; yet what lay revealed to her gaze was not a void, however scintillant, however serene, but the shadow of a dark object which itself was not visible, but which appeared to pulsate with steady rhythm. Something beat in time to her own pulse in that still and mysterious centre, and without realising what she was doing, she unfastened the catch of the cabinet and slipped both her hands inside it. Cupping them round its fragile form she gently eased the sphere out of its setting.

Louis Bruhm was beside her in an instant, wringing his hands in spasms of anxiety: 'Please! please be careful! it is so light, almost like a bauble, do not be deceived by its appearance of solidity, do not let it fall'.

Flavia flashed at him an angry glance as she held the precious object in her hands and scrutinized it closely. Ruth had come up beside her. Together they looked at it with unfeigned wonder; the Holy Graal itself could not have evoked such adoration.

Bruhm recovered his composure and stood rubbing his hands together in the manner peculiar to those who preside over curio shops.

'I see I was right', he beamed. 'Only this morning I placed it in the cabinet knowing that the Misses Keene and Chalmers would come in and find it, and - abracadabra! - am I not right? Say if I am not right!'

'But what is it?', murmured Ruth, 'it doesn't really look like a crystal - and', she gasped in astonishment, 'look! it's changing colour, it's changing shape...'

'What is this object?', asked Flavia, levelling a strangely abstracted gaze at Bruhm. He was silent for a moment, an almost imperceptible moment:

'It's a shewstone', he replied, and did not enlighten her further.

19

Flavia was instinctively aware that he was struggling against a sense of revulsion; it manifested in an expression he was unable to conceal:

'Please replace the stone', he said.

'But I want it', said Flavia, immediately.

'Please replace it', he repeated.

The words came from his lips like a command, imperious in its intensity. He turned his back and walked away. Flavia replaced the stone almost mechanically, lowered the lid and fastened it. Then she walked over to Bruhm, and there was fire in her eyes. He was smiling now, enigmatically.

'If this is play-acting', she said, 'then I've had enough. I wish to buy that stone; will you be so kind as to tell me its price'.

'Certainly, Miss Keene', he replied. He was still smiling, but she thought she detected a whitening of the lips, a suspicion which was confirmed when she saw his tongue appear to moisten them. An uneasy, furtive expression rippled over his features like a silent wave. He glanced quickly at the door from which he had emerged on hearing the chink of the chain which Ruth had disturbed. He bent his head close to Flavia's and whispered something in her ear. Not a tremor passed over her face; she drew out her cheque book and, resting it on a showcase made out the required amount.

'Will you have it sent, or..?'

'I'll take it with me; now.'

He seemed extraordinarily relieved, and yet, as he took the proffered cheque, Flavia noticed again a shadow of disquietude hover for an instant over his features before it was wafted away by the breeze of his smile.

'As you wish'.

He bowed deferentially, removed the stone from the cabinet - without, however, looking at it - and disappeared with it through a small door concealed by a green curtain to the left of the main entrance door.

Neither of the women spoke as they waited for Bruhm's return. Ruth, in the statuesque silence of her outward calm, entered an inner inferno of envy and fury, while Flavia, enveloped in the coolth of her perfumes, dreamed of a bodiless heart beating in a luminous void.

Louis Bruhm returned, extending in Flavia's direction a neat parcel: 'See! I have wrapped it for you myself so that no other should even so much as look upon so precious a ... relic'.

'Relic?', queried Flavia. Bruhm smiled deprecatingly: 'It is very old, of course', he said.

'It must be', she virtually spat at him, 'for that price!'

Her eyes were still blazing when she turned to Ruth, who was carefully gathering up her selection of ornaments.

'Forgive me, forgive me, Miss Chalmers', Bruhm exclaimed: 'Please let me help you; I must apologize, but the matter of the .. the stone... ', he looked in Flavia's direction and smiled, 'quite distracted my attention. Shall I have them sent, or...?'

'I shall take this now; please send the rest', said Ruth as she detached the medallion from the remaining articles.

'Permit me; pray permit me', began Bruhm, and he placed the chain about Ruth's neck so that the gold pendant hung with the heavy costliness of all rare things above the valley of her breasts. Flavia drew close to her, and Ruth felt the heat of her breath on her throat as her friend remarked: 'how lovely that is; surely it's the image of a cat'.

'But you are mistaken, Miss Keene, is it not the head of a lady of...' Bruhm bent closer towards the object, '...of Egypt?'

'Of *ancient* Egypt', said Ruth in a toneless voice.

Bruhm glanced swiftly at the inner door and complimented her on her choice of so appropriate an ornament.

'Will you have me enter the purchases in your account or will you follow the fashion set by Miss Keene?', he asked, smiling dubiously at Flavia.

'As I cannot imagine that the sum total of my purchases can amount to a tithe of the price of my friend's single piece, I think I'll risk your crediting them to my account; thank you'.

As she said this, Ruth smiled coldly at Flavia, and together they left the shop.

2

The Inner Room

As Louis Bruhm entered the room, Ralph Carter smiled sourly. He was dark, saturnine, and he suffered periodically from fainting fits. One of these had left half his face paralysed. He was an erudite person and possessed a store of unusual knowledge. He was also - and this was why Bruhm cultivated him - a member of the Beaumont Club, which ranked not only as the most exclusive but also as the most occult of its kind. Most of its members were creative in their respective spheres. The Club also contained some extremely wealthy individuals, not many, for the rich are seldom creative in the sense in which the Club understood the term. It was Bruhm's partiality for the rich and the famous, merely because they were rich or famous that barred him from the charmed circle, he might otherwise have gained admittance, because he was genuinely interested in curious personalities, and if he had little creative ability, he prided himself that one day he would prove useful to the Beaumont crowd. But his shop, his establishment, as he liked to call it, acted against his interests in this direction. In actual fact it was not the sort of club that Bruhm imagined it to be, for creativity often goes hand in hand with a passion for solitude, of 'not belonging' to any given category or class of human affairs. It was rather in the nature of an 'astral drawing-room', an affinity of souls, than a tangible salon.

Ralph Carter, because he cared for little but the past, not merely the historic past but that pre-human past which exists at subjective levels, enigmatic and profound, and because he had discovered ways of tapping these levels, had been admitted to the fold and was honoured by the elect. He now sat in the inner room which was connected with the shop by the door with the green curtain.

'What did I hear about a shew-stone?', he asked. A queer half-smile illumined the unaffected side of his face, leaving the other frozen in its perpetual calm.

'Nothing, nothing at all; a mere bauble my dear boy; some skryer's crystal, no doubt, but nothing that would interest you, I assure you'.

Bruhm splayed his hands upon the table, exhibiting the immaculate perfection of a pair of snow white shirt-cuffs linked by glittering gems.

'Do you remember Hilary Morgan?', asked Carter, suddenly.

'Of course, my dear boy. Who doesn't remember Hilary? I sold some of his first pictures, long before your time'.

Bruhm's face lighted up at the recollection of one who had unwittingly lined his pockets. But then the luminosity departed, for he then remembered that Hilary Morgan had sponsored Carter for the Beaumont Club. Morgan had thought very highly of Carter, and of young Basil Seton who was turning out canvasses in the Morgan manner. Bruhm drew his hands together; the fingers touched as if in prayer; yes, he well remembered Morgan. He had hinted as much to Seton in the hope that he also would let him handle his pictures - Bruhm could get a high price for them - and in return act, perhaps, as his own sponsor to the Club. But the gain to Seton, and the double gain to Bruhm had remained in the empyraean.

'Morgan had a very peculiar crystal', went on Carter.

Bruhm started, and withdrew his thoughts from the Beaumont Club.

'Did he indeed? I am surprised to hear that he took an interest in such things.'

He wished Carter would keep off the subject of crystals; he was not at all sure that he had acted wisely over the Keene transaction, although the sum he had acquired thereby was astronomical! He squirmed uneasily under Carter's gaze, especially that which emanated from the unmoving side of his face. Carter sat back in his chair and resumed the conversation:

'One day Morgan confessed to me that the crystal had changed his style and endowed him with genius. As you know, his early work was unexceptional, technically good, perhaps, but not creative. But on becoming possessed of his talisman, as he called it, his work changed; it was not a matter of development, but of total change.'

Bruhm was stirred by the allusion to the talisman, and he realised that the afternoon's encounter with Flavia had added another dimension to his memory of Hilary Morgan.

'I think that Morgan in his last period surpassed anything he had hitherto achieved'.

Carter paused. Bruhm nodded and forced a smile of agreement which lacked sincerity: he was uneasy and beginning to be afraid. Carter went on, relentlessly:

'If I had to describe Morgan's work to someone totally ignorant of it - though well acquainted with the works of contemporary painters - then I should summarize it as a mingling of certain elements which go into the make of a Spare, a Sime, or a Wunderlich. Morgan's subject-matter is, of course, anything but modern, and some people deplore the obsession with ancient Egypt which his later work reveals. But why deplore it? He treats the subject in a non-traditional manner, but why should he depict only those aspects so far confirmed by the discovery of historical fragments? I fail to understand how anyone can criticize a work of art because the painter depicts Isis holding an instrument that is unidentifiable.'

Bruhm was familiar with the painting to which Carter referred. 'My point is', went on Carter, 'that it was only after Morgan became possessed of his talisman that he began painting those really extraordinary pictures. Previously, he had treated usual

22

subjects in an unusual and - let us admit it - in a rather uninteresting manner; after he acquired the talisman we see a complete reversal - a straightforward treatment of extraordinary subjects. In this sense he may be compared with Dali, although the atmosphere of antiquity is not present in Dali's work. And the quality of light which pervades Morgan's work, this surely is his most remarkable achievement. Have you ever - before or since - beheld a picture in which the light seems to change as you look at it?'

Bruhm smiled assent, genuine this time:

'How did Morgan acquire this talisman?', he asked.

Carter raised his hands expressively, and let them fall to his sides: 'Nobody knows; at least, nobody I know. And he permitted no one to see it, as I expect you know'.

He paused, observing Bruhm with one mobile eye; he had been on the point of adding that nobody at the Beaumont Club had seen it, but, remembering Bruhm's ever-open wound, he modified his remark. If no one at the Club had been allowed to look at it, then Bruhm could rest assured that no one outside it would have been accorded the privilege.

'I heard rumours - only rumours, mind you - that Basil Seton was to have inherited the talisman, but I doubt whether he ever actually saw it. He used to talk about it a lot several years before Morgan's death, but during the eighteen months or so before the end, he did not so much as allude to it. Its disappearance at the time of Morgan's death was suspicious, and Seton was accused, but he would hardly have bothered to spirit away an object which he knew he was to inherit anyway'.

Carter paused and directed at Bruhm another peculiarly disturbing glance.

'Seton was Morgan's chosen, was he not?', asked Bruhm.

The question was put more to keep his mind from the subject of the stone than for information.

'Yes, he was beginning to paint well under Morgan's influence. The stone's effect on Morgan was so pronounced that I see no reason why it should not have had the same effect on Seton. Morgan claimed that it had the power of inducing inspirational frenzy, and I see no reason why it should not have done the same for Seton. This is merely a theory of mine; Lawrence Hector would merely laugh at the idea'.

'Hector?', queried Bruhm, searching his mind for the names of Club members.

'Lawrence Hector, scientist, inventor, whatever you like to call him. Personally, I don't know why anyone tolerates him' (Carter meant 'tolerates him at the Beaumont Club'), 'but there you are! He's made one or two significant discoveries, I believe, in the realm of nuclear physics, and so...'

Bruhm nodded. He remembered Hector when Carter mentioned the man's pursuits. It was characteristic of Bruhm that he could recall a person only when he had classified him as this or that, rarely by reference to name, face or character. The Misses Keene and Chalmers, for instance, were not elegant women whom he enhanced even more by adorning them with his curious treasures, they were daughters of the joint shipping-line owners Marshall Keene and Raymond Chalmers. Bruhm did not take into consideration their personal tastes and interests, any more than he would put any store by Hector's famous contributions to science. Likewise, even though Ruth Chalmers was herself one of the Beaumont crowd, Bruhm believed this to be due solely to the influence of her father. It was, in actual fact, due to quite different reasons, one of them being Ruth's poetry which was attracting attention in literary circles, another being her interest in the ballet which had led to her friendship with Flavia, a woman of peculiar tastes and great creative potential. It was Flavia who had been determined to see Ruth accepted in the Club *despite* the almost insurmountable obstacle of her father's wealth!

After Carter had left, Louis Bruhm returned to his chair and sat thinking for a considerable time.

3

Louis Bruhm Remembers

Exactly three years previously, Bruhm had been sitting thus before the table by the chair that Carter had vacated. It had been a sultry afternoon and Bruhm had received few calls. But on this occasion the door of his shop had opened,and he had left the inner room to attend to his client. At first he distinguished nothing in the bright pathway of the sun except the black bar of the metal grille which covered the door. Then he noticed, with a start, a kyphotic figure in curiously black cloth that had a faint greenish bloom upon its shiny surface. Bruhm's intense preoccupation with this peculiar habit was - he later realized -due to his total disinclination to look at the face set on the crooked neck which rose from the green shadow. It was not so much that it was distorted, as the faces of dwarfs sometimes are distorted, but that there was in its expression so hideous an intent, that Bruhm - accustomed to contemplate rare and lovely objects - found it impossible to accept such an antithesis of his aesthetic ideal of normal beauty in this incarnate form of abnormal ugliness.

For the space of a few seconds, though to Bruhm it seemed an eternity, the two stood beside each other, and then fluttering yellow hands plucked at his sleeve. Bruhm stood motionless, paralysed by the oblique entry into his domain of an element the very reverse of the solar gold which flooded the silent afternoon. A nausea that was wholly physical laved his being, as the heavings of stagnant water would have laved his body and coated it with a veil of greenish slime, had it lain immersed in some polluted backwater. If a spectre swathed in rank seaweed had risen from a pool scummed with scarves of green putrescence, and protruded *in lieu* of a hand a tongue-like flipper, Bruhm could not have been more completely introduced to fear, stark animal fear. His petrification was absolute; but within the immobility of the flesh which embalmed him, as in marble, his consciousness attained a lucidity, a mirror-like perfection, that enabled it to detect the finest shades of movement, and to register the subtlest gradations of the surrounding atmosphere. Carter would have said that Bruhm's body, having relinquished its task of receiving impressions, had identified itself with its own aura, which, registering all sensation, interpreted the slightest inclination towards itself in terms of pure physical impact.

Simultaneously, Bruhm was conscious of the advance towards him - as on a calm rivulet which the sun's rays fleck with gold - of an aqueous bubble about the size of a pomegranate. It was of a shining substance that reflected the sun's rays in spearheads which stabbed him from all sides. Borne upon the same current, a voice seemed to accompany it. Although no human mouth was capable of uttering the sounds he heard, and because he was able to interpret them in terms of words, and therefore of human speech, he was compelled to acknowledge the activity of some human agency.

And so it was that Bruhm heard what he was to do, and how he was to do it, for he was the recipient of commands which he had to obey. He received them, not with his reasoning mind, but with a layer of consciousness normally inaccessible to direct influence. His waking mind informed him that he was receiving instructions from a hunchback with an evil face, and with hands that fluttered like wings, idly beating the summer air. He also knew that he was being hypnotized by an exterior intelligence that was implanting ideas that were to take effect, immediately, with regard to a specific matter, and were to remain dormant for a period of three years with regard to another specific matter. In three years, to the day, he knew that he had to bring out the 'thing' from the place where he had, for safety's sake, been commanded to secrete it, and display it in his shop; and that a certain person would ask for it, would acquire it in her own name at a specified price, which he, Bruhm would be permitted to retain for his share in the transaction. That was all. That so simple a thing as secreting the sphere in his safe, and displaying it at the appointed time, seemed little to require of anyone in return for so large a sum of money.

And yet, during those three years Bruhm had known no peace. The sphere had been duly concealed, and he had not once felt any further curiosity concerning it; but there had hung before his inner vision the monstrous impression of a dwarfish shape, like a twisted cloud around which seeped brilliant sunlight. Even so, he had risen from his bed on the morning of the day appointed as if it were a morning like any other, and not the morning of the day he had dreaded. It had been a matter of moments unlocking the safe and withdrawing what he had placed there. A shadow had fallen across the small square aperture as the heavy door swung outward; he had not turned his head, and had dared scarcely to breathe.

As he ascended the steps from the cellar with his weightless burden, he thought it seemed heavier than anything he had ever lifted. He placed it in the cabinet prepared for it and fastened the lid, and then he saw the substance of the shadow that had slid its silent length between the sphere and himself as he had drawn it from hiding. There it was, peering through the grille of the entrance door, as a trellis-work whereon flowered the noxious rose of its deformity. The shafts of sunlight behind it illumined the darkness with its presence; the yellow hands pawed and fluttered like restless leaves in a breeze, or like moths around a flickering flame. Then it was gone. Bruhm's three-year prayer that it should not enter, should not invade with its substance what it had invaded with its shadow, was granted. He broke out in a sweat of terror as he thought of the possible consequences of having forgotten, or of having bungled his task. Madness, surely; perhaps death, in a manner totally beyond his power of imagining.

He had been standing thus as Ralph Carter entered the shop. Bruhm turned swiftly, his back shielding the show-case from Carter's gaze, which was fixed questioningly upon him. He took Carter's hand, greeted him effusively, drawing him with him into the inner room.

A few minutes later, Flavia Keene and her friend had entered the shop. Bruhm, paralysed by a dread he was unable to combat, submitted to the inner power that now controlled his physical movements, excused himself to Carter and entered the shop to carry out the final stage of his instructions. Even the process of wrapping up the globe, of receiving Flavia's cheque, and of dealing with Ruth Chalmers' purchases were effected automatically by an intrusive intelligence which directed all his actions. Now, after Carter's departure, Bruhm recalled these events as if a series of indelibly vivid pictures had been branded upon his conscience.

As he had entered the cellar containing the stone, he had noticed several canvasses which he had stored there some years previously. They were mostly paintings of a pretty or charming nature which he exhibited from time to time; but among them were two or three by Hilary Morgan. Bruhm had forgotten the paintings and something now induced him to go down and look at them. He passed once more into the shop, and paused on his way to the curtained doorway through which he had disappeared with the shew-stone after Flavia had asked him to wrap it up. He looked at his watch, it was nearly ten minutes past four; he usually closed shop at a quarter to five, but something prompted him now to lock the main door. This he did not usually lock until the outer grille had been closed over it, but he feared that by opening the door he would invite the evil presence which he sensed in the near vicinity. He therefore locked the heavy door and drew into position the double-barred aitch-lock. Then he pulled down the dark green blind. The shop was now illumined by a glaucous light which bathed the show-cases in an even sheen. Their contents appeared as motionless fish in a vast aquarium, and, owing to the passing of traffic without, sudden flashes of light streaked into its depths. In front of Bruhm, heaped on a central cabinet, were the shining baubles which Ruth Chalmers had let trickle through her long white fingers. He saw them now, caressing the hard cold brilliancies with a sterile and feverish excitement. A ring had gleamed on one of her fingers, it displayed a dark green stone that flashed its sullen cool spears against the coins and medals which she let fall upon the velvet cushions. He gathered up the little heap and dropped it carelessly into the cabinet, as one showers, idly, the calm surface of a pool with a handful of pebbles. Passing through the curtained doorway he traversed the small room in which he had wrapped the sphere, and approached the staircase descending to the strongroom.

4

The Encounter on the Pavement

Paul Chisholm was strolling in the afternoon heat, returning to the hotel where he was staying with Dr.Irving Starke, an old friend who directed in Chelsea a clinic for nervous disorders. It was a little after three o'clock. Catching sight of a coffee bar he decided to take refuge from the gruelling heat and, sitting over a cup of coffee, he mused upon recent impressions received at the clinic.

Chisholm had been invited by Dr.Starke because he was puzzled by certain symptoms exhibited by some of his patients. He had thought instantly of Chisholm, whose wide knowledge of occult matters might enable him to explain them. Although the doctor was a specialist in the psycho-therapeutic treatment of nervous disorders, and dealt with a wide range of disturbances of psychoneurotic origin, he did not undertake extreme psychotic cases. It was his practise to pass them on to other institutions, but in the particular circumstances alluded to here, Dr.Starke had not pursued his usual procedure.

Among these special cases were three women who for the past two or three years had proved intractable to his methods of treatment. Their nervous systems showed signs of extreme disorganization, but they were not, strictly speaking, psychotic cases.

Within the past six weeks, two more, similarly afflicted patients - also women - had been committed to his charge, and he had decided that they exhibited symptoms of an 'occult' nature.

Chisholm had come down, therefore, to study the cases directly. He had given considerable attention to the doctor's written reports, and these had been supplemented by private discussions as certain observations that touched upon the occult borderland had not been entered in the reports. The latter testified to a morbid condition of nervous functioning, combined with partial amnesia where certain specific matters were concerned. A marked anxiety-state was present which, in all the cases, was characterised by a dread of children or exceptionally small adults. This fear was so acute that one of the nurses at the clinic, owing to his diminutive size, had caused in the patients outbursts terminating in a total collapse of the psycho-physical organism. The nurse in question now no longer did duty in the wing tenanted by these patients.

Concerning treatment: hypnosis induced a comparatively lucid state in which each of these patients described a more or less similar experience, though at a certain point a barrier supervened and every method failed to elicit further material.

In conversation, Dr.Starke had told Chisholm that hypnotic permeability ceased always at the appearance of a curious geometric symbol or design, which each patient drew automatically on a sheet of paper. The symbol thereafter acted as a veil covering an entire layer of the subconsciousness, which resisted all further attempts at exploration. The accounts up to this point resolved themselves into a single story representing an experience common to all three patients. This experience terminated in obsession by the symbol, which seemed to epitomize and at the same time 'seal off', the trauma. Chisholm recognized in the symbol a close similarity to an occult sigil known as *seeing through the oblivion of Time*, which was based upon an ancient Egyptian hieroglyph. Beyond this close resemblance, more marked in one patient's version of the symbol than in those of the other two, he could detect nothing remotely familiar. In one of the other cases he noted certain additional sigils, one of which closely approximated to the Egyptian hieroglyphic for 'water', while another resembled a crudely drawn star. The patients exhibited no particular reaction to the ideas or actualities connected either with time, stars, water, or with vision, although - of course - the idea of oblivion could be associated with the amnesia which afflicted each patient. On confronting them individually, however, with the notions of water: of the sea, of running water, of water-clocks; or with ideas of time, stars, eyes, vision, and so on, no noticeable reaction could be detected either in the hypnagogic state or during waking consciousness. Violent reactions were produced only by the sight of children, by the sight of the nurse already mentioned, by bright lights or shining objects, and by personal adornments or trinkets which induced in all three patients paroxysms of fury. The women were, in all cases, similar psychological types, possessed of forceful personalities combined with unusually strong aesthetic sensibilities. One woman was - as was Dr.Starke himself - a member of the Beaumont Club, a fact which seemed to rule out congenital weakmindedness and similar defects.

To Chisholm's mind, the similarity in type appeared the most startling feature. He had not that day seen the patients in question, having been occupied solely with Dr.Starke's account of them. He had with him a portfolio containing everything pertaining to the case which the doctor had collected during the previous three years.

Chisholm left the coffee-bar and strolled leisurely along the blazing strip of pavement until the heat forced him to take refuge on the other side of the street. He had been walking for some time when his reverie was interrupted by an alarming spectacle. A little way ahead of him a young woman appeared to be wrestling with a grotesquely shrunken old gentleman who was trying to pinion her against a shop window. In the glare of the afternoon sun, Chisholm watched this drama being enacted as if it were an isolated cameo suspended in a shimmering gauze before his heat-engendered fancy. The street was strangely silent and still, although a small group of people was advancing in the direction of the disturbance. As Chisholm drew abreast of the scene, the elderly assailant emitted a gasp and sank to his knees. The woman glanced fearfully at Chisholm:

'Oh, he's fainted; the heat has been too much for him ... I tried to hold him up, but he struggled against me.'

Chisholm did not believe a word the woman was saying; she seemed not to be addressing him, but the advancing crowd. There was an urgency in the words she had just uttered, and the look of terror in her eyes seemed too genuine to be simulated.

'She attacked him; I saw it!', said one of the group, a hard-faced woman with a malevolent expression. As the accusation was levelled against her, the young woman moved closer to Chisholm and stood slightly behind him.

'I happened to observe the whole scene', said Chisholm, in a tone which made it clear to his listeners that they should go their various ways. 'The young lady is perfectly correct in what she has said'.

By this time the man had revived sufficiently for Chisholm to help him to his feet. A shopkeeper emerged from a doorway and offered a glass of water, but the man declined it, and, glancing queerly at Chisholm, shambled down the street. As is usual in such cases, nobody had observed closely what had occurred, and the accusation which had been flung at the young woman arose from the desire for trouble which some people delight in initiating. And so the group slowly dispersed, melted almost literally in the relentless heat.

The young woman at Chisholm's side was plucking at his sleeve in an agitated manner, the momentary expression of relief on her face having now given way again to one of panic. She was pulling him forward in the direction in which he wished to go, but not by any means at the speed he wished to go on such an afternoon. She urged him on, and there was some quality in her insistence, coupled with her obvious anxiety, which impelled him forward at the rate she would have him go. She muttered under her breath a disconnected account of the violent encounter, which she explained away as a distressing accident caused by mistaken identity. She referred, repeatedly, to a curio shop which - so Chisholm gathered - was situated not far away. She said that some indescribable abnormality had entered the shop and emerged a few minutes later. Her brief glimpse of the figure had inspired in her such terror that she had been compelled, despite her abhorrence, to follow in its wake, to confront it, and so to assure herself that her senses had deceived her. On catching up with it, however, she had found herself face to face with the elderly gentleman whom Chisholm had saved from the efforts of her temporary derangement.

Chisholm tried vainly to reason with the woman. They had reached the shop in question and she had grasped the door knob. The door did not yield to her pressure; she pushed frantically, hysterically, until Chisholm laid upon her shoulder a detaining hand. As she turned towards him - her eyes glazed with the veil of impenetrability that often indicates a state of interior upheaval, sometimes of ecstasy - she noticed a florist's shop on the opposite side of the road, and, before he realized her purpose she was urging him over the road. The traffic surged about them as they wove a zigzag path to the opposite pavement. Once inside the florist's, Chisholm was barely able to restrain his companion, until a white-smocked figure detached itself from a cluster of blossoms foaming in an enormous tub, and advanced in their direction. Chisholm cast an anxious glance at the young woman, who then addressed the florist quite casually:

'I wish to see Mr.Bruhm, but unfortunately his shop appears to be closed.'

The man she was addressing looked at his watch: 'A quarter past four', he said thoughtfully. 'He usually remains open until a quarter to five; would you care to give him a ring?'

'If you would be so kind, I think this gentleman will oblige me'. She motioned in Chisholm's direction as she finished speaking. The florist looked at him queerly and led him into a small side room. Chisholm turned, held open the door, and the woman followed him to the telephone.

'What's your name?', he whispered, as the florist withdrew.

'I'll ring him', she said, heedless of his question. 'I know his number; I've bought things there.'

She seemed calm and collected now as she took the receiver in her long tapering fingers, the nails of which - he noticed - were lacquered in mauve. At last he was able to take stock of the enigmatic and erratic creature beside him. Her face was full, round, and unusually soft, he thought, for a woman whose other features suggested an age between thirty-five and forty years. Her small arched mouth was also full, and the eyes, liquid and large, lent to the face a curiously voluptuous, almost oriental appearance, except that the finely chiselled nose and the receding forehead suggested a vaguely African provenance.

Her call was in vain. She looked anxious, but not distraught, as she replaced the receiver and looked blankly at Chisholm. He recalled his attention from wandering over other of her attributes and proceeded to choose a lavish bouquet of flowers which he then presented to her. He left his card with the surprised and delighted florist, and, together, they left the shop.

She seemed speechless with gratitude, but he deliberately refrained from paying any attention to her exclamations, when they came. Instead, he hailed a passing cab and suggested she should go home and rest. He heard her give an address in St. John's Wood, mentally noted it, and, giving a note to the driver, waved her goodbye.

He then hailed a cab on his own behalf and arrived back at his hotel between half past pour and a quarter to five. He was tired, hot, and hungry. After a light meal, he retired to his apartment and remained there until morning, his mind reverting to earlier episodes in what seemed to him to have been a long and confusing day.

But although the encounter on the pavement was pushed into the background by his study of, and reflections on, Dr.Starke's case-histories, Chisholm was nonetheless conscious of the presence, perpetual, vague, of a lovely face distorted in turns by apprehension and frustration.

The day that followed was fresh and bright, the buildings shone against a flawless sky as if the entire town, and he in it, were floating in a chalice filled with azure foam. He decided to walk and revolve in his mind the thoughts which yesterday had deposited. In Hyde Park the profusion of fresh blossoms which quivered slightly in the ghost of a breeze, cleared his mind of the baffling case-histories.

He had been strolling for some time before he realised that he was again in the vicinity of the curio shop. As he approached it he heard a clock strike twelve; and what he saw made him quicken his pace. Two policemen, a small group of bystanders - among which he recognized the florist - and a large vehicle, were disposed around the shop's entrance, and it was evident that a legal entry of the premises was being effected. As he drew abreast of the group he recognized the florist, who motioned to one of the policemen and said: 'This is the person I was telling you about'. He then produced the card Chisholm had given him the previous day. Both florist and policeman looked at him a little queerly, but when Chisholm mentioned his friend Dr.Starke, matters were made easier, by the florist who occasionally supplied flowers to the clinic, and by the policeman's acquaintance with the doctor who directed it. The policeman was relieved to find someone who might contribute a more substantial justification for his entering the curio shop than that with which the florist had furnished him.

It appears that Bruhm had lived in constant fear of some sort, and he had asked the florist to inform the police the moment anything unusual occurred. Apart from Bruhm's having closed his shop earlier than usual the preceding evening, the florist had noticed the omission in the matter of the closing of the metal grille. Having become uneasy when Bruhm did not open his shop at the usual hour next morning, and urged by his wife, the florist informed the police. Now, at a little after midday, Chisholm was observing the result.

As the policeman turned once more to the door, two things occurred simultaneously; one of them observable and explicable: the sudden yielding of the heavy door against the iron bars that were crossed behind it from within; the other, invisible and inexplicable: the sudden realisation by Chisholm that this rather irritating matter in which he had become involved had a definite connection, and a vital one, with the cases of nervous disorder which his friend Dr.Starke had under observation. And so it was with that impulsive spontaneity that sometimes overcomes all barriers, that he entered the curio shop in the presence of two policemen and came upon the dead body of Louis Bruhm lying at the foot of the stairs in the strong-room. A broken neck, caused by his fall, seemed the obvious cause of death. An empty safe stood open in the wall to the left of the stairs. Chisholm recognized it as a Hummel-Sauvage recess-safe of foreign manufacture, little used in England. While the police were busy taking notes, Chisholm quickly took out a pocket handkerchief, and, placing it over the catch recess-slide, released it. Inside lay a slight brown-covered notebook which he slipped into his pocket. Why he had engaged in so risky a procedure he was unable to explain, but a face haunted with fear, a face that had come to have some meaning for him, appeared to his inner vision, its eyes prompting by the intensity of their expression, the action he had just performed, quite unnoticed by the policemen, who now waited for him to precede them up the stairs and out of the shop. They smiled courteously, as if obliged to him for some useful service.

Chisholm's imagination had enabled him to see more than the apparent. And so it was in the case of Louis Bruhm's death, to which the police gave no further attention, its circumstances being devoid of any of the features normally associated with foul play. Even the vacuity of the safe did not stimulate a query in minds conditioned to observe only positive facts, and these were lacking precisely because Louis Bruhm had indeed fallen down the stairs and broken his neck.

But Paul Chisholm sensed a very different state of affairs, one which the law could in no way discover owing to a total ignorance of its existence.

5

Strange Ecstasies

Ever since Flavia Keene and Ruth Chalmers had acquired their treasures there had been a decided change in their relationship. In the first place, Flavia had said goodbye to her friend in a rather sullen fashion, and in the second, she had not called her each morning, as was her usual habit when her friend was staying in London. And although Ruth herself seldom took the initiative in these matters she had telephoned Flavia three days after their outing, more out of curiosity about the shew-stone than out of any inclination to speak to her friend. Flavia had been vague and non-committal, which, of course, determined Ruth to persist in enquiring about it. Flavia became positively rude, and an uneasy silence was established between them.

Largely because of this state of affairs, Ruth had spent the remainder of her stay in London at the Beaumont Club. Herbert Roydon was a bit of a problem, but as it happened, Ruth was out of town during the first phase of Flavia's passion for him, and now he had been conveniently spirited away to Nigeria, so that Ruth could come and go at the club without embarrassment.

But if Ruth spent more and more time thinking of Flavia's shining sphere, Flavia herself, although absorbed in her new toy, could not help thinking of Ruth's medallion. And, oddly enough, on arriving home that sultry afternoon, Flavia had gone straight to her bedroom and laid the sphere - still in its wrappings - in a drawer of her cabinet. As she did so, her eyes rested on a painting by Hilary Morgan, purchased several years previously, which hung above a divan upholstered in golden damask. The painting contained several human figures, one of which possessed features remarkably similar to the head of the woman depicted on her friend's medallion. But the figure in the painting was not of a woman, but of a sphinx-like creature, half human, half feline, which explained Flavia's mistaking the head on the medallion for the head of a cat. She now looked at the picture from an entirely new viewpoint; no longer as an 'adventure in line and colour', no longer as a purely aesthetic expression, but as a vaguely sinister and ambiguous hint of certain strange yet somehow familiar mysteries.

She unwrapped the sphere and placed it upon the divan. In the well-known symbol of the ancient Egyptian goddess, with which, in Morgan's painting, the sphinx-woman appeared to be crowned, she saw, instead of the golden disc of the sun in the arms of the moon, the glowing sphere embraced by a horned head-dress in which it was exalted to the status of a crest-jewel. The symbol was repeated as a star in the ominous sky which hung, low and heavy, above a dark-walled temple. At its portals crouched two sphinxes, flexed to spring. Great winged creatures circled about the pylons of the temple, the interior of which was brilliantly illuminated. A gold sarcophagus inscribed with memorial hieroglyphics gleamed behind a veil of incense which billowed from the temple, seeping through cracks in the cyclopean masonry. But what most had fascinated Flavia were the two shining globes, one set in the nightsky, the other in the head-dress of the High Priestess who seemed to be performing a sabbatic rite. And through another aperture there seemed to lie, on a slab of obsidian, the image of a man. Instead of sacrificial blood, a luminous current - as of lightning - flashed from his body.

As Flavia sat contemplating this weird drama, of which she could not grasp the significance, she became uncertain as to whether her eyes were on the shew-stone or on the painting, uncertain from what source emanated the fantasies that assailed her. She was aware only that two distinct streams of imagery were obsessing her.

Firstly, she was haunted persistently by the dark and horrible shape of a man bent double, or twisted grotesquely out of shape. It appeared to throb at the heart of the shew-stone, which suddenly darkened until a leering face alone remained in its depths, a smouldering presence. Sometimes the form changed, and the creature's fingers, like the ivory stays of a fan made visible by old age, snapped at her with a sickly rhythmic insistence which drummed in her mind a tune that she was beginning to loathe, but which she could not shut out merely by stopping her ears. Secondly, and at times when the distorted form faded or remained in a state of cloudy indistinctness, Flavia saw the surface of a calm lake shining in the waning light of a summer evening. Fringeing the lake were reeds, rushes, and trees, violet with the mists of dusk. Beside the still water, and wheeled in an invalid-chair, was a man with silvered hair and refined features. He was propelled forward by a silent form which Flavia could hardly distinguish from the dusky shadows. On one occasion, and thereafter on succeeding occasions, the figure wheeling the chair turned suddenly, and Flavia saw the features of a young man, although bodily he seemed old and stooping, and wracked with pain. But always the same turn: an awkward, startled gesture of surprised intimacy, the eyes glowing with an expression of ecstasy as the head was turned to confront some thing, or person, unknown but expected. But the face of the man with silvered hair was constantly serene and tranquil, and Flavia noticed that his expression was oddly interchangeable with the stillness of the water, which shone behind the reeds at the sick man's feet.

Then the trailing curtains of mist would thicken and obscure the vision in dense fog, impenetrable, more profound than night. When this occurred, Flavia felt that

32

some great drama was being enacted behind the veil; but no sound emerged, no light, nor the slightest tremor to betray the presence which she knew still lurked in the depths of the dark and unyielding shew-stone.

The weeks passed. Flavia seldom went out, and when she did it was merely for physical exercise. She barely noticed the fierce onset of summer as that unusually warm spring merged with it almost imperceptibly. Nor was she conscious of the pain she caused Ruth, whose telephone calls, letters, and even a personal visit, were all equally ignored. Yet Ruth felt bound to admit to herself that it was the shew-stone upon which she longed to gaze again, and that whatever joy she may previously have taken in Flavia's company, it all was eclipsed by the thought of the certain satisfaction she knew she would derive merely from gazing upon the mystic stone. She did not allude to this in her letters to Flavia, which became less frequent and which ceased finally at midsummer, when all hope of a reconciliation seemed lost. She wept, when alone, when June drew to a close, for, soon after, she would be leaving London for her home in Glamorgan where she would remain until the Christmas holidays.

But of Ruth, Flavia was totally oblivious as she spent her days and nights in unceasing communion with the bright sphere that enthralled her. Towards midsummer, however, as the heat pressed upon the curtains which she kept perpetually drawn, she began to notice a change in the pattern and sequence of events which unfolded themselves in the depths of the stone. No actual scenes or figures now manifested themselves. The twisting clouds, which seemed to express the coiling columns of heat that rose above the house in which she was immured, as an anchorite lost in the solitary ecstasy of his meditations, were pregnant with a great secret which was soon to declare itself. Her intuition proved correct, for as the days gathered themselves into autumn a curious shape, or sign, made itself apparent in the shew-stone. It came mostly at night, when the cloying perfumes of the flowers with which her room was strewn hung in stifling drifts, almost sickly in the intensity of their fragrance. Two lamps in burnished metal holders beneath the solitary painting, shed upon the shew-stone a radiance like antique gold, and a lustrous form emerged from a Sign, as a cocoon, breaking suddenly, might eject a fragile chrysalis to leap like light upon the bright damask.

At this stage of the revelation, when the mysterious Sign had burst open to give birth to the figure, Flavia took up the stone and, swathing it in a specially consecrated vesture of mauve, secreted it in the cabinet. Then she reclined upon the divan, her limbs shining like ivory in the golden light, her hair cascading over shoulders whose virginal paleness responded to the light's caress and took on the hue of roses. From her lips came a soft crooning, and the air echoed with the sighings of violins.

It was during the period of these strange ecstasies that Herbert Roydon, on a brief and unexpected visit from Nigeria, took away with him the first dark uncertainties as to Flavia's sanity. Although all appeared outwardly normal, except her refusal to relinquish her solitary habits, Roydon had sensed a subtle change in her personality, no less than in her surroundings. She had not told him of the stone, and so he was unaware of the source of his disquietude, for while in Flavia's presence, or even while sitting in her room, he found it almost impossible to concentrate his mind. Whenever he attempted to do so his thoughts were forcibly dispersed, as if dissolved by a corroding agent no less effective for being invisible and inexplicable.

Flavia had removed Morgan's picture during the period of Herbert's visit, as well as the lamps which illuminated her nights of mystical vigil. He found an absent Flavia, an indifferent, statuesque replica of the living woman. Yet her whole being gave evidence of being enhanced, exalted. Her features, which normally exhibited rare beauty and refinement, were now etherialised to an almost alabaster spectrality. They reminded him of those exquisite oriental ornaments of Indian and Singhalese craftsmanship, figures of divine beings whose filigree draperies were wrought in threads of ivory as fine as hair. She had become like a monstrous spider, spinning, not a web but a sphere of gossamer which entangled and strangled the thoughts projected towards her. She was ungraspable, unattainable, a fact which aroused in Roydon that form of desire which exists only when its object is infinitely remote and utterly inaccessible.

He had but three days in which to savour such ecstasy and such anguish, and on the last he experienced a phenomenon of a totally different order. As he had come up the stairs, he noticed that Flavia's door was ajar, and he supposed she had recently left her room. He slipped inside with the idea of awaiting her return, and of rehearsing a final declaration and appeal to her. But Flavia had not left the room. She lay, with eyes closed, on her bed. All was still, and although no sound percolated from the street, Roydon was aware of a constant vibration. He likened it to the whir of a dynamo. Puzzled, he gazed about him until a sound behind him caused him to look back at the door. Standing on the threshold he glimpsed, fleetingly, framed like a portrait in the doorway, a person of indescribably loathsome appearance. Then it vanished, and the door closed. Roydon rushed in its direction, aware as he did so that the whir which had diverted his attention from Flavia now hummed shrilly. He wrenched open the door, dashed down the stairs, and a housemaid on the ground floor looked at him so complacently that he began to wonder if his eyes had deceived him, as she evidently had seen no one precede him down the stairs, and the main entrance-hall was empty. He passed her in silence, looking first into one room, then another. Then he retraced his steps, feeling giddy and sick. As he approached Flavia's door, which he thought to find open, he heard a faint sound of scurrying feet, and a low pitched murmur, as of a voice chanting, intoning. But the voice was not Flavia's; it was harsh, like a dog's growl that had suddenly acquired a semblance to human speech. He burst unceremoniously into the room, a flush of anger staining his throat and neck. Flavia turned sharply as he entered. She had been about to close the door of the cabinet beside her bed. There was fury in her eyes as she turned on him, and then - abruptly restraining herself, or, as Roydon thought, being compelled to restrain herself - she faced him in silence, an immaculate figure, statuesque, imperious.

Roydon realized that the silence was absolute, that the humming vibration that had risen to a pitch of frenzy a few minutes earlier, was stilled, abolished; another figment, perhaps, of his bewildered brain. For he had also realised, with a shock, that whereas Flavia had accepted his unexpected presence as an unavoidable interruption of her ritual, her new way of life, she was now leaving him in no doubt that she wished him to withdraw his attentions from her, forever.

6

Hilary Morgan's Statement

Several months before the events just related, Paul Chisholm and Dr.Starke had discussed the matter of Louis Bruhm and a slight brown-covered notebook. As its contents form an indispensable key to some of the mysteries surrounding the shew-stone, it is necessary to reproduce them here.

The notebook belonged originally to Hilary Morgan, and its contents were written in the artist's own hand. It takes the form of a history of the shew-stone and is addressed to Basil Seton, who was to have inherited it at Morgan's death:

'All my success in painting, both in an inner and in an outer sense, is due to the shew-stone, which it is my wish that you should inherit after my death.

'I have told you something about this curious object, which is not a stone in the strict sense of the word - precious or otherwise - but a talisman constructed according to precise occult principles about which I know little. There now remains to tell what I have not already told you in private conversation, and which I did not wish you to know until you had proved yourself worthy of possessing the stone.

'Firstly, you must understand that I was entirely truthful when I admitted ignorance as to the stone's origin and significance. I was directed towards its discovery at a certain stage in its history, a history that had already embraced many hundreds, if not thousands, of years. I have never regarded myself as anything but a guardian of the stone. It seems to have the habit of selecting with infallible precision the indivi-dual destined at any particular time to receive it into his custody. It may be that you will not inherit it, or this document, because the power responsible for its destiny may have decreed otherwise. There have been other candidates (for want of a better designation), striving sometimes consciously and sometimes unconsciously in its direction, but none so tirelessly, and, I must say, so sensitively as yourself. Hence my fervent wish that destiny will favour you.

'With these matters in mind, I shall now relate the stone's history as it affected the brief phase of my life in which it featured, I might say, to the exclusion of all else except my art.

'As you know, I spent eleven years in Egypt, where I steeped myself not only in the physical atmosphere of the land, especially that about Fayoum in the Nile Valley, but also in the more rarefied and magical atmosphere in which its mighty monuments lie perpetually embalmed.

'I visited Egypt, originally, as an artist in search of material which I considered to be more potent to stimulate the creative faculties than the devices of modern civilization. I endeavoured to approach the real sources of primal energy that had given rise to the artistic achievements for which that ancient land is celebrated. But you should understand that I did not consciously entertain any idea of participation in the dark and ambiguous mysteries that formed the inspiration of those achievements.

'I had exhausted, or so I imagined, most of the avenues of approach to Art which the Western world had to offer, and I went to Egypt well knowing that it was not the Egypt of today that would absorb my interest, but that of ancient times, replete with all the mysteries which even the vulgar mind associates with it. I regarded these mysteries as concerning themselves primarily with the problems of aesthetics, problems which had intrigued me since my youth. That these Mysteries were sprung of other, occult, arcana, I became gradually aware during the years that followed. But in the earlier years of my residence there, I sought out individuals professing interests similar to my own. I was then unknown, even in artistic circles, and the particular coterie that attracted me consisted of men and women who, from a worldly point of view, were similarly undistinguished. This is not to say that they lacked talent, but all of them lacked genuine creative ability. It was creative ability, if not genius, that I desired of life more than anything else; nor was I concerned to restrict it to artistic pursuits alone. I should have been happy to have discovered my genius and to have let it express itself in any sphere or endeavour in which it felt at home. I did not at the time know that I possessed any abilities other than those associated with Art, and they were of a kind inferior even to talent, much less to genius.

'I soon tired of the coterie. The activities of its members approximated to those of numberless similar groups existing in Europe, with the one difference that in Egypt persons "belonged" more by virtue of race, of being white (no matter how purple many of them were by a devotion to Bacchus more sincere than to the Muse), than by virtue of their merits as artists. In fact with the sole exception of the Beaumont Club, which I hold in high esteem for its uncompromising attitude in respect of artistic creativity, the coterie was fast absorbing more and more of my time and health and was similar to any of its counterparts in Europe. So far from painting better pictures, I had - at the end of my first year in Egypt - painted nothing of note, cheating myself with the idea that I was 'working', when I turned out idle sketches 'for future projects', or pretending to myself that by sketching some ancient monument I was working towards a release of the creative spirit. Truth to tell, I felt listless, hopeless of myself and my ideals, which seemed mere sham and pretence. The only things for which I seemed to have any energy or interest were the incessant drinking parties, and other amusements in which I indulged in a vain effort to hide my despair and laziness. But, one evening, in a smoky room occupied by the coterie which I had grown to detest, but which I felt powerless to quit, a strange experience occurred.

'Midnight was approaching, and the club presented its usual appearance: clouds of smoke hung in drifts over the plush sofas, chairs, and tables littered with ash trays, bottles and glasses.

'The subdued lighting, the shadowy forms plunged in morose silence or drunken reveries, the dismal wailing of a pipe or the reverberations of a muffled gong, all combined to cast over the senses an evil glamour. And out of the writhing smoke, the nauseous reek of alcohol and drug-laden fumes, the figures that surrounded me assumed the grotesque appearance of human beings wearing bestial masks reminiscent of the gods of that ancient land. I had to remind myself that the figures were in fact human, that the faces were those of my kind, even if twisted into hideous grimaces. I was sitting quietly, contemplating the futility of my life, and the lives of those about me, when I became aware that a woman whom I had not previously noticed was regarding me with a curious, I might almost say a compelling, gaze. I smiled back at her; at least, I had the intention of smiling, although I had barely the energy to do so. I was astonished therefore to find myself rising to my feet, and propelling myself in the direction of the curtained alcove from which the woman gazed. I entered it, barely noticing the poppy-drugged bodies lying on the floor in unhealthy sleep, so fascinated had I become by the woman who had attracted me. She was dissimilar to anyone I had noticed that evening. She was dressed in a costume of most unusual style. I know that none of the women belonging to the coterie would have assumed such dress, not so much for fear of ridicule, but because all of them adhered rigidly to conventionally fashionable European styles.

'These observations flashed through my mind in far less time than it takes to recount them, but what enthralled me about the woman was not so much the odd nature of her attire as the dominance of her personality. She was, perhaps, thirty years of age. Her eyes and her mouth were the most outstanding features in a broad dusky face framed in foaming waves of hair which cascaded over her shoulders. Her nose was short and delicately modelled, and seemed to connect the luminous dark eyes with a small and exquisitely formed mouth. Such was the magnetic intensity of her eyes, and the urgency of desire which she aroused in me, that a sensation of oblivion engulfed me. The only phenomenon of which I was aware at that moment was the pleasurable feeling of total surrender to the sovereignty of her gaze. The eyes - as raying lamps of black fire - poured into me a deep current of desire. This was not all; with the desire, poured also the power, necessary to its fulfilment.

'Long after the curious events that followed, I wondered what subtle emanations of drugs, alcohol, and the toxins of my own fevered fancy had combined to produce this remarkable image. Although incapable of responding to her in a normal manner, a part of my consciousness seemed to remain unaffected by the impact of her personality. I found myself not only able to hear and understand what she was saying, but I was also able to move my body in such a way as to conform to her instructions. But I did not so much as touch her during the entire course of the experience, nor do I remember even so much as brushing against her body during the difficult manoeuvres we undertook.

'I followed her out of the club into a pitch dark night, astonished that she should be able to guide me on a journey which my legs declared interminable, but which my desire to accompany her, to be controlled by her, registered as of no duration at all. I know now that we covered many miles, sometimes in a night so utterly black and starless that I have never been able to understand how we accomplished the journey without mishap. And throughout its entire length, I experienced, in another compartment of my consciousness, an indefinable dread, supposing the whole experience to be a dream often slipping over into nightmare. Indeed, if it were not for the stone which I actually possess, and which you - by this time - will possess, I should ascribe the experience to a derangement of the senses.

'During our journey I noticed that objects were springing up around me, objects that I recognized as vaguely familiar. I recognized the landscape as one I had visited some time previously while exploring the land and the monuments in it. I had stumbled by chance upon a valley containing the nearly obliterated remains of an ancient temple. The sky was now begemmed with stars, and a full moon hung above us like a white lantern. Before I had time to wonder at the sudden luminosity, the woman beckoned me into the shadows of an ancient gallery.

'For some time she stood beside me, in silence. I noticed that her hands were beautifully formed, the nails were long, and glittered in the moonlight. She motioned me to follow her. The gallery declined more and more as we proceeded, until we arrived at a shaft cut into the rock at an angle of approximately forty degrees.

'The night and the stars vanished from view as we entered a vault which still declined steeply until a small aperture appeared, and we crawled on to a narrow ledge. We now made our way by the light, eerily phosphorescent, of gigantic fungus-like creepers that flourished in profusion in the stifling subterranean atmosphere. They emitted a rank odour which became overpowering as we advanced along the narrow ledge. We then traversed a long corridor and descended steeply once more, this time emerging in a circular basin lit by the radiance glimmering from grotesquely shaped plants. The form of my guide stood out suddenly, darkly etched against the green effloresence. I then detected a distinct aroma, it rose from the mephitic odours exhaled by the fungi. It suggested chloroform; there was about it a sickly intensity, an overpowering density of fumes. I learned later that the similarity to chloroform was created by a pungent aromatic that overlay the stench, rank and miasmic, which rose from swampland adjoining the underground basin.

'My eyes, grown more accustomed to the greenish radiance, discerned a series of symbols painted or incised upon the walls which surrounded us. Before I had had time to study them I was startled by a harsh grating sound proceeding from the far side of the basin. At a sign from the woman beside me I pressed myself against the wall in the shadow of a cyclopean monolith, one of many which rose from the rock like monstrous inverted stalactites. The sound reverberated and reached a deafening pitch, made somehow even more disagreeable by the fact that my hands, on coming in contact with the walls, met with a viscous slime, as if blood seeped out of the symbols. I swiftly withdrew them, and did not have to hold them under my nose for confirmation of its nature, but thinly disguised by the sickly aromatic. There was on the face of my guide a blank expression, a void of passivity which stretched apart her eyes and clamped her mouth in a rigid line. Where had been beauty and fascination, was now a vapid mask that filled me with repulsion. But in a flash, and as if she were conscious of my feelings, her face resumed its oriental and barbaric beauty. She smiled, and I would have lain for her, a willing sacrifice beneath the rock that was now moving with hideous gratings along the slippery ground at the far side of the basin.

'Sweeping round the aperture revealed by the rock - it was like a door of vast proportions - quilted drifts of smoke formed arabesques about the floral lanterns. These were charged with the sweet odour I had already noticed, and I realised that I was in some kind of temple or sacred enclosure, and that behind the door a rite was in progress. The fumes of incense clouded my consciousness and I became incapable of motion. The woman turned her eyes upon me and I drifted into oblivion. It was as if my lapse of consciousness permitted a change of scene the mechanics of which I was not intended to observe. I awoke to find myself beside an ornate cask raised between braziers of billowing incense set on a magnificently wrought pedestal. While my vision became adjusted to this inner, darker chamber, I sensed a movement to the left of us, against three sarcophagi standing upright against the overhanging wall. Before relating what followed, I shall describe them:

'One was very large, of regal appearance and raised on a slab of obsidian. It was flanked on either side by less imposing casks at ground level. My vantage point enabled me to see the lid of the sarcophagus to the left of the central cask, the lid of which was above my level of vision. The cask on the far side was almost totally obscured by the darkness and the smoke of the incense.

'I could not resist an impulse to pass through the curtain of smoke, which I did, and was surprised to find myself looking down into the first cask. It had a transparent lid, not of glass but a curiously opalescent substance. It revealed an inert form in its swathings, but with the head exposed, and I recognized with a start of horror that the shrivelled and decaying face bore an unmistakeable resemblance to that of the woman beside me, who, at that moment, emitted a stifled cry. She buried her head in her hands, and her body shuddered convulsively. Then she became calm and I was able to see the cause of her alarm. Something had emerged from behind the central sarcophagus. At first, I thought it was a dog, or, perhaps, a jackal. But the suggestion of anything canine soon vanished. As the creature turned in our direction my mind refused to accept that which my eyes saw, for the tentacled abnormality which shambled towards us bore little resemblance to any concept of humanity. It advanced at one moment with a crab-like motion, and at the next moment it collapsed and slithered along the ground. And then, as a climax to my horror, I saw that the woman was responding to the teratoma's advances.

'I cannot relate exactly what followed; by some miraculous intercession I was able to close my eyes, and the blending of inhuman sounds which echoed outside that chthonian cell, lit only by the radiance of monstrous fungi, was something I shall not succeed in banishing from memory. How long the coupling endured I cannot say. My eyes opened after a prolonged silence, when I became aware of an intense vibration which palpitated almost inaudibly. A cloud-like column of vapour hovered over one of the sarcophagi, which suddenly tilted at an angle. Within it, like a fly embalmed in amber, I again recognized the features of the woman who had led me to this cavern of nightmare. Then, as a snake glides silently beneath a slab of rock which appears to offer no means of ingress, so the vaporous column seeped beneath the opalescent lid of the cask.

'Behind the sarcophagus I saw the huddled body of the teratoma, exhausted by its frenzies, immersed in sleep. I gazed again through the lid, not knowing what I expected to see, and there, replete and ruddy with vitality lay the woman with whom I had journeyed. She was swathed in the cerements of the dead yet she appeared even more desirable than in ... I was about to write 'life' ... but what, then, had led me here? If my guide had been living, what was this object before me, which had resembled a shrivelled shadow of her now bloated corpse?

'I sensed that I had little time at my disposal, and that the sleep of depletion in which the dog-like anomaly was sunk would not outlast the trance of repletion which the woman now enjoyed, for the curve of her lips suggested ecstatic dreams. I dared not look into her eyes although they were open and unblinking in the narrow tomb that was no longer a house of death but a womb of abhorrent life.

'It was then that I began to sense an invasion of strange desires, of morbid hungers no less insane, no less unhallowed than those which had found expression through the teratoma. It was then also that I noticed the curious sigils upon the sarcophagi. They resembled Egyptian ideographs but were less sophisticated in conception and design. One of them represented a star; it was embossed on the central, imperial, cask. I mounted the pedestal and noted with relief that the lid was opaque. Its sides were deeply incised with hieroglyphics similar to those I had seen in the circular enclosure outside the chamber. It was not until I stepped down from the pedestal that I noticed that the third cask, like the first, had a transparent lid. I saw a pallid head beneath the glacial sheet of misty substance that covered it. At that period of my life I knew no face to which I could have likened it. Embalming salves had preserved its expression of refinement, of true nobility.

'Accompanying this statement you will find replicas of the predominant hiero-glyphics which I then made in great haste and therefore imperfectly. I have had some of them transliterated and translated by Ralph Carter, a close friend whom I introduced to the Beaumont Club. One of the ideographs represents the name of a royal person-age, Hat-Abaft-Sume, probably a queen and certainly a high priestess. Her cartouche was inscribed upon the central cask. The flanking casks contained the remains of a priest and a priestess, also of noble lineage. The priest's name seems to have been Sutechem or Sutekh-Khem. It is repeated on the mortuary stélé inscribed on the side of the cask. The name of the priestess is unfortunately undecipherable owing to the inaccuracy of my transcription.

'I came, at the last, to a small and exquisitely wrought casket set between the two braziers. There is no need for me to tell you what I found within it, after I had - with great effort - prised open the lid: even the shew-stone, now in your possession. I cannot refrain from giving you an account of my first impression of it.

'It lay in a dark cavity, nestling in foaming silks of glaucous green, like a rayed star flashing its brilliance to the farthest recesses of that abominable crypt. I discovered, months later, that the crypt lay beneath the Lake [1] itself. I gazed into the depths of the casket, knowing intuitively that it was my duty to extricate the stone, to take it with me, back to the world of the living. As the idea of the 'living' flashed into my mind, I could not help feeling that this magnificent jewel was infinitely more alive, more vital in the true sense of the term, than anything I had left behind me at the club in which the mysterious woman had appeared to me.

'As I lifted out the fragile sphere, colours flashed from it with a vibrancy which I likened to the barely audible pulsations which seemed to beat like a heart within it. At that moment I understood the nature of the object I held in my hands. It was not a heart, but a soul which shed its lustre in the dark recesses of that lugubrious cavern. As it dawned upon me that the form of my guide was not a form of flesh and bone which we call a body, but a body of astral substance, so it also dawned in on me that this scintillating globe was the astral or stellar body of the occupant of the regal tomb, that the stone contained, indeed, the soul of the Queen Hat-Abaft-Sume.

'If the legendary identification of stars with souls is an exact, a scientific fact, as I have believed from that moment, then I did - in truth - hold in my hands a star, a ball of stellar energy as shining, as glorious, as holy as the Sangraal itself. I thought of how much our friend, Lawrence Hector, would have appreciated my incredible discovery; how he would have been enraptured by a mere glimpse of this truly magical casket which contained, in a strictly scientific sense, the essence of a human being, the motivating, intelligent, guiding principle which the fleshly envelope merely obfuscates and expresses in its ponderous, unsubtle, manner. In a thoughtless frenzy

[1] These events occurred in the Fayûm, or Country of the Lake.

of scientific curiosity, might he not have liberated the bright energy in order to analyze it or to put it to some unnatural use? And perhaps its future history will show that such would have been the wiser way, for then something not human, something that came from the stars, might have merged again with its ancient source and thus withdrawn from our terrestrial sphere influences it had rather not known.

'It would be tedious to describe the obstacles which threatened to foil my attempts at finding a way out of that infernal temple. I shot a final glance at the abnormality on the great stone flags. A hideous and deflated mass of semi-liquid matter, it lay in a comatose state midway between ectoplasmic and astral substance. I never understood by what occult law it had a partially substantial form, for, before the loathesome coupling had occurred, it had, like my guide, appeared of non-material substance. After the phantomous union, however, both participants assumed tangible forms; the one, a mummy revivified with unlawful vitality, the other, the quasi-entity now lying on the flags. Both were immersed in an unnatural and magnetic sleep, the one of ecstasy, the other of exhaustion. How many times during the centuries of her interment this vampire had risen in the manner which I had witnessed, will never be known, but I suspect that that ghastly miscegenation had occurred but rarely, and that it was due to it, and to it alone, that I had acquired the stone.

'It may have been the will of the Priestess that I should steal away the stone, the act being impossible for an unsubstantial creature, or for one whose chances of substantiality were circumscribed by laws of which I was totally ignorant. Whatever her object, it had failed of effect owing to the horrendous intervention I have described, and which, paradoxically, she appeared to welcome once her panic had subsided. In this manner she resembled the majority of her sex, however cultured, however strongly willed; women will suddenly forego an object which they have taken immense pains to acquire, merely for the chance of satisfying that part of their natures which they had repressed and whose energies they had dedicated to their original objective. As Glanvil observed:

Man doth not yield himself to the angels, nor unto death utterly, save only through the weakness of his feeble will.

'The remainder of this history is known to you, at least in general terms. I have told you about the curious sigil that always glows in the depths of the sphere, prior to the outflowing streams of inspirational energy which I harnessed and used in my later work. In every one of those later paintings, some adumbration of the occult forces which inspired them makes its appearance in one form or other. We often discussed this as you wheeled me by the lake in Brankley Park. What I did not tell you, however, is that the face which appears so many times, and in so many painted scenes of subterranean temples, is the face of Queen Hat-Abaft-Sume as I have often seen it in the stone, nebulous at first, but growing more precise towards the end. Her face bears such similarity to that of the woman, the priestess who led me to that fantastic sphere, that miraculous star, that I often wonder whether she were not indeed a sister of her whose essence has congealed in that coruscating avatar.

'Whatever I have accomplished, has been accomplished under her aegis. She it was who set revolving my long dormant and creative urge, made it blossom in the works with which the world is now familiar, but which - like myself - it cannot fully

41

understand. My realization of beauty has become perfect, has been attained for myself and within myself, by a certain synaesthetic initiation into the identities of touch and vision which she has made possible by a dissolution of the barriers of Time. But of all this we have talked in great detail.

'I will conclude this Statement by committing to your care that which accompanies it, that for which I can find no satisfactory name and which must therefore remain nameless to eternity.'

7

The Triumph of Ruth Chalmers

Ruth Chalmers and her sister Abigail often enjoyed each other's company, especially since the time of Flavia Keene's defection, which Ruth had, at first, pretended to conceal as much from herself as from her friends. But the Beaumont crowd were quick to detect anything amiss. Ralph Carter suspected a luckless love-affair; but Abigail, who knew her sister, was a little irritated that Carter, with his flair for esoteric sodalities, had not understood Ruth's nature. However, Abigail herself was unaware of Ruth's obsession with the shew-stone.

Ruth had not been content with the old gold medallion which she had bought on that fateful day at Bruhm's, when, for the first time in her life she had glimpsed something she had desperately wanted but which she could not have.

Abigail supposed a tender current of thought to flow from Ruth to Flavia, and she would have been aghast, had thought assumed visible form, to see the very reverse: a malevolent current tinged with the peculiar physical emotions that Ruth once bore towards her friend. Those emotions had indeed always contained an element of envy, and Abigail had sometimes feared that a day might come when their relationship was disrupted, but the end had not come in the way that Abigail feared. There had been no violence, merely a folding in, as of a flower, of Flavia's receptivity to the outflowing of Ruth's affection for her. It was therefore with mingled feelings of excitement and dread that Abigail heard from Ruth of an unexpected summons from her former friend.

Ruth's journey to London had seemed endless and she underwent agonies of anxiety in case Flavia, regretting an impulse induced by loneliness, or by some less obvious cause, should suddenly have changed her mind.

Ruth arrived in Chelsea on a torrid afternoon that reminded her of their afternoon expedition to the curio shop. She remembered vividly that other afternoon as she rang the bell set in the white wall of Flavia's house, smothered in bright blossoms. A maid admitted her and led her up the narrow staircase. Flavia was in bed, the curtains of her room tightly drawn against the brilliant afternoon. One of the first things Ruth noticed was that the painting by Hilary Morgan, which used to form the room's centre-piece, had been removed; that a slender and elegant cabinet stood against the wall beside the bed, and that the usual tubs of flowers were absent, although a cloying aroma hung heavily in the air, a scent suggestive of a conservatory devoted to the culture of tropical plants. The impression evoked the image of venomous orchids emitting from the fleshy violet of their hair-lined mouths the fumes she now inhaled. Then again, and Ruth thought how odd this was - she was reminded of a laboratory she had once visited, although on what occasion she could not recall. These thoughts flashed through her mind as soon as she entered Flavia's room, but they were dissipated an instant later by other, more direct and powerful impressions, one of which was the sight of her friend.

Flavia lay beneath a coverlet of azure which her maid had no doubt arranged in anticipation of Ruth's visit. Ruth noticed how still she lay, how pallid the languid arm that extended its marble on that void of blue. Flavia's eyes were open, vacuous globes of green. A slight breeze displaced a corner of the curtain and admitted a lance of golden light. In its beam, Ruth saw a dancing child spring into life, only to plunge its luminous form into a menacing cloud that drifted from the cabinet which flanked the bed. A wave of jealousy aroused by the sudden revelation of her friend's condition harassed the cloud, almost dragging it down to the bed to smother its occupant. But Ruth's will revolted against the hateful ease with which murder could be encompassed, and it enabled her to regain control of her mind and to pursue the real purpose of her visit. She wanted to see the stone again, if only for a moment. But Flavia refused to comply with her repeated requests. The cloud seemed to gather itself together, it swirled and eddied about the azure, shimmering on the bed; it blossomed in the heavy air and discharged a sickly, unfamiliar, perfume which blended with the radiance pouring from the crucible of flashing panes behind which the sun's rays were transformed to aureole rose. It acquired the precision of a cloud that might have floated out of a painting by Morgan, and in its mobile convolutions the veins of deeper darknesses traced the mystic web of blood-rains which burst from its heavy womb, submerging Ruth in forgetfulness.

As she lost consciousness, two distinct images manifested through channels appropriate to their respective natures: the one a rhythmic pulsing beat, the other a vague smile glowing on a face of incomparable nobility, the eyes of which implored her to surrender the secret treasure which she could now possess. She could possess it because she had permitted the cloud to eject from its perforated shell the soul of her friend.

The consciousness of the astral atrocity she had just permitted by the mere passivity of her attitude, when she could have aroused herself - and Flavia - to avert it, remained as a shadow behind the two fading images of vibration and vision.

8

Abigail Breaks Her Word

Flavia Keene appeared to have died of a rare form of glandular disease concomitant upon pregnancy. Her father became obsessed by the idea that Herbert Roydon - whom he supposed to have been engaged to his daughter - had committed an indiscretion which had cost her life. Ruth, however, was glad of any explanation that enabled her to conceal the theft she had committed, and she nourished the rumour by making it known that Flavia had had absolutely no time for her after Roydon had returned from Nigeria. The matter was generally accepted, and Roydon determined to fathom the mystery of the double crime, for that Flavia had had another lover he refused to admit.

Shortly after Flavia's death, two things happened to Basil Seton. He learned from Dr.Starke of the existence of Hilary Morgan's statement, and he fell in love with Abigail Chalmers. They had met at a party where he had hoped to strike a clue, however slight, as to the whereabouts of the shew-stone which he was to have inherited, and which was, until Abigail's advent, his sole preoccupation. Dr. Starke had not, until then, told Seton about the Statement for two reasons, one of them being Paul Chisholm's investigations into the mystery of the stone, the other being that Dr.Starke had no desire to attract attention, which would most certainly have been forthcoming from certain quarters if Seton had decided to publish his claim to the stone, thereby instituting an official enquiry as to its whereabouts. Having determined that this was not Seton's intention, the doctor could no longer justifiably withhold the document from him. After obtaining his assurance that Chisholm would not in any way be implicated, Dr.Starke handed Seton the notebook containing Morgan's Statement.

Dr.Starke and Paul Chisholm had been able to establish the fact that on the day preceding his death, Louis Bruhm had received a large sum of money from Flavia Keene. It was also known that in the episode of the encounter on the pavement, the woman involved had been incited to violent action by the sight of a dwarf, and that Morgan's Statement lay in Bruhm's safe at the time of his death which occurred soon after.

Dr.Starke and Paul Chisholm had decided to take Basil Seton into their confidence because, as is frequently the case with people who decide to make another the recipient of a particularly enigmatic and fragmentary intelligence, they hoped that by so doing they might learn more than they were able to impart. They had thought also of annexing the services of Ralph Carter, but had not actually approached him before Seton, of his own accord, suggested it. Carter was learnéd not only in matters ancient and modern, but also in the more obscure aspects of occultism.

In respect of his cases, Dr.Starke had traced a system of symbolic images corresponding to the pattern now familiar to him and to Chisholm. The images resumed a traumatic dread of children or small persons, and this was naturally associated with the dwarfish creature that had so horrified Morgan and terrified the young lady of the pavement encounter. The symbol which Chisholm had compared with the ancient Egyptian hieroglyphic, 'seeing through the oblivion of Time', suggested a glyph which Hilary Morgan had appended to his statement, and which he had copied from the "regal" sarcophagus. It resembled a rayed star, and showed a further point of comparison, in that a peculiarity common to Dr.Starke's patients consisted in the dread of a bright light or disc. Morgan had written:

> If the legendary identification of stars with souls is an exact, a scientific fact, ... then I did, in truth, hold a star in my hands, a ball of stellar energy as shining, as glorious, as the Sangraal itself.

And so it was that they began worrying the symbols into a strange life, almost imploring them to yield their secrets. When Flavia Keene died, they thought that a great step forward would be made because the stone would at last come to light. In order to forestall any possibility of its being disposed of before they had seen it, Dr.Starke had arranged to view it through the courtesy of Dr.S.M.Mitchell who attended Flavia during her last days. Even so, the stone had eluded him. He had, however, been able to view a possibly significant painting by Hilary Morgan which Flavia had had in her possession, significant, that is, in the context of Dr.Starke's investigations.

In the meantime, Abigail, by virtue of a passion stronger even than her devotion to Ruth, had been led to betray her sister's secret to Basil Seton. Having learned of his search, and of his presiding obsession, she had broken the pledge which her sister had exacted from her before the altar of their personal sorority. Seton was unable to believe that the stone lay hidden in the little whitewashed cottage on the banks of the river Ewenny, in Glamorgan; that it was, in fact, the Cor-Abbenic which enshrined his ultimate Graal. But Abigail had caught a glimpse of the sphere in an unguarded moment, when her sister - dazed by the trance of ecstasy which it had induced - had omitted to return it to its hidden shrine. The ecstasy had turned to anger, and to Abigail - who stood before the stone as before a fragment of azure fallen from the heavens - it seemed as if clouds obscured that sky; and as the waves of Ruth's anger blackened it, Abigail resolved to remain silent. But the strength of her resolve, the fear of her sister's rage, were as nothing beside Basil's despair, and she had told all. It had brought her nothing but misery, for not knowing where Ruth had concealed the stone, Abigail was powerless to prove her story. It therefore remained for Ruth to reveal it, and she did so in a manner that was to leave Seton no alternative but to investigate Abigail's assertion.

Ruth was haunted by guilt. She read in the glances of strangers, even, their certain knowledge not only that she was a murderess but - and this was, to her, infinitely more heinous - that she had slain her friend for the object whose startling brilliance surely all eyes could see. Wherever she might hide it - in earth, in iron, in wood, or stone - the glow of its glory must cleave any prison, making of it a translucent cask flashing with its incredible rays. Her terror subsided, partially, when she immured herself in the cottage and found relief from the gaze of passers-by, of people who knew her, or thought they knew her, and who also knew her secret. But Abigail knew that the glow on Ruth's face was the flush of forbidden ecstasy rather than the serenity of interior illumination. Her dress now consisted of a single seamless garment, adorned by the medallion of antique gold which she had bought from Louis Bruhm one unforgettable summer afternoon; the medallion which - later - Basil Seton was vividly to remember.

This particular phase of Ruth's activities began with experiences similar to those undergone by Flavia, except for the manifestation of the dwarfish horror. She saw the lake beside which Seton had wheeled Morgan during his last illness. When Seton later appeared at the cottage as her sister's lover, Ruth conceived for him an immense hatred. Being members of the Beaumont Club, they had previously met. It was at this time that the hieroglyphic finally discharged its contents, as a sigil might suddenly give birth to the entity of which it is the linear expression. Ruth had experienced inner raptures comparable to those which Flavia had known, although in Ruth's case they took the form of joys bestowed by the phantom woman who, at

Ruth's desire, had slain her friend. These joys gave way to periods of profound revulsion, when Ruth came near to taking her own life, and they were followed by a phase of perverted fantasy which gradually dissolved in vacuous silence. She rarely showed herself, even to Abigail.

It was during this period that Abigail noticed a thickening of Ruth's features; they became heavy and lugubrious where before they had been delicate and serene. An unhealthy pallor spread over them, as a white bat might trail across a sullen face fashioned in clay, on which the lees of wine have traced mauve veins, its drooping wings. And in her eyes there swam a slow horror, as sometimes observed in the eyes of the insane. And there seemed to sprout on this mask of clay the ambiguous foliage already bursting from the seed quickening within her, embalmed as an alabaster statue.

Basil Seton, convinced at last by a compelling inner certitude regarding Ruth's treasure, terrified Abigail by demanding to see it. He feared that Ruth's incipient insanity would swamp her reason, washing away all memory of its whereabouts. Abigail waited with dread for his emergence from Ruth's room, for she could not believe that her sister's pregnancy had proceeded from a natural cause. Seton was aware of Ruth's peculiar proclivities and he was infuriated by Abigail's fears, because of certain suggestions implicit in Hilary Morgan's Statement. These confused threads of irritation and apprehension were submerged by the most urgent requirement of settling once and for all whether or not the secret nurtured by Ruth was identical with the object of his search.

Yet Abigail, even in her extremity of foreboding, was not prepared for Seton's discovery. He came into the room in which she sat, and it was a long time before he was able to tell her that in an agony of guilt and revulsion Ruth had rid herself of the stone that had destroyed her. He told Abigail that Ruth had looked upon her body, whilst speaking to him, as if it enshrined the soul of a demon, to which - slowly but surely - she was feeding her blood, her intelligence, her vitality. Her hands had plucked at the air, her hair, her breasts, as if despair had sought expression in the senseless motion of her fingers which conveyed more of horror to Seton than all her words. When she told him that she had rid herself of the stone, the fact did not immediately imprint itself upon his mind. Then, as a flaming brand sears the flesh, he felt its impact. She had thrown away the shew-stone, had 'thrown it into the bright water' - she did not know where!

Abigail, recalling the nocturnal movements of her sister, remembered that three or four evenings previously Ruth had left the cottage for a short while. Abigail supposed that she had then disposed of the stone. But where? In what water? The cottage stood on the east bank of the river Ewenny, not far from the estuary. Perhaps she had flung it into the sea. It would have taken her precisely twenty-five minutes, Seton proved, for Ruth to have reached the sea and returned to the cottage. But Abigail observed that it had been at the ebb of the tide, and that it would have taken Ruth a longer period had she in fact done so, unless, of course, she had let it fall into the river, which she could have done without setting foot outside the cottage. But even had she done so, what chance had anyone of retrieving it? Seton himself came near to insanity when he contemplated Ruth's action. Had he known how Flavia Keene had died, he would perhaps have remained unmoved, but the thought of the abandoned stone plunged him in a passion of rage.

Abigail had calmed him, one evening, after such a spasm, when Ralph Carter appeared. She had, in an extremity of despair, written to Carter - whom she did not know, personally - because Seton had mentioned his name in connection with occultism. Furthermore, Abigail knew that Carter was a member of the club to which Seton and her sister belonged. What she did not know was that Carter had recently been informed of a great many matters concerning Seton, in consequence of the latter's suggestion that Dr.Starke and Paul Chisholm should enlist Carter's aid. Seton was, to some extent, able to collect himself when the visitor arrived, and Abigail was almost happy to be able to share her burden. It gave her a chance to grapple with the problem of Ruth, and of what was to happen to her now that she needed medical care and attention. Carter relieved her of this anxiety by suggesting Dr.Starke as the best possible source of advice. But he brought even more hope to both Abigail and Seton when, on hearing the story of the stone's disposal, he demonstrated that even a casual interest in ancient place-names could sometimes be useful. Seton had reported that Ruth had thrown the stone into the 'bright water', and Carter observed that Ewenny - the name of the river running past the cottage - meant just that. Abigail, knowing the locality intimately at once associated the words with a certain pool. It lay parallel with the river, and almost exactly opposite the cottage. It lay, in fact, in the district named Ewenny, which was so named after both the river and the pool. Furthermore, she knew that it would take approximately fifteen minutes to reach the pool, and ten minutes to return from it, lying as it did in a hanging wood on the steep hillside leading up from the cottage. The cottage itself lay without Ewenny proper, and bordered the locality known as Sutton, which commenced just before the road swept round the base of the hills near the mouth of the river. Abigail wondered if she should risk awakening an uncertain hope in Seton. But he had already seen the light. He was all for going, at once, to the pool, but Carter persuaded him to postpone the excursion until nightfall.

At the time the two men were about to set out, a telegram arrived for Carter requesting his immediate return to London, so Seton went alone to the pool of bright water.

9

The Pool of Bright Water

A full moon shone over Glamorgan, its pale brilliance bathing the sleeping village of Sutton, with its whitewashed dwellings and the ghostly road which linked them with Ruth's cottage and the hamlet of Ewenny on the farther side. It drenched with a distillation of snowy light the hanging wood, and communicated a glacial calm to the sultry air, redolent of summer scents.

Seton found the pool without much difficulty, though the wood was in places so dense that he had to hack his way through thickets of bramble. The trees were set closely together, and thick creepers swathed the overhanging boughs from which drooped spectral blossoms, which, like inverted chalices poured into the atmosphere a sickly balm.

Ruth had evidently not approached the pool by this route, because every so often Seton had been forced to slash through curtains of foliage that had not previously been disturbed. His progress had been a gradual and continual ascent, and he was surprised by the wildness of the terrain which, seen from the cottage, seemed a mere wedge of darkness driven into the verdant slope of the hill.

He reached level ground and saw again the pale bloom of the moon which hung like a lantern in a field of stars. It now shone at his feet in the dark black hollow of the pool. In the clearing about it the trees stood like spectral sentinels, withdrawn from the water's edge and leaving a narrow rim sprung with tall grasses and motionless fern. He circumambulated the pool several times, while the moon's brilliant pathway crossed its surface unobstructed by overhanging branches. He could observe with ease in its light the limpid depths, but he saw no sign of that other bright sphere. Congeries of giant water-weeds were spread here and there over the water, hiding some of its abysms, although the long tapering stems of their delicately tinted blossoms were clearly to be seen in the crystal depths. The calm and translucent expanse was aptly named Bright Water.

He sat upon a lichened stone that time had weathered into a shape suggestive of some antique deity, thrusting from the earth its defiant token of forgotten ages which yet lived on in the tranquillity of such unvisited retreats. And the thought reminded him that he himself sought from black aeons an unknowable survival.

A profound serenity, and an almost voluptuous indifference to his failure to discover the object of his quest, contrasted stangely with the rage and hatred that had possessed him a little earlier. But it did not strike him as odd. He felt a different man, calm, assured, receptive to the cool lunar rays which drenched with their ethereal radiance this secret sanctuary. He no longer strove to coerce to visible appearance the object of his obsession, but contentedly surrendered himself to the subtle influences that enveloped him.

From afar he heard the muffled thunders of breakers echoing in rocky caves, and as the sound of the surf merged with the scents of the woodland he felt a delicious lulling of his senses and a compelling and hypnotic suggestion irradiating from the shining surface of the pool, reflecting so purely the bright and exalted orb.

Thoughts of Abigail and Ruth sailed across his mind, but they left no impression. A great peace possessed him. After what seemed an immeasurable time, he became aware of intense activity taking place around him. The pool, limpid in the moonlight, was violently agitated, a shuddering convulsion disturbed its calm surface, and, as if heaving itself massively into another dimension, it gathered itself together - and vanished! Rather it left a residue of brilliance which Seton mistook for the moon itself. It was as if the moon had dried out the pool, or frozen it utterly, and then descended upon it. But the pale orb still hung in the night-sky, and Seton knew that in some inexplicable manner the pool had distilled its quintessential luminosity in the object of his search. The shew-stone lay before him, as it were the soul of the bright water. He tried to rise, but his body refused to move. He then had a vivid impression of wheeling Hilary Morgan by the lake at Brankley Park. He remembered how, from the depths of the lake one summer night - a night similar to this - he had seen arise a vaporous mist in the form of a column, as it were the pillar of a temple.

Above it shone the full moon, and at its base gleamed hieroglyphics reminding him of Egypt. But the vaporous column was not the pillar of a temple, but the support of a catafalque upended on the shining surface of the waters. Morgan had grown excited, and wished to remain, alone, by the lake. Seton had gone up to the house, wondering at what he had seen, knowing it was no mere hallucination.

Seton now recalled that other evening as he watched this incredible phenomenon. A mist hovered over the dry basin, veiling the stone in a shroud through which, occasionally flared pinpoints of brilliance. Then a star shone out, and a crescent moon emerged and cupped its curve beneath the star. Seton knew what he was about to see, and he shuddered. The star was the reality of which the glyph on the sarcophagus was the lineal expression.

Several other matters became plain to him as a long dormant memory awoke within him of ancient, yet vaguely familiar, things. The moon-cupped star resembled the head-dress which surmounted - how well he remembered it now! - the face of the Queen Hat-Abaft-Sume. She regarded him steadily through a gauze of violet mist; it was a haughty and imperious regard, and in the face which concentrated in that gaze an infinite arrogance combined with an irresistible fascination, Seton recognized familiar contours. But some image which he struggled to identify eluded him. He seemed upon the brink of making a momentous discovery, yet each time the veil was about to lift, he floundered in seas of forgetfulness.

The face rose slightly, its head-dress outlined against the trees encircling the pool. Gradually, an entire human form materialized before him. Seton's rudimentary knowledge of the hieroglpyhics that appeared upon her violet robes, told him that he looked upon one of the most evil and alluring queens of history.

The sense of calm assurance that had descended upon him on his taking up a position by the pool, seemed now perfectly natural and necessary as he rose to greet this ghostly figure of an immemorial past. His lips formulated the old salutation, now lost to the world, which he remembered as if he had uttered it but yesterday. Her ringed fingers, her jewelled arms, rose musically in the sign of acceptance as he stood before her, his arms folded upon his breast. When she addressed him at last it was by the name he had never really lost, but merely forgotten: Sutekh-Khem, High Priest of the Temple of Sevekh, in the reign of Hat-Abaft-Sume, Queen of the XVIIIth Dynasty of Ancient Khem.

Her voice came through the veil as golden chimes gliding on moonbeams. Her glittering eyes were sometimes veiled by long-lashed lids of amethyst, and her mouth - as if painted with fresh blood - curved in a smile which the unsmiling eyes belied. Then she spoke; and her speech was a sonorous, almost caressing breeze of music, with a slight huskiness, rich in *timbre*, resonant, infinitely refined. It possessed all its old and hypnotic potency, and he was once again as clay in the hands of this woman who had defied even the Gods. Indeed, she herself claimed to be the Creatrix, the incarnation of Sevekh-Khepsh, that primal Star-Goddess who was old before the gods of the Sun and moon had been conceived in the womb of Time.

He bowed his head before the Power which streamed all about him, enclosing him in azure folds of starlight, voluptuously cool and soothing him to sleep.

49

In that sleep she instructed him. She would again take birth among men, and Ruth was to be the medium of her return. Before the appointed time he - Basil Seton - was to enshrine in his work the Mysteries of her Cult, as Morgan before him had done; and his paintings - entering the homes of her chosen - would prepare the ground for her secret work. At a certain specified time, after the birth of the Child, he was to give the Stone into the keeping of Lawrence Hector. For slaying the previously appointed medium of her reincarnation, and for abandoning the Stone, Ruth would languish many years, a prey to madness. Before this came to pass, the Stone would avenge a death, and rid the world of a monster.

Silence ensued, and Seton sensed the onset of her anger. Her eyes flashed, and Seton - only partially aware of objective phenomena - heard, as through another body, reverberations of thunder echoing in the surrounding hills; heard the distant sea boil as a cauldron seething with fury; saw the summer-lightning flicker in the night-sky. Her rage thrashed the elements to fury, and it seemed as if Ruth - against whom the venom of wrath was directed - must perish in the storm. Then, suddenly, all was calm; the winds became a gentle breeze, fragant with sweetness of summer; the sea laved the rocks, far away, with insidious whispers; the lightning no longer violated a cloudless sky.

Flashbacks of Seton's life then appeared to him as it had been in those distant days. He knew that a submarine crypt in Egypt housed the mortal remains of Sutekh-Khem. They lay beneath the glaucous lid in a royal chamber lit by incandescent vegetation. He remembered that Hilary Morgan had been reticent about certain matters that occurred that night by the lake in Brankley Park, when the catafalque had formed out of mist before their eyes. Morgan had not, in his statement, revealed the identity of the occupant of the third sarcophagus, he merely had written, tersely, ambiguously, concerning the features he had seen: 'At that period of my life I knew no face to which I could have likened it. Embalming salves had preserved its expression of refinement, of true nobility.'

Morgan had recognised in Seton, long after the incident described in his statement, the priest who had played a vital role in some ancient magic involving two priestesses of the royal house of the Eighteenth Dynasty. Seton was reminded of that other priestess, as another memory awakened from its age-long sleep, explaining why he recognised the Queen. She was the sister of Sesh-Bâst, the priestess enamoured of Sutekh-Khem. The course of the couple's life together, and the final vengeful act of the jealous Queen against their passion reawakened in his consciouness. But he now had no time to re-live the anguish of that long forgotten drama.

Seton awoke as from a trance, stiff in every limb. He had fallen from the lichened outcrop and lay huddled on the dank moss. In the even illumination of early morning the clearing had assumed an air of cold detachment, in marked contrast to the intimate warmth it had possessed the previous night. Rising painfully, he saw the pool; not a tremor disturbed the cool glass of its tranquillity. The giant waterweeds were locked in sleep, each fragrant flower closed in upon itself. The trees, reflected in immaculate stance, emitted from their foliage the melodious cries of birds. Beneath a drooping lotus, and almost concealed by its emerald stem, lay a dark object scarcely distinguishable from the mud in which it was embedded. Above it, irridescent fish wove phosphorescent arabesques. Seton, not at all surprised, heaved out the object, disturbing the calm surface of the pool and the sleep of the lotus which opened shyly, and offered the pure chalice of its flesh to the virgin morning. A black box resembling an old sea-chest secured by metal clasps, relinquished easily its aqueous abode as Seton lifted it out and laid it on the bank. On its lid, in brass, were the initials R.C.

He descended from the pool of bright water by the way which Ruth must have approached it, for he encountered no obstacles on his return journey. He emerged from the hanging wood and was suddenly rooted to the spot as he took in the vista of wreckage caused by the night's storm. The cottage had been all but devastated by lightning, its seaward side had crumbled and was still smouldering. A clot of people and cars, some of which were now pulling out across the hummocky turf, confirmed his worst fears. He thrust the black box into a thicket of gorse, careful - even in his panic - to mark the spot near the limestone rock which jutted from the turf. He then plunged down the hillside and joined the little group which eyed him with astonishment. He gazed with mute horror at the body which two men were carrying out of the ruins. It was Abigail's. There was somebody at the rear of the cottage, but she had locked herself in. They would soon have her out; and they did. Seton felt desperately ill and was helped into a neighbouring house and given refreshment. Then he departed to roam the wood until the light faded. He sought his treasure but the box had disappeared.

10

Seeing through the Oblivion of Time

Dr. Starke and Paul Chisholm were discussing Ruth Chalmers, who had recently been admitted to the doctor's clinic in Chelsea.

It had been a difficult task persuading Ruth's father to commit his daughter to the doctor's care. Raymond Chalmers, however, respected his daughter's peculiarities, and he realized that Dr. Starke more than any other could give to her the help she needed.

Ralph Carter was gradually deciphering the hieroglyphics appended to Hilary Morgan's Statement, and Basil Seton was expected that afternoon to tell them more about the Stone, which had been lost again so soon after its retrieval. Morgan's Statement had been purposely withheld from Carter in order not to prejudice his interpretation of the hieroglyphics. In Seton's case, a rather more delicate motive had dictated their withholding; not only the fact that Abigail had been murdered on the night of the storm - which he already suspected - but also the fact of a previous sexual assault upon her.

A police officer had been sent down from Bridgend - the nearest town - to enquire about Ruth, who had been extricated from the debris. While the matter of her mental health was being investigated it had been confirmed that her sister's death had been due to murderous assault. Seton, although unable to supply an alibi had been dismissed because there was no evidence against him. He was, however, in the invidious position in which an innocent suspect often finds himself. It had been all that Dr. Starke could do - and for Dr. Starke, in this instance, read the Beaumont

Club - to obtain for Seton some respite from enquiries which had assumed, in view of his previous relationship with Abigail, the proportions of an ordeal. What had further complicated matters, and made things worse for Seton, was the fact that the police had been informed of the unusual manoeuvres of a motor car, later discovered to have been stolen. The report had come from a farmer in Ewenny who had noticed the car heading for the coast. He had also observed it on his return journey, for it had stopped near his farm and backed into a field where the driver had left it and walked in the direction of the coast. Next morning, the car had gone; it was found later, abandoned, at Reading. As nothing further had come to light concerning it, and as the police were satisfied that Seton had no part in the matter, it had been dropped.

Seton was careful to omit, in his narration to Dr. Starke, any reference to the erstwhile priest of the Temple of Sevekh. The omission was not due to fear that his sanity would be doubted, but because a part of his nature revelled in the certain knowledge of his destiny, and he wished to preserve inviolate his secret. He felt it to be more a part of his essential nature than did his present personality, which seemed but a cloud obscuring his true identity. He had felt more himself by the pool of bright water than he did as a member of the Beaumont Club, or even as as artist.

The ease with which he was able to give a sincere account of the occurrences at the pool, without introducing the one element that would have made the event intelligible to Chisholm and the doctor, proved the correctness and supplied the authentic seal of this identity. His sense of frustration at losing the stone was understandable to Chisholm and to the doctor, without reference to any other factor. Seton told them that he had 'seen' the 'Queen' mentioned in Morgan's statement; that she had revealed the hiding place of the stone; that he had predicted the perpetuity of Ruth Chalmers' insanity, and the birth of the child. He omitted to mention the part he was to play in respect of the stone and its destiny. He sincerely desired to help Ruth Chalmers, Dr. Starke, and his friend, but opposed to this desire was a powerful sense of loyalty to pledges made in antiquity, pledges to a person he both desired and feared. This person, this object of his age-long desire, exercised so powerful an influence over him that he had no option open to him. Although he had loved Abigail, a lessening of that love had occurred, even as had his love for the sister-priestess of Queen Hat-Abaft-Sume, centuries earlier. In this matter he sensed the existence of past memory, as if a veil obscured the mysteries of a sudden change of heart, the shock of which had obliterated all but the most nebulous traces of an experience too violent and terrible to recall.

When he had finished retailing his experiences, Chisholm drew attention to various facts apparently unnoticed by any of them:

'It seems to me', he said, 'that the sigil which we have agreed to identify with the ancient hieroglyphic known as *seeing through the oblivion of Time* has a double effect, according as to how it is applied. For Hilary Morgan, and for Basil, here, the appearance of the sigil in the stone stimulates creative energy which later manifests in artistic expression. In other words, the sigil possesses the ability to open cells of psychic activity and to evoke forces which rise up into consciousness in order to express themselves in artistic creation. This seems to apply to men. To women, however, the sigil fertilizes emotionally and physically, and when improperly conceived, produces results such as are observable in Dr. Starke's patients, *who fear children, and adornment*; and in Flavia Keene and Ruth Chalmers, who, conceiving the sigil completely, were rendered physically pregnant. The overpowering aversion to adornment is proof of my theory, for all jewels - and the Stone is the Jewel of Jewels - were associated, in the ancient mind, with insemination, fertility. And what is the ancient mind but the subconscious mind?

'It seems fairly certain that the Stone, which we know to have been a magically constructed object, was designed originally to incarnate something other than physical children'.

Seton nodded agreement, and Dr. Starke then took up this line of thought:

'According to Carter's translation of the hieroglyphics, Hat-Abaft-Sume was the materialization of a primitive stellar goddess. The Queen was obsessed by a desire to reincarnate this deity at some future time, when she would be able to manifest to the full the peculiar powers with which she had identified herself'.

Chisholm continued the doctor's reconstruction from this point:

'I have investigated this matter rather thoroughly. In the thirteenth dynasty, a priestess - a royal priestess - identified herself with this same unearthly power. In the dynastic Lists she is designated Queen Sebek-nefer-Ra-Nu, and she reigned during the first thirteen years of the XIIIth Dynasty. Her consort was the Pharaoh Amen-em-Hat IV. There then followed a very long lacuna in the records of ancient Egyptian history. When the lists are resumed again it is with the reign of Aahmes, in the XVIIIth Dynasty; Hat-Abaft-Sume was his consort.

'The prolonged silence between the beginning of the Thirteenth Dynasty and the beginning of the Eighteenth Dynasty has been explained (by some historians) as due to successive invasions, resulting in the almost total obliteration of religious monuments and temples, by powers intent on substituting in their stead their own cults. Other authorities claim that the phase of oblivion is to be accounted for by internecine and religious antagonisms between the followers of the Star Cults (of which Sebek, or Sevekh, was the supreme and primordial concentration), and the Sun Cults, which eventually prevailed.'

Seton indicated that he favoured the latter explanation, and the doctor was surprised by the vehemence with which he professed his conviction, surprised by his having any particular opinions in the matter. He was even more surprised when Seton took up the conversation, and said:

'For all the superficial resemblance it bore to the solar cult, the reign of Hat-Abaft-Sume was a revival of the power she had previously wielded as Sebek-nefer-Ra-Nu in the thirteenth dynasty. This is why her tomb was despoiled and had to be set up again, and reconsecrated in the crypt in the Fayûm. Fayûm means the 'country of the Lake'; it was a centre of the Stellar or ante-solar Cult, and as such became the secret temple of its worship'.

Chisholm, apparently oblivious of the stress under which Seton laboured, added:

'That fits nicely into the symbolism. Is not the crocodile the chief symbol of Sebek?'

'It is', replied Seton, 'the priests observed that as the sun-god, Ra, slid each night into the pool of Amenta, at that supreme moment of solar death, the crocodile was the last object visible upon the horizon. It was as if, with its mighty jaws, it devoured the sun-god in the waters of Space, thereby giving birth to Night (Nu) with her stars, and to the Moon, splendid in her solitary triumph.'

'So', resumed Chisholm, 'as symbols, the Lady of the Lake and the Crocodile are identical. The waters consume the sun and give birth to the moon - and the stars'.

'And the Star', added Seton emphatically.

'How very apt is all this symbolism', remarked Dr. Starke, 'it undoubtedly explains the hieroglyphic for 'water', as well as for 'vision'; for the moon is the eye of the sun at night'.

'If we study the manner in which the stone was fashioned', said Chisholm, 'we come to an even clearer understanding'.

The doctor assembled a sheaf of papers bearing copies of the ancient hieroglyphics which Ralph Carter had been elucidating. The papers, summarised and illuminated by Chisholm, aroused intense interest in Dr. Starke, who had been unable to interpret their significance. As for Seton, he lived again through experiences that had occurred several thousands of years previously, as if they had occurred yesterday; and so vivid were they at times that they seemed to synchronise with Chisholm's reconstruction of them.

'We should realize', Chisholm continued, 'that the ancient Egyptians were in the habit of identifying the subconsciousness with the Underworld, known as the Amenta, the 'hidden place', the Land of the Dead. The dead lived on in another world, similar to the *Bardo* of the Tibetans, about which certain facts have in recent years been made known to the world at large. In remote times there existed a science of death which did not necessarily involve the actual decease of the priest-magician. By this I mean that by a special magical process he was able to enter the Underworld before his physical death, and he did so by identifying his subconsciousness with a particular god-form, or symbol.

'Ancient Egyptian god-forms combine human and animal qualities, such as the hawk-headed Horus, the cat-headed Bâst, the ibis-headed Thoth. Each magician had his own formula for entering the Amenta, his own peculiar mode of identification with this or that god or goddess. He did not identify himself with the actual animal connected with these deific forms, but with the magical power of which the animal was a symbol. For instance, the cat's ability for nocturnal vision, the lion's strength, the flight-power of birds, or the faculty of seeing in the Underworld represented by the serpent, and so on. One could go on indefinitely elaborating the layers of such a system of symbolism. But once a symbol or a sigil had been annexed by the subconscious mind of an Adept, once it had been 'charged' with the peculiar magnetism latent in the subconsciousness, it acquired a vitality and an identity of its own. It is true that this vitality derived from the source of its origin, the mind of the magician, but this did not automatically prevent its developing peculiarities over which the parent-source had no direct control. Before applying these observations to the hieroglyphics, I shall explain the manner in which the sigil was vitalized.

'The ancient Egyptians embalmed their dead, and committed them to the Underworld by means of elaborate ceremonies, the details of which we really know very little. Some authorities consider the rituals of embalmment and entombment to be symbolical in themselves of further mysteries. The Egyptians knew that for magic to be effective, desire, or Will, must coincide with subconscious vitality; that is to say, the Will must be magnetized by subconscious or occult energy. If the desire remained conscious, however, it would achieve fulfilment only at some future time, a time determined by the laws governing material manifestation. They therefore rendered desire subconscious by so formulating it that the conscious mind remained unaware of it. In other words, they 'forgot' the desire, and submerged it in Amenta, and this process was symbolized by the swathing of the mummy in anonymity, and then entombing it.

'We do not know the actual means employed, but the sigil known as 'seeing through the oblivion of Time' was charged by the occult vitality of an advanced Adept - in this case, the Queen Hat-Abaft-Sume. The hieroglyphics contained in Morgan's Statement show how this magical rite was performed more than four thousand years ago.

'A duly consecrated priest was charged with the office of vitalizing a sigil which meant nothing to him; that is to say, he was unaware of its hidden meaning and of its object. This we now know to have been 'the reincarnation on earth of the *Khu*, or magical personality, of the Queen Hat-Abaft-Sume'. The sigil was then steeped in magical fluids in a curiously constructed vessel that embalmed it, as the mummy-swathings embalmed the symbol of the Living God in the Underworld, of which the perfectly preserved corpse was the supreme symbol. The chalice of forgetfulness, in this case, took a very novel form. Queen Hat-Abaft-Sume possessed magical knowledge far beyond that of the more advanced magicians of her time. She had discovered a way of blending the influences of the stars with their corresponding astral counterparts in a human being endowed with supreme magical power.

'According to the hieroglyphics it was the priest, Sutekh-Khem, who was chosen for this high office. He performed the operation successfully with the assistance of a priestess whose name, unfortunately, is not recorded. The operation took time, probably a long time, for there are indications that many moons passed before the stone reached the degree of density necessary for the introjection into its depths of the magical sigil. The vitalised Will was thus embalmed in this magically created star, as a fly is embalmed in amber. Yet, unlike the fly, which may be seen by the physical eye, the sigil is a subjective phenomenon, which on being infused into the solar consciousness of the male, inspires intellectual and artistic creation, while a similar infusion into the lunar consciousness of the female engenders physical offspring.'

'Not only physical offspring', interjected Seton, 'but the specific physical offspring of Hat-Abaft-Sume, who will be able to take up her abode on earth once more.'

Dr. Starke was unable to fathom Seton's fervent interest in the long-dead Queen; he could not imagine that Seton really believed in the substance of Chisholm's researches. However, all he said in reply was:

'It looks as if Ruth Chalmers will have her child, after all.' Chisholm looked at him, blankly, as the doctor added: 'She is well on the road to recovery, and as sane as we are at this moment'. He eyed the two of them rather doubtfully. Seton breathed a sigh of relief.

'To revert to the hieroglyphics', said Chisholm: 'As I remarked earlier, such a magical operation - so deep in its nature, so vast in its scope - could generate effects in a distant future of which the initiators could know nothing. We must suppose this to be the case here, since there is no mention of the Guardian Elemental of the stone, referred to in Morgan's Statement. Can it be that that abnormality was born accidentally, caused by a flaw in the original magical rite? We may never know.

What is certain is that the priestess with whom Sutekh-Khem performed the rite, so enflamed the anger and jealousy of the Queen that the latter consigned to perpetual exile in the Underworld her sister's *khu*, or magical personality. This is now, therefore, fixed perpetually in that incarnation in which it was bound by bonds of blood to Hat-Abaft-Sume. This awful fate precluded any chance of reincarnation. This was, then, the vampire form seen by Morgan, which, in its despair, compelled him to search out the lode. It wanted him to destroy it, or perhaps in some way to change the sigil within it, thus enabling the *khu* to reincarnate again in the world of humanity, and reverse the Queen's evil spell. But the attempt was unsuccessful.

'What I fail to understand is the rôle played by the Guardian-Elemental, since it did not in fact protect the stone from violation.'

'I can enlighten you on that point', said Seton in a slow even tone. It was as if some profound level of his being had opened and flooded his conscious mind with strange knowledge. Was he merely guessing or had he learned these things at the pool of bright water? Dr. Starke had no time to decide; he was too amazed by Seton's explanation.

'The High Priest, Sutekh-Khem, was enamoured of the Priestess, but he also desired the Queen, who was to him forbidden fruit, both as an Initiate of supreme degree, and as a lady of the blood royal to whom none but the Pharaohs, or gods incarnate, had a right. And the Queen, in her turn, desired Sutekh-Khem, and a fire of jealousy consumed her because the creation of the Star-Stone that would enshrine the vehicle of her future reincarnation required that the priest and priestess unite in a magical marriage differing from the union of ordinary mortals only in its ultimate process. She therefore determined that the priestess should die, even as she herself would die, at the culmination of the Rite which ensured her own return to earth. But, unlike the evil queen, the priestess would be unable to reincarnate in a self-possessed form. The Elemental had been created after the fashion of an *homunculus*, though of astral, not physical matter, with the purpose of guarding the tomb. This office it successfully fulfilled, for although the tomb was desecrated by marauders after the Queen's mortal remains had been consigned to it, the dwarf protected the sarcophagi, and the cask, and caused them to be removed to the sub-aqueous cavern which Morgan described. How this was achieved we do not know, but as Chisholm has already mentioned, the Cult of the goddess Sevekh - of whom Hat-Abaft-Sume was the incarnate focus - continued to flourish and to become extremely powerful. It possessed all the resources required for the secret transportation of the sacred bodies, and of the mysterious cask which thus remained unopened until Morgan himself sundered the seal.

'The cause of the Elemental's waning power lay in the vengeance of the priestess. After her death, her *khu*, or magical body, remained for centuries in a sleep of oblivion. But on awakening from that age-long sleep, she remembered both her identity and her sacred office. To her it seemed as if she had slept but a moment, and uppermost in her consciousness was the fear and the hatred inspired at the time of her death by her sister's action. Her sleep had been, as it were, nourished on the sweet essences of vengeance, extracted from these bitter fruits of hatred and fear.

To the Guardian-Elemental, the passing of the centuries had been as corrosive as are time and change of temperature to all chemical substances, however tenuous, causing them to undergo subtle and sometimes unpredictable transmutations. The process had engendered a personality where previously there had been but a reflex of the Will of the magician who had created it. The Elemental, being composed predominantly of masculine energy, the priestess had been able to turn the slave of the Stone into the slave of its own desires, into her slave, in fact, since she was the closest and most potent object to which those desires could apply. And so the power of the Elemental diminished, and the priestess waxed on the energy which she drew from it. This enabled her to project an almost tangible body in which she could move about and be seen by mundane eyes, and desired by mundane flesh. She soon tired of playing the vampire, however, for she realized that only by possessing the stone itself could she nullify the sigil within it, and substitute for it another which would enable her to achieve her long desired end. She therefore directed some incarnate spirit to acquire it on her behalf'.

Seton concluded his statement abruptly. Chisholm was astounded:

'Which explains the Encounter on the Pavement', he said. 'She was *almost* physical; materialized in some kind of ectoplasm which lent her the appearance of a living human being'.

Dr. Starke, who had been profoundly affected by Seton's account, then said:

'Ruth Chalmers has told me that a materialisation such as Morgan described appeared also to her, *and, in a fury of revenge, killed Flavia Keene.*'

Seton and Chisholm rose to their feet simultaneously. Chisholm's face was a mask of horror: Seton was smiling a queer smile:

'You see', Seton explained, 'if Flavia Keene had given birth to her child, if the Stone had burgeoned, the priestess would not have had long to live - a few years; perhaps fifteen at the most; and what is that in aeons of time?'

'Do you mean', asked Dr. Starke, 'that the Queen could destroy her soul?'

Seton did not reply; a new fear had possessed him. He looked steadily at Dr. Starke: 'Every care must be taken of Ruth Chalmers'.

'But the Stone', interjected Chisholm, 'where is the Stone?'

'That I do not know', replied Seton bitterly, 'but wherever it is, we can be sure that Sesh-Bâst, the Priestess - will not rest until the sigil is changed; and she has little time if the operation takes several moons in which to effect such a change'.

'But surely', said the doctor, 'surely this dispossessed spirit, this *vampire*, could have secured the Stone with ease whilst Bruhm had it in his keeping! After Morgan had removed it from the cavern, what was there to hinder her?'

Chisholm could not answer the question, but Seton did, and he spoke again with that authority which the others now sensed as proceeding from another personality, though neither of them guessed the incredible truth:

'Time in Amenta is not as our time on earth. Although I spoke about time a moment ago in connection with the Stone, I wished to convey the idea that from the point of view of an incarnate soul, or embodied spirit, the Chalmers' issue will write *finis* to the Stone's potential, so far as concerns Sesh-Bâst. But Sesh-Bâst is not motivated by considerations of time, any more than a fly on the ceiling aims at gaining the wall before darkness falls. She is impelled by interior impulses of which terrestrials can know nothing. When the Lode responds to particular vibrations, as when it emits a rhythmic beat resembling that of a heart, or when it flashes forth colours, then her sleep is stirred. Why, it is not possible to say, You must remember that her own essence went into its composition, and this the Queen herself is - possibly - incapable of destroying, even of neutralizing. One who sleeps for centuries, and awakes with memory unimpaired, and who supposes herself to have slept a mere night, cannot be expected to calculate precisely the infinitesimal degrees of time of which we, in our comparatively brief acquaintanceship with it, are capable. Only when some particular condition of the Stone has rendered her consciousness of it external, or actual, has she manifested in accordance with the laws governing her peculiar nature. The Stone, being partly herself, perhaps she can never wholly possess it objectively; some unpredictable factor always hinders her acquisition of it. As with ourselves, we can think about ourselves up to a certain point, but when we try to seize the Self and analyze it, we fail, for the instrument with which we would grasp it is more truly ourself than the object of our quest. The case may be similar where she is concerned'.

'What you say about the heart-beat of the Lode is significant in view of what Ruth Chalmers had told me', said Dr. Starke. 'She experienced this phenomenon shortly before Flavia died, and her insanity derives from her sense of guilt, for she desired the death of her friend so that she herself could possess the stone.

'Poor Ruth!', exclaimed Seton: 'How terrible are human agonies, how awful the pits to which they consign us, but...'

His attitude changed, abruptly: 'We must retrieve the Stone', and he added, almost in a whisper: 'Ruth's child shall be the glory of the stars!'

11

Transformation

Basil Seton again found himself in quest of the Stone. The priestly side of his nature encroached more and more upon the man, who, in contrast, seemed a mere bundle of disconnected tendencies. He sought fulfilment not only in art - the culmination of aesthetic ecstasy - but in that other, more occult art that has its origin in ecstasy. He set himself to find by deep unremitting introspection the source of that fulfilment which was the lode-stone of his soul. He, no less than Hilary Morgan, Flavia Keene, and Ruth Chalmers, had been attracted to the lode, and Lawrence Hector - to whom Seton had been charged to convey the stone in due course - was also to be attracted. And the cause of this immense attraction which consumed every life and soul drawn into its orbit, was the Queen Hat-Abaft-Sume, whose earlier avatar was Sebek-nefer-Ra-Nu. The affinity with the Stellar Consciousness which she embodied was the real lode. This consciousness, which is experienced by those who live in the ambiguous atmosphere of artistic creation, flowers mysteriously in the artist devoted to that hidden aspect of Beauty of which the evil queen was, perhaps, an impure reflection.

There are certain shadowy and oblique natures that recoil from broad daylight, and seek pleasures in strange ecstasies. There are some who prefer the unfamiliar, the dark byways, to the well-trodden highways prostituted to the uses and abuses of indifferent travellers. These go in the same direction as their fellows, and at the same rate, but they have nothing to report at the end of their journey beyond unreliable impressions of the way they have come, and of those with whom they have travelled, and an even less complete understanding of themselves, whom they appear to have forgotten on the way. The Beaumont Club tended to consecrate candidates to the more oblique pathways, and the stellar consciousness had nourished and directed the artistic genius of Hilary Morgan, who had succeeded in expressing the soul of the Stone. He had painted many pictures while under its influence, and every painting produced after his experience in the temple, enshrined, materially, some of its vibrations. Seton was unable to fathom this mystery during Morgan's lifetime, but after his own experience of the lode he began to understand its subtle workings. He knew that it emanated a mysterious effluvium; that it communicated to those who beheld it, an actual though immaterial part of itself, and that this in turn flowed out of the beholder and into the painting, sculpture, or music, which formed under the artist's hand. These works of art, in their turn, communicated to the beholder a portion of their charge, and this inspired reactions as diverse as the individuals concerned.

When Louis Bruhm began selling Morgan's pictures - and it was Bruhm who first made the world at large aware of Morgan's genius - his curio shop became the flourishing establishment that attracted clients such as Flavia Keene and Ruth Chalmers. It was, in fact, after Flavia Keene had come into possession of a 'Hilary Morgan', that she developed the strange and powerful personality which so attracted Ruth Chalmers. And in Ruth, the stellar charge stimulated a latent store of creativity which resulted in the poems first sponsored by the Beaumont Club. Yet this had been a side-issue, for an inscrutable force had already chosen her to be the matrix for its next incarnation. That which was to awaken in Lawrence Hector a genius for scientific inventiveness, in Seton a fulfilment of artistry hitherto denied him, proceeded from the soul of a unique personality who had lived upon earth many centuries previously, and who now was attempting another fully conscious incarnation. It was the intention of this soul to revive the ancient Stellar Cult with the added powers and experiences that had accrued to it over the intervening aeons.

The Beaumont Club had no specific headquarters. Wherever several members gathered together, there was the Beaumont Club. One evening it happened to be assembled in the rooms of Lawrence Hector, on the top floor of a house in Gloucester Square.

Seton was talking to Hector and others, and the conversation naturally touched upon Ruth Chalmers, whom nobody had seen since the disaster at Ewenny, and whose pregnancy - in view of her inclinations - had come as a surprise.

Dr. Starke was at the gathering, but beyond volunteering the news that Ruth was recovering, and that she had begun again to write poetry, he did not have very much to say. Everyone felt mildly resentful since it was due to the Club that Dr. Starke and Paul Chisholm - who was not present on this occasion - had been able to make such an interesting addition to their collection of unusual cases.

The entrance of Ralph Carter was - to Dr. Starke at least - a welcome diversion. No one had seen Carter recently. Ill health and the strain of devoting much time and energy to the decipherment of the Egyptian hieroglyphics had not only kept him away, but had caused a reappearance of the distressing fits to which he had for many years been subject. He looked haggard and pale, and the static side of his otherwise mobile face seemed more rigid than usual. Seton joined him and they talked about Egypt and the Queen Hat-Abaft-Sume. As was becoming increasingly apparent, when Seton directed his mind to these matters the priest gained ascendancy over the artist. Carter was surprised to find him dogmatic about incidents concerning which nothing was certainly known. And Seton, in turn, was surprised to find Carter equally emphatic about minute differences in interpretation where the Morgan hieroglyphics were concerned. Their interchange seemed to lack an essential element, which made it a curious combination of fact and fantasy. It was as if a couple of relatives discussed a family problem without reference to their own relationship, as if the knowledge of their relationship had been totally forgotten.

As the evening wore on and their discussion became more and more animated, Carter exhibited the unhealthy flush, which, superimposed upon his usual abnormal pallor lent him a ghastly appearance. Seton, looking back on that evening, realized that moment to have been the starting point of Carter's attack. A spasm of pain stabbed him as he rose from his chair, struggling for breath. At that moment Seton was talking about the Lode and had made a casual remark, so casual in fact that he was later unable to recall it. As he went to Carter's assistance and loosened his collar, Seton noticed something which made him recoil as if he had been physically struck. Beneath Carter's shirt there glowed darkly the medallion of antique gold which Ruth Chalmers had been wearing on the night upon which the lode had disappeared, and Abigail had died. And in a flash, he understood; understood the deceit behind the telegram that had called Carter away - Carter himself had sent it; understood the story of the stolen car; understood ...

Seton's thoughts, careering confusedly in a chaos of conflicting impulses, were suddenly stilled, frozen like an ice-bound lake in a paralysis of terror. There, before him, the body of Carter -naturally diminutive - seemed to have shrunk to half its usual size. An added horror lay in the peculiar twist which now contorted it into a spiral deformity; and the man's face had grown suddenly *hideous*. Before Seton's gaze there reeled and simpered a dwarfish creature bereft of all human characteristics. The garments which clothed it - now many sizes larger than the form they concealed - were stirred by violent paroxysms as the creature fought for breath and wheeled blindly about the room. Its hands resembled talons, yet in a sense they were delicate, fragile hands, the swift movements of which reminded Seton of butterflies, or moths, fluttering in dark foliage. The medallion encircling the crooked neck, now curiously hirsute, flashed beams of light that danced before Seton's gaze like sunshine on cascading water. Then, in a spasm of pain or passion - induced perhaps by its inability to accept the truth of its identity - the creature leapt upon the window-seat and hurled itself through the heavy velvet curtains draping the French windows. The splintering of glass accompanied an in-human shriek which recalled - to Seton - awful invocations in a subterranean temple.

Seton sank to his knees, shocked into unconsciousness. On his exit from waking life he entered the place of the tombs, and saw, through the translucent lid of the cask of Sesh-Bâst, a strange transformation. The lips of the priestess had parted in a moment's agony; it seemed as if that inhuman shriek had proceeded from the pale throat, and - even as he looked - the face and the form crumbled into dust. Then the shade of a breathless form slid over the lid, leaving in its wake a viscid trail. The

Guardian's eyes - so like, yet so unlike, the eyes of Carter which had glared at him a moment earlier - now no longer saw him. The dwarf had dissolved into the realm of shadows.

In this way was fulfilled the prophecy of Queen Hat-Abaft-Sume: a death had been avenged, and the world had been rid of a monster.

12

Paul Chisholm Explains

Dr. Starke was talking to Paul Chisholm in the private room of his Clinic: 'I, too, have disturbing news', he said, in reply to Chisholm concerning Ralph Carter's death: 'My most interesting patient has vanished'.

Chisholm did not seem surprised: 'Does Seton know?' he asked.

'No one knows, yet, except her father. I discovered the fact only this morning. She took her usual turn round the garden in the company of her nurse, who, as it happened, was called indoors for a moment. When she returned to the garden, the patient had gone, and the gate of the enclosure was wide open. It is very distressing'.

Then the doctor fixed Chisholm with a steady gaze and said:

'I do not go as far as you seem willing to go, in believing that her child would differ in any way from other children, unless ...', he hesitated, and Chisholm waited for him to conclude, but the doctor seemed irresolute: '... but I do', he went on, 'believe that we should have had a great deal more light on the matter from Ruth herself. We may even have learnt something about Carter's death'.

'As I understand things', replied Chisholm, 'both Seton and Carter are clear cases of double personality. If Seton is correct, then Carter was responsible not only for Abigail's death, but also for the special cases you have had under observation for so long'.

'You suggest that Carter went about in his other personality, terrifying people out of their wits?'

'Not exactly. I believe the dwarf-like elemental attached itself to him during the spells of unconsciousness which he habitually experienced. As they grew more frequent and of longer duration the obsession became physical, so that whereas an astral entity is at work in the cases under your care, in Abigail's case Carter's physical body was also involved. He may not have suspected the precise nature of the obsession, although I have no doubt that he supposed himself to have been inert during his lapses of consciousness. He would shut himself away on the excuse of illness or debility, but I think there was more to it than that, and that he feared some eventuality such as occurred when Seton brought the obsession into his conscious mind. If he had been unsuspecting, how account for the Abigail tragedy and the bogus telegram?'

Dr. Starke nodded: 'But why did Carter want the stone? Seton, by the way, had no difficulty in tracing it; he found it in Carter's rooms.'

'Yes, I know', replied the other, and then he added: 'I think you'll find that each of your patients have - or have had - in their possession a picture by Hilary Morgan.

According to Seton, the paintings emit an influence, in a diminished form, identical with that emanated by the lode itself. A further point of interest struck me last night as I went through Carter's papers and translations of the hieroglyphics. He did not once refer to the Guardian of the Stone. Was this intentional, because he suspected the identity, or is there in fact no mention of it in the hieroglyphics themselves?'

Chisholm was unaware that Carter had suppressed allusion to the dwarf for precisely the same reason that Seton himself had withheld knowledge of his own identity with the high priest, Sutekh-Khem. But although the reasons were similar, the two cases were of an entirely different order. Carter's was a case of gradual possession; Seton's, one of actual identity.

'But why should Carter have been the one to be possessed by this creature?', queried the doctor.

'I think that Carter's interest in the occult predisposed him psychically, as he was predisposed physically by his disease to influences of this kind. His involvement with Hilary Morgan, Louis Bruhm, and others who were under the lode's spell, made of Carter a suitable vehicle for possession.

'Seton, who plays an ambiguous part in this ghastly affair, tells me that the medallion found on Carter was the one that Ruth habitually wore. It came from Louis Bruhm's establishment. On one of its sides is a portrait of the priestess, Sesh-Bâst, who had a direct link with the dwarf. It seems to me that when Carter tore from Ruth's neck that medallion, and left her locked in the burning cottage, he had assumed to himself - totally - the monstrous soul of the Guardian Elemental which had taken substance from the long-dead flesh of the priestess. For as long as the flesh remains - embalmed flesh being no exception - it exudes a subtle effluvium which may act as a materialising agent for any obsessing entity able to make use of it.

'I know nothing of Carter's origin, but I am prepared to wager that no living person can give a satisfactory account of it'.

'But this is utterly fantastic', exclaimed Dr. Starke: 'I thought you implied by your earlier remarks that Carter - like any other victim of obsession - once had a human soul that was ousted by malefic influences.'

'There was', replied Chisholm, 'a human soul in Carter, but it was not Carter's; it was a soul-fragment of the person who created the dwarf.'

'You mean the Queen Hat-Abaft-Sume?', the doctor asked, incredulously.

'I do', replied Chisholm: 'She had cursed Sesh-Bâst, and, by magic spells, prevented her from reincarnating. But the Elemental, which the Queen had created, enabled Sesh-Bâst spasmodically to materialize, by virtue of its desire for her. And so, in a sense, she endowed the dwarf with her own humanity. As time went by, the human component created for itself a centre, a nucleus, and Ralph Carter was the end result. When he died, she with whom he was magically united, also dissolved, owing to their unnatural occult affinity. The soul of the priestess, cursed long ages ago by Hat-Abaft-Sume, was then freed from the vampire body it had been doomed to inhabit in order to prey, for its continued existence, on creatures like the dwarf.

'If we understood the mysteries of incarnation and of reincarnation, we should have to evolve an entirely new system of psychology and psychiatry. I think the time is not far distant when we shall be obliged to readjust our theories of the soul, and review the Stevensonian theory of a plurality of selves, of several obsessive entities going into the make of a single soul. And if we, as individuals, are constituted of all the souls and personalities which we have ever been, then our future selves no less than our past selves partake of a vast congeries of influences, animal, human, divine; perhaps stellar, lunar, and solar! a ramifying complex of subtle vibrations, any one of which, at any time, may - by a chance word or a glance - be evoked into present reality.

'Magic is a matter of memory; of re-*membering* the past images of ourselves, be they images of beasts or of gods, or both, as in the weird hybrid entities of the ancient Egyptian pantheon. If we could remember ourselves completely, we should become as the Gods; by remembering incompletely we become monsters, abortions; by not remembering at all, we are the so-called normal creatures of everyday life.'

'You mean', asked Dr. Starke, 'that we are all involved in some way or other in this affair of the Egyptian Queen; that we have all played a part, you and I included, in this drama of thousands of years ago?'

'Undoubtedly', replied Chisholm. 'The reappearance of the stone has unsealed in some of us the cells of elder memories; in others - ourselves, for instance - there remain, mercifully, barriers to the full remembrance of those past identities. And yet, it would, perhaps, be better if we could know, and accept, as poor Carter came at the last to know'.

'So that by an arbitrary series of incidents, in the present case the stone and its vicissitudes, one or other of our past selves is awakened again to life?'

'Not arbitrary', corrected Chisholm, 'but as rigidly predestined as Seton's recovery of the stone; as Flavia Keene's madness, and Ralph Carter's death. These things were determined long ago, and could doubtless have been 'read' in the stone by any competent skryer'.'

'But why should the stone, and not any ordinary object, awaken such deep strata of memory?'

'Because the lode is the perfect example of a talisman charged with magical vitality by the ancient Egyptians, the vitality of the subconsciousness. Its seemingly miraculous power lies in its longevity, in its ability to transcend vast cycles of time. But is this any more mysterious than that a celestial orb is capable of similar longevity? How do we know but that the stars themselves were not created in a similar fashion?'

Dr. Starke remained silent; deep in thought. The sun's rays slanted through the rich blue of the curtains draping the diamond-paned windows.

'Then it is inevitable that Ruth Chalmers disappears at this vital moment of time; that no amount of effort to trace her will avail?'

Chisholm smiled and raised his eyebrows:

'You must not fall into the error of fatality, inferring therefrom that all your actions are outside the workings of fate. Might it not be a part of fate itself that we are destined to make every effort in our power to find her and bring her back? How may we judge of these matters from the limited, and therefore distorted viewpoint of the conscious mind alone? In the present circumstances I think we can do nothing but wait, but we should wait watchfully, not inertly, so that our very awareness may reveal in the light of consciousness the clue we are seeking'.

'Then you think disaster may be averted, that evil may be avoided?'

'I do not think disaster may be averted, that evil may be avoided, but I believe that 'evil' may be transmuted, so that that which we normally interpret as disastrous becomes an experience of positive value for the future embodiment of our selves'.

'I take it, then', said Dr. Starke, 'that Seton's recovery of the stone will lead to fresh revelations; that it unseals the subconscious mind, which is a universal reservoir available to all who are able to dive into it.'

'Precisely. Those aspects of ourselves which *appear* to be outside us are merely crystallizations of memories which we have, in the course of time, forgotten. The Sigil called 'seeing through the oblivion of Time,' is an engine that effects a release of memory from the thraldom of forgetfulness. Your patients are unable to awaken this sigil. I believe that if they were brought into contact with a sentient symbol, a living and exteriorised subconscious projection, such as the Stone, then the Sigil would swing inwards, like a door whereon a sign is painted, revealing the totality of their past selves. I believe that their appalling visions of the Elemental - perhaps occurring in the presence of one of Morgan's paintings - caused a violent shock, the impact of which threw their minds out of gear without effecting total recall'.

Chisholm paused awhile, then he continued:

'I should be interested in Lawrence Hector's ideas of the lode, its chemical composition, its physical laws, properties, and so on; but now that Seton has salved it a second time, nothing short of his death would make it available for examination.'

'What has become of Seton?', asked the doctor.

'He has shut himself up with it. I gather he spends his time painting under its influence. Remarkable results will no doubt be announced before long. In the mean time, we can do little but wait for a clue as to the whereabouts of Ruth Chalmers'.

'You have spoken about god-forms, sigils, sentient symbols, and Egyptian sorcery, but what exactly is the purpose of the Star-stone, the stellar lode?'

'I think it is an instrument of reincarnation. Hat-Abaft-Sume was herself a reincarnation of an earlier queen, Sebek-nefer-Ra-Nu of the Thirteenth Dynasty, who, in turn, concentrated and transmitted certain cosmic forces. She was not human in the strict sense of the term; her assimilation to the Star Goddess was, no doubt, a mythical mode of explaining her extraterrestrial origin.

'The Egyptian Mysteries were derived from the Inner African worship of stellar deities, of which the later goddess Nu, or Nuit, is perhaps the most celebrated. She is sometimes depicted on all fours, a posture indicating animal origin, and arched over the earth on to which she sheds starlight, indicative of her extraterrestrial connections. Nu and Isis are two distinct forms of one and the same idea expressed at two levels: the terrestrial and the extraterrestrial; and we are on the point, perhaps, of seeing the dead or mummified Hat-Abaft-Sume-Isis reintegrating her stellar nature as Sebek-nefer-Ra-Nu.'

13

The Years Pass

Basil Seton had long relinquished the inner struggle that had caused him so much anguish before the second recovery of the stellar lode. The consciousness of his power as a Priest of the Mysteries, as a Magician in the service of Queen Hat-Abaft-Sume, flowered in spite of the limitations of his present incarnation.

Seton had received an ordinary education; had passed through the various phases usual to a man of his class and circumstances, and had approached middle age with no exceptional achievements either to his credit or to his discredit. Yet there had existed in him from his earliest youth a keen desire for freedom greater than his status - in every sense of the term - permitted.

He had been drawn irresistibly to the work and - later - to the personality of Hilary Morgan, and, once under the sway of that artist's genius, had gone far to evoking his own. At first, he had not developed beyond mere talent, and a gift for assimilating his master's creative *ethos*, without any originality on his own part. Now, however, influenced directly by the talisman which had released Morgan's store of creativity, Seton found himself, also, the vehicle of forces which all but overwhelmed him. So much was he obsessed with the idea of transmitting to canvas the emanations of his genius, that he had not the slightest interest in the fate of Ruth Chalmers, or even of the issue about which the witch-queen had spoken. He knew, with absolute certainty, that the latter would manifest again; that her powers of magic were equal to any eventuality; that she would triumph in the end. It was the deep conviction of the fanatic, who does not stop to consider that equally fanatical personalities in the opposite camp are doing their utmost to frustrate his designs. But such a state of mind enabled Seton to work unhindered by desire, anxiety, doubt, by all the obstacles that strangle the lukewarm attempts of mediocre artists. He worked as he had never worked in his life, tirelessly, ceaselessly, absorbedly. Painting upon painting seemed to fall from him, as leaves from the silent Autumn trees. His canvasses were thronged with unfamiliar shapes engaged in strange rites, in the consummation of ineffable mysteries, the central sacrament of which was none other than the Stellar Lode. He communicated to each one of these remarkable works a certain sinister quality which impressed - as a tangible radiation - the sensitive beholder. The Lode glowed for Seton in sunshine or in darkness, but the bright luminosity occasionally departed from it, and a swirling mist troubled its depths, in which appeared the violet-lidded mask of the witch-queen.

As the days merged into weeks, and months, the lode underwent a subtle change which Seton barely noticed, until, one day, he realized that the queen's image no longer appeared. He sensed in this withdrawal a strange connection with reawakening memories of Ruth Chalmers, and he knew without doubt that the child would be born, and that She would come again.

The thought inspired him with even greater creative fervour, and it reacted on him more powerfully even than had her appearance in the lode, for that were but a glamour cast from another world. And so, when the moment came for parting with the stone, he relinquished it calmly, determinedly, and in an almost casual manner.

Lawrence Hector had called upon Seton at his London address. Seton had taken him aside and, without any ceremony, given him the lode wrapped in a mauve-hued veil. And such was the inevitability and the necessity of the occasion that Hector had carried it away, knowing that his life would be transformed.

Seton's works, unlike those of Morgan, were an instantaneous worldly success. This was part of the Plan, and Seton accepted the ordeal of publicity as a strengthening of the bonds which united him to the witch-queen. He saw the sudden flooding, so unlike the slow trickle of his master's works through obscure channels as beginning with Louis Bruhm's curio shop. But Morgan's work had paved the way, had made possible Seton's enormous success, although few were aware of the single source of their inspiration.

Hector, on the other hand, although acclaimed by the Beaumont Club, was unknown to the world at large. His peculiar genius had revealed itself in the realm of nuclear physics, in which he had made important discoveries. But there was one discovery about which even the Beaumont Club was unaware. It lay in a unique contribution to astrophysics: the projection through the Stone of sidereal corridors which linked the stellar zones with earth's astral atmosphere, thus forming a network of space-tunnels for the traffic of extraterrestrials. Being primarily concerned with the study of objective and measurable phenomena, the lode did not affect Hector in the manner in which both Morgan and Seton had been affected. In the highly specialised laboratory which served as the field of Hector's scientific creativity, he had submitted the lode to tests involving enormous extremes of temperature, exposure to subtle rays, nuclear and atomic radiations, and submersion in electrically charged fluids which constituted the solution employed in generating the astral corridors.

One still and sultry night, a slight explosion had wrung from the lode a rose of green smoke, which, had he read Morgan's Statement, he would instantly have associated with the curious illuminations emitted by certain nocturnal flora that had - in the course of aeons - developed strange magnetic properties. And Ruth Chalmers - had she seen the plume of smoke - would have recalled a visit to Flavia Keene, and an aroma suggesting poisonous flowers and the cloying odours of a laboratory. And the faint pulsations within the stone would have recalled - to several people - unforgettable moments. This pulsation, which combined the highest frequencies with the most profound resonances, indicated, as Hector had discovered, the presence of astral entities. By altering the frequencies, totally different entities would be evoked into the stone. But of the laws determining such operations he remained ignorant for many years.

The only incident which distracted Hector from his researches in the years following his acquisition of the lode, was the news of Seton's death at a time when the artist's fame had reached its zenith. Hector, withdrawing temporarily from his profound absorption, regretted that he had not questioned Seton more closely about these matters, and he realized with some annoyance that he had gradually arrived at an acceptance of certain 'occult' hypotheses proposed by Seton and various other members of the Beaumont Club. Hector's attitude to the stone now embraced all the transcendental categories implicit in the influence which it had wielded over Seton, and others, himself included. It brought about in him the realisation of the part which he himself had played in the lode's creation thousands of years previously. The years he had devoted to its investigation had effected a subtle realization of identity, so that the fact came to his notice, objectively speaking, quite casually and as if by accident.

It was while signing his name that the realization dawned on him with the certainty of irrefutable conviction. The name Hekt-Ankh-Khonsu was that of a priest-magician in the Temple of Sevekh, and it reminded Hector of a brother-priest named Sutekh-

Khem, whom he knew - in a flash - to be one with Basil Seton. He marvelled at the sport of destiny that had given the same names to the same forces manifesting at intervals of thousands of years. Hector had once been Hekt, a name of Isis in her dark and sterile phase, so characteristic of the scientific mind and its approach. Sutekh and Seton, too, were identical, for Set was the son of Isis, and On was his solar brother, Horus, which, as the single name Set-On, combined the two-fold character of the priest of Isis, known in her stellar phase as Sebek. And was not Sutton - where Ruth's cottage had stood - the abode for a time of the stellar lode itself, and the town or place of Sut, or Set? Carter, even, was remembered as the Khart, that aspect of Isis who - in her waning or lunar phase - was represented on the monuments by the hieroglyphic of the dwarf, or crippled child.

So engrossed was Hector in these reveries that he lost touch with mundane events and the changes that had occurred since he had embarked upon his researches; changes, not only in the Beaumont Club but in the outer world generally. He was not aware, for instance, that a mysterious individual known as Besza Loriel presided over and dominated the more progressive coteries, which was a remarkable phenomenon in that she was an extremely young and beautiful woman. So great was her influence that she was forging into a vehicle for her wild ideas the machinery of the Beaumont Club and its continental counterparts.

It is one of the ironies of fate that when news of this person finally penetrated to Hector, he dismissed it with irritation and engrossed himself yet more profoundly in his study of the lode. Absorption had given way to devotion. He was no longer a scientist pretending to investigate an object without admitting the subjective element - his own self, but a priest, who, through total identification with the object of his worship, had himself been initiated directly into its mysteries.

14

The Star of Nu-Isis

Changing each moment, she defied all analysis, her essential identity remaining concealed from all, Besza Loriel fell upon the artistic and intellectual circles of London and Paris, as a tiger on its prey. She swept all before her. Her presence was an inexplicable mixture of elemental power, ancient wisdom, extreme sensibility, and ravishing beauty. Those whom she favoured with her attentions were exalted and strangely transformed. Not only did lovers find their mistresses more amorous; artists, their models more beautiful; poets, their muse more pliable, but these vehicles of creativity emanated a subtle current of energy which affected profoundly those with whom they came into contact. Each woman became a source of creative inspiration, and powerful to arouse the cosmic mind refracted through her mate; and men began producing work in their particular fields of activity, of an order transcending anything of which they had, previously, been capable. Men who had relegated their lives to the limbo of the might-have-beens, the failures, the eternally frustrated, now blossomed afresh, like stunted trees which, after years of sterility, burgeon again. Yet behind the complexity of these flowerings, a discerning person -

such as Basil Seton - would have detected an order, a pattern, a preparation for some greater manifestation yet to come. These individual fulfilments constituted a strange arabesque which formed a vast tapestry only to be apprehended by one who patiently had watched the threads, bright and dark, interweaving on the loom of Time.

In addition to these manifestations of genius were the few specially chosen individuals, consecrated by past initiations, who came under Besza Loriel's direct influence. The immediate proximity of a battery charged with energies transcending all known powers, animal and human, exercises a profound attraction over anyone who experiences it. But when that transmitter is not, strictly speaking, of a human nature; when it partakes - in its essential being - of the cosmic currents it is constantly discharging, then indeed its power of fascination is absolute. Such was the influence of Besza Loriel on those of her inner circle. She was to its members the supreme sovereign of their souls, as she had been to them a Queen in remote antiquity.

Although the distorting lens of history had endowed her with 'evil' powers, as a prism breaks up pure white light into multiple colours which stain its original perfection, personal contact with her dispelled this illusion. She appeared immaculate to those who adored her and would have died to fulfil her slightest wish. Lawrence Hector, alone, of exclusive coteries such as the Beaumont Club, remained aloof and absorbed in matters which he considered of greater import than those connected with Besza Loriel and her circle. His reserve protected him from the overwhelming glamour of her presence, and it was this quality in him that singled him out for her special attention. Even Seton, absorbed as he had been in the creative frenzy which she had inspired, had not had the strength whilst in her presence to remain withdrawn. In the artistic consciousness, emotion predominates; in the scientific, the intellect rules. Hector's cold and unemotional nature responded to her in the depths of his work, not in the depths of his individualised personality, and through his self-effacement he accomplished for her the supreme and most exacting task.

In the white interior of his laboratory the shining sphere was held fast between the clamps of a highly sensitive instrument which he had perfected during the course of many years. Two dark globes, like lodes of darkness, drained the sphere of its hidden lightnings. The process was prolonged, of exquisite subtlety, and invisible to the naked eye except at certain times determined by lunations, when a flash of azure leapt between the two dark globes. There was then a faint hiss which rose to a shrill shriek of sound, as a bat falling prey to high voltages emits its death-squeal as it plunges earthward. That squeal, vastly amplified, would suggest, vaguely, the sound which sporadically sundered the silence of the laboratory. Invariably, it would be followed by a muted throbbing, like the whir of a dynamo. Muffled explosions denoted the venting of extreme compressions of energy, or faults in the apparatus transmitting the magnetic currents from the lode itself. Then a cloying scent would fill the air, accompanied by greenish coloured vapours. In his record of the Great Experiment, Hector referred to these manifestations as 'the incense of Isis'.

Many months passed without any appreciable alteration occurring in the lode, and then, one night, a barely noticeable change became apparent. The stone had diminished in size; so slight was the change that Hector may not have noticed it but for the fact that a minor explosion had caused the sphere to stir in the clamps. Had he not noticed, a time must have come when the fragile sphere, slipping its moorings, would have fallen. The idea filled him with dread not unmingled with horror, and he prepared a bed for the lode's reception in the event of any such accident. His attention was then completely absorbed in trying to fathom the significance of the stone's diminution in size, for the mass of its content was in no way diminished, there being no modification in the physical density or in the activity, molecular or atomic, of its complex constitution.

In that other sphere of Besza Loriel's circle, chemical and other observable reactions (had they been scientifically recorded) would have told a different story to that unfolding in Hector's laboratory. Such was the brilliance of the explosions discharged in her atmosphere, electric with her presence, that she found it easy to draw the attention of a multitude to a startling phenomenon. This was the appearance in the night-sky of a new star, which, she declared, would soon transfigure the earth.

Astronomers in several parts of the world - independent of Besza Loriel's declaration - had observed the star's *primum mobile* without being able to explain its origin or its sudden appearance. Theories abounded, ingenious, conflicting, fascinating, but none approached the truth of the matter. Nor did Lawrence Hector suspect any connection between the sinister luminary and his own unremitting labours. He knew only that vast quantities of dissipated energy were going *somewhere*.

The votaries of Besza Loriel knew that Hector had provided the vehicle for her cosmic influence, and that she would soon withdraw from earth and establish her centre, once more, in the sphere of the stars. Proclamations were already being circulated in various strategic centres of scientific and intellectual activity. One such proclamation declared itself in the following terms:

'A new and compelling influence is enveloping the earth, and, as yet, there are few individuals who are open to the influx of its subtle vibrations. Its rays proceed from a source as yet unexplored by those who are not at one with it in essence and in spirit, and it finds its present focus in the outer universe in the transplutonic planet Isis.

'In the inner being of man, also, this influence has a centre which will slowly begin to stir in mankind as a whole, as the influence strengthens and flowers. As it is at the beginning of its course in relation to man, however, many ages will pass before he may avail himself fully of the great powers and energies which this influence is   silently and continually bestowing on all who know how to identify the inner core of their being with its deep and inscrutable heart...' [2]

It went on to state that a special arcane school had been founded in order to disseminate information concerning Nu-Isis, and to enable each individual to enter into the stream of its subtle vibrations. It was further stated that 'the Mysteries of Isis and her ensouling energies, as radiating forth upon man from her macrocosmic centre' were 'gradually revealed' in this sodality.

Besza Loriel, although not mentioned by name in the Proclamation, was the High Priestess of this Stellar Cult.

As time passed, the star waxed in size and in power, and Lawrence Hector became aware that the lode, in its diminishing, was transferring its peculiar vitality to the vehicle prepared for it in the Outer, where its rays descended through the prism of

Extracts from *The Manifesto of New Isis Lodge*, London, 1955.

the ultra-saturnian planets, and the Uranian, Neptunian, and Plutonic astromagnetic rings.

Paul Chisholm thought it possible that such a star - a seat of trans-human Intelligence - could attract sympathetic particles from all the planets in turn, from Pluto down to the Earth, and that the essence of these orbs would contribute to this single and supreme concentration of power.

As the Great Experiment proceeded, Hector saw the sphere shrink perceptibly. At this period, Besza Loriel's appearance in society also grew appreciably less. Also at this period, Flavia Keene's lover, Herbert Roydon, engaged Hector in one of those private dramas which the newspapers are seldom able to explain. If a murder is committed and the chief suspect is known to have benefitted materially by the crime, the fact is considered as an almost positive proof of his guilt. And so, when Roydon broke into Hector's laboratory one night, and shot him dead, the press - unable to discover that Roydon would benefit materially by the crime - concluded that he was a madman. And when, later, his own body was discovered lying beside the corpse of an unidentified woman, from whom nearly all traces of humanity had been effaced by prolonged illness, it was suspected that some version of the eternal triangle may have been the cause of the scientist's death. But the newspapers were not to know - how could they? - that Roydon had once been a Priest of the Sun in the Temple of On in ancient Egypt, and that having learned the story of Besza Loriel's birth, from her own mother, he had set out with the sole purpose of destroying a reincarnation of Sevekh, which he regarded as an abomination.

It had not been difficult for Roydon, obsessed as he was with the occult occurrences surrounding Flavia's death, to piece the puzzle together. He knew that if the star gained ascendancy, the outcome for humanity would be disastrous. Terrestrial tyrants, and other, lesser demons, fed on blood; but Besza's lust was for creative energy, the very soul of man, which, after transfusion with the spawn of Outer Space, would be injected by Besza into the wombs of women to breed a monstrous and non-human race.

And so, when Hector died, and the physical medium of one of the most resourceful intellects in the history of science was no more, the stone, shrunken to the size, almost, of a child's marble, burst from the clamps, as Hector's body crashed against the apparatus of his strange sorcery. There were blinding flashes of flame, and tremendous explosions as azure lightning blanched and shattered the dark terminals. Roydon escaped destruction by a miracle, to die by his own hand, together with the mad mother of Besza Loriel.

In all that chaos of smouldering destruction, a small black stone, a mere cinder, bespoke the death of a star. It is possible that the cinder, if polished, would shine again with the glistering luminosity - supremely fascinating, supremely compelling - of infinite and forbidden things, for it was once the soul of the Queen, Hat-Abaft-Sume.

Perhaps, if Dr. Starke still lived, he would recall a remark of Paul Chisholm's: 'And even then, at the moment of fulfilment, and after vast cycles of time, a course of events often seems to be thwarted by a trifling 'accident' which renders the whole operation futile.'

Epilogue

When emerging from one of those reveries that occasionally possess one in the compartment of a railway carriage, and which are induced by a mingling of all the essences which a hot summer afternoon distils, one sometimes finds oneself - as I once did - gazing uncomprehendingly at the first object which falls within the range of vision.

A lustrous sun, suspended in the frame of the compartment window, induced my sleep; a brightly glistering object met my gaze when I awoke.

It takes several seconds for thought to readjust itself at such moments, to reintegrate the flow of ideas which claimed one's attention previous to the lapse. It took a full minute therefore before I realized that I was staring at a brilliant pendant - onyx, obsidian, jasper? - which nestled at the throat of a remarkably beautiful woman seated opposite me in an otherwise empty compartment.

In order not to appear churlish I turned away my gaze, only to discover that I was quite incapable of letting the ornament out of my sight. It was on glancing at it for the umpteenth time that I became aware that I was being subjected to a scrutiny just as intense as that with which I had initially scrutinized the pendant. I became aware also of large eyes gazing at me steadily from beneath violet lids. They reminded me of luminous flowers whose fragile blossoms glow in waxy sheaves of foliage recalling the texture of flesh, but not of living flesh. The woman regarded me languidly, yet so intensely that I recoiled as from the glance of a snake.

The chance similarity between an actual person's face and that of a creature fabricated by the mind - particularly in sleep - could be attributed to the fact that having noticed the person's face before falling asleep, the subconsciousness merely weaves about it a fantasy. A sense of positive uneasiness amounting almost to anxiety occurred, therefore, when I remembered that the compartment had been empty when I entered it. It had remained empty, as far as I was concerned, until I awoke a few minutes later to find the seat opposite to mine, occupied. As the woman had evidently entered the compartment at some station *en route*, it might be argued that I had but half awakened, caught sight of her face, and relapsed again into reverie, taking with me the memory of it.

However fortuitous the connection in my mind between the cinerial soul of Queen Hat-Abaft-Sume and the jewel adorning the throat of my travelling companion, it was not unique, for there now hung about the carriage a cloying odour with which I was strangely familiar, but which I was totally incapable of placing.

I began to recognize and to analyse various other elements of my recent reverie, some of which definitely partook of ascertainable actuality; ascertainable, that is, to myself, for one of those elements was a friend of mine named Irving Starke. In fact, my dream-Starke differed from the actual person of that name only insofar as his relationship with others was concerned. He had, to my knowledge, no friend by the name of Paul Chisholm, and nor indeed had I; and yet Dr. Starke appeared in my reverie with knowledge he could have gained only from Paul Chisholm, who was indeed an actual person and well known in certain occult circles.

And so I began to conjecture that the woman opposite me might possibly bear some relation to the Queen of my dream, although in what manner I had no means of determining, *unless I asked her*; unless - in fact - I appeared to her as a person, it were wiser not to engage in conversation.

I cast at her a furtive glance. The nails of her pallid and slender fingers were lacquered with mauve and rested on a leather handbag; they seemed to *bleed* about her an atmosphere of mauve which was reflected from her eyes, which glowed with a mauve luminosity. My gaze rested on the glistering gem which stood out in sharp relief against the statuesque stillness of her throat. I was about to ask my question when I noted, almost with revulsion, that the gem was not what it seemed, but - like the dream-queen - that its polished surface failed utterly to conceal its abominable essence.

I looked again at the woman. Her sole adornment consisted of the black gem suspended from a chain of antique gold. Her hair was wound high upon her head in a fashion suggesting African or Asiatic influences. Her clothes well suited her smooth, almost reptilian elegance. She was a paradox of barbaric sophistication, yet I still could not formulate my question.

She, for her part, did not encourage me. Her face, like the faces of women who are conscious of their irresistible fascination, remained an impassive mask. She might indeed have been a Queen-Priestess; forbidding, inscrutable, yet the large liquid eyes suggested strange violences which smouldered and flickered like lightning over the calm surface of her features. But I was still no nearer to the intimate communion I was struggling to initiate.

It then crossed my mind that this woman, proud, haughty, disdainful, defiant in her calm and barbaric loveliness, may have chanced upon the gem as Flavia Keene had chanced upon...I was about to write *that other gem*...in the hidden places of my subconsciousness. In that case she would know nothing whatever of its history, its properties or the influence which it had exerted upon so many lives. This thought flooded me with hope. Should I not warn her? Were it not a crime to let an innocent woman attach herself to so malevolent a talisman? I sensed her eyes upon me; their expression dispelled instantly all thought of her needing any warning, all thought of her being an 'innocent woman'. Yet had not Flavia Keene herself been the type of all sophistication and mystery? Would it not have been better (had it been possible) to have warned her of the danger in the jewel she was buying from Louis Bruhm?

Suppose, on the other hand, this woman had chanced upon the stone, blackened, unpolished, lying in the vicinity of the explosions that had been the cause of its corruption; suppose the lode had drawn her towards itself; what purpose might it not have in directing such chance patterns to determined ends? The idea was a terrible one because it implied that the stone still lived. was still a sentient entity possessing volition, a will that must inevitably lead her to certain destruction.

My cogitations were interrupted as the train gave a sharp jolt. I became aware of two things simultaneously: firstly, that the train had been stationary for some while, and was now pulling *out* of a station; secondly, that the woman had vanished. I had been so sunk in thoughts of her that I had not noticed her disappearance! I gazed confusedly out of the window, but it was too late; all the passengers had left the platform; a solitary porter stared blankly into my compartment, then he, too, was gone. I sat back, a little breathless, my eyes fixed on the shining clasp of the handbag resting on my knees! My hands shook as I opened it and took out the small mirror sheathed in its lining. My eyes were heavy with recent dreams, languid, the arched violet lids half veiling their too bright lustre in vaporous drowsiness. I thought how melancholy I looked, how strangely beautiful. My hair was white, but very becoming in the way in which it coiled and reared like a serpent-crown upon my head.

The train was slowing down; I had arrived. Stepping out on to the platform I was surprised to see Dr. Starke himself coming towards me; he was wearing the anxious expression I had lately observed in his tired, worn face.

'I began to think you were lost', he said, and he smiled a little wanly. 'You know, it makes it difficult for me to let you go out like this when you come home so late. Roberts was here to meet the two previous trains; he thought he'd missed you completely. So what could I do but come and find you myself?'

Perhaps my thoughtlessness had reminded him of some similar incident in the past.

'What did you say my mother's name was?', I asked.

He stared at me; his eyes searched mine and then directed their gaze, almost fearfully, to the black jewel about my neck.

'I don't think I ever knew', he replied, tonelessly.

'Then I'll tell you; it was Chalmers - Ruth Chalmers'.

His face was inscrutable. 'Where have you been?', he asked, suddenly.

'I've been asleep'.

'I can't think the sun has been very kind to you; it has been quite unbearable here all afternoon', he said.

'I suppose that is why you have always called me Stella; I think that is quite clever of you.'

He smiled a deprecating smile as we approached a line of taxi-cabs and entered one.

'Come now!'. He took my hands in his: 'Let us not trouble ourselves any more about these matters.'

But I broke away.

His eyes were moist, and in a moment I believe they would have filled with tears; he was such a kindly old gentleman; so considerate; so sympathetic. He looked once more at the black irregular gem which nestled at my throat. I smiled at him.

'I've heard of a person wearing her heart on her sleeve', I whispered, 'but I think I can claim to be the first person of whom it might be said that she wore her soul about her neck'.

Dr. Starke looked into my eyes with infinite compassion, but very sadly, I thought.

Kenneth Grant wrote this tale in the mid nineteen-fifties.

Graal Mortum

"METAPHOR, MEDIA, MAGICK: AND THE BURIED CROWLEY"

Do what thou wilt shall be the whole of the law.

(N.B.: Spelling. It is explained in *Book Four* (Part 2) by Aleister Crowley that the original spelling of *magick* was adopted "to distinguish the Science of the Magi from all its counterfeits." This convention also applies throughout to the following, and is the reason why references made to "black magic" do not contain the "k" suffix.)

THE METAPHORS OF MAGICK

I

There are many definitions of Magick - at least as many as there are magicians. One of the most familiar is written in *Magick in Theory and Practice* by Crowley, and states that: "**Magick is the science and art of causing change to occur in conformity with will**". Another, less well-known one from the same source is: "**Every intentional act is a magickal act**". But whichever definition one gives, in all likelihood it will contain no mention of colour, because magick is fundamentally a colourless act. Whether it is "black" or "white" in the commonly accepted moral sense of those words is purely subjective, and based upon the motivation of the magician, rather than on the judgmental perspective of any onlooker. It is a curious anomaly too, that although magick is, at least in part, *hidden* or *para-* science, there have been no analogous descriptions of "black science" or "white science", even though these same moralistic considerations would apply - e.g, for a neutron bomb, or a cure for cancer.

Although the magickal act is, at root, one without colour, in the magician's temple it can involve and engage the other senses, in addition to that of vision. In ritual, the result of rightly using the relevant Correspondences (tabulated in *Book 777* by Mathers / Bennett, revised Crowley), is that all six senses are heightened. Enjoyment is then Had from the holy rapture which is a part of, yet beyond them.

When magick is spoken of as having a colour, the term is used as a metaphor; the sense in which it is employed throughout this essay. Whether any such metaphors are used with accuracy or not is something else, to be dealt with in due course. But they are, however, of vast significance: because what society perceives as reality is formed by, and based upon, the use of language, and the neuro-linguistic means by which information is transmitted. The figure of *Tahuti*, or *Thoth*, the Egyptian God of Language and Magick, is usually depicted holding a style and papyrus. Yet, as Crowley has written, this serves to indicate that "Thoth was merely a man who invented writing, as his monuments declare clearly enough. The whole subject of Magick is an example of mythopoeia in that particular form called Disease of Language." [1a] Moreover, the message is that "Writing is the real Magickal Art: a "grimoire" is nothing but "grammar"; "to cast a spell" explains itself; and an "angel" is merely a "secretary"..." [2a]

Metaphor describes *associatively* that which a purely factual description cannot ever hope to convey. It is of the essence of poetry, which, by attempting to describe the everyday, elevates it. When an everyday thing is described in metaphorical terms, it is foolish to first dismiss it as being unreal or immaterial, without asking what the **underlying** meaning might be which the author has **mentally constructed** in terms of communicating something to his or her peers. Naturally, this applies to speech as well as it does to writing; also, figurative symbols are non-literal metaphors. What is the nature of that underlying common ground of communication, the **cultural consensus reality,** which is being referred to?

II

In the 6th Letter of "his" posthumously-published book of correspondence *Magick Without Tears* (otherwise known as *Uncle Aleister Explains Everything*), Crowley established that the metaphor of *Schools of Magick* originated from an essay by Gerard Aumont, a French journalist and associate, which he had translated verbatim into English. Dr. Israel Regardie, one of Crowley's biographers, refuted this notion, and drew attention to the fact that, although Aumont was a real person known to him, the belief, style and opinions were unmistakably Crowley's own - a point with which I am inclined to agree. But whatever might have been the **reality** of the situation, according to Crowley-Aumont:

> "There have always been, at least in nucleus, three main **Schools of Philosophical practice...** It is customary to describe these three Schools as **Yellow, Black and White...**These Schools represent three perfectly distinct and contrary theories of the Universe, and therefore, practices of spiritual science. The magickal formula of each is as precise as a theorem of trigonometry. Each assumes as fundamental a certain law of Nature, and the subject is complicated by the fact that each School, in a certain sense, admits the formulae of the other two. It merely regards them as in some way incomplete, secondary, or illusory. The Yellow School stands aloof from the other two by the nature of its postulates. But the Black School and the White School are always more or less in active conflict; and it is because just at this moment that conflict is approaching a climax that it is necessary to write this essay." [2b]

For many centuries there have been the traditional metaphors of only two types of magic(k), "White" and "Black" in the collective consciousness. The current usage of the colours "**Black** (magic)" and "**White** (magick)" originates from the French *magie noire* and *magie blanche*, where the former only used to describe "magic which involved the invocation of devils" - contrasted with the latter, which did not. **Yellow,** as well as being the colour of the sun, was seen in the ancient Orient as the colour of the middle way; a holy and a favourable hue that signified that something was correct. In the modern West, it has degenerated to the degree of its now being known chiefly as the badge-colour of cowardice, and the description of a magazine or newspaper of a recklessly or unscrupulously sensationalist character.

Inasmuch as the ideal is absolutely minimal activity to the point of there being a total **non-reaction** to phenomena, the practice, if there were to be one, of the Yellow School would be that of a third colourful metaphor, "Yellow" Magick. This is because the magickal end involved would be identical with the School's goal, which is to lessen any disturbance being caused to the universe by not actually saying or doing anything at all, and trusting to the slow dispersion and absorption of any ripple so created. So profound is the bottomless deep **Silence** of this approach, that the Yellow School has consistently maintained that the **Magickal Language** of the White School is always bound to be unsatisfactory by comparison; and that in it there has always been some degree of corruption involved, again, through means of "disease" of language: by the process of "chinese whispers" in the oral tradition; and, in the days before a widespread ability to read, through "bowdlerisation" or the editorial "improvement" of ideas in the written texts, especially in translation.

The essence of a concept such as Yellow Magick concentrates on an attitude of indifference, as opposed to action, and has more in common with mysticism than with magic(k), either black or white. It relates closely with Taoism in viewing all "earthly" activity (as distinct from "heavenly" : the changing of the seasons, the sun and rain, etc) from whatever benign or compassionate motive, as unsettling the perfect, heavenly equilibrium of the universe. The demeanour is one of a "scientific and philosophical detachment" and a passive contemplation of the "**lila**", or play of the universe. According to the Yellow School, there is only one way to clear a vessel of muddied water, and that is to leave "well" alone. This can be shown by a sublimely simple practical experiment using a glass of water, earth, and a stirrer.

For these reasons, there are not, nor can there ever be, any written or oral yellow magickal texts. The *Tao Teh King* and the *I Ching* remain the closest attempts at realising the pure spirit of the tao. In seeking to reduce any resistance between an individual and the universe, they advise taking whatever action is needed at the earliest sign of trouble, before it is given a chance to grow. "So far as (the Yellow School) attempts to influence the course of events at all," Crowley-Aumont remarks in the essay, "it does so in the only intelligent way conceivable, by diminishing internal friction." [2b] But it is in this very attempt to influence the course of events "at all", that it ceases to be truly yellow.

III

A much larger distinction has to be made between the White School of Magick, and the popularly held belief of what constitutes White Magickal practice or technique; with an even greater distinction needing to be made between that of the Black School, and "Black Magic".

The main philosophical idea behind the Black School is that not only is the universe verily indeed a "vale" of suffering and tears and gnashing of teeth; but that there is no thought that anyone can have, or deed that anyone can do, which will ever be able to improve this gloomy prognosis. Christianity, especially evangelism, has come to partake of this food of the Black School; yet so also does Buddhism, whose Four Noble Truths lead one to the conclusion (in the real sense of the finality of that word) that the only way to escape from the endless wheel and whoa of suffering is by means of annihilation - for every man and every woman to actually cease to exist at all. The ideal fulfilment of the formula of the Black School would ultimately result in the destruction of all positive *as well as* negative qualities in human affairs, with the devastation of all life and thought and civilization in the universe seen as some kind of a *fatal necessity*. As shown by the subconscious enthusiasm that underlines the growing fundamentalist hysteria with regard to the end of the millenium - which in itself is prompted by feelings of inner worthlessness and despair - to the Black School, some sort of a global nuclear apocalypse or viral epidemic would suit this end extremely well, providing none survived. It is in this area of personal destruction that the distinction lies between the objectives of the Black School and those of the Black Magician. Such destruction is absolutely not in the interests of the latter, whose concern above all else would be with the acquisition, retention, and expansion of personal power. Annihilation of the ego - which is the final **objective** of the Black School, and that which is also entailed for the highest **operation** of "white magick" (bordering on mysticism and known, again metaphorically, as *crossing the abyss*) - would not suit these self-centred individuals at all!

By contrast, the belief of the White School is that all existence is not only devoid of suffering, but a state of pure joy. Furthermore, this joy is not in the nature of some targetted Goal to be lusted after (because then it really would be unattainable), but is to be found in the "going", or progress of life itself, as symbolised by the ancient Egyptian **ankh** or sandal-strap. Whatever is *perceived* to be pain and suffering can be transformed and transcended either by a process of direct **initiation** - fire "brought down" from "heaven" in the "hollow tube" of metaphor; or by means of an **interior spiritual alchemy** - the aspirant "ascending from earth to heaven", in its counterpart. (Metaphorically, "Jacob's Ladder" or "Double Wand of Power" could be other means of expressing the same thing.) The non-religious consensual understanding of the metaphor *white magick*, though, is something very worthy and bordering on the pious: that its practitioners carry out good works for the betterment not only of their own selves, but also (selectively and judgmentally) on behalf of others. An example might be the activity of a (so-called) "white witch" in curing a neighbour's ailment or ill cow by raising some sort of a spell for their benefit. Money might even change hands these days and the situation would not be regarded irregular - more's the pity. But unless what was being done was in alignment with the other person's true **will**, or purpose in life, what would be going on - although quite probably compassionate and done from the best humanitarian motives - would not be white magick at all but black, as will be illustrated subsequently.

Who can really tell for sure what might, ultimately, be the best outcome for all concerned in the universe of all living creatures? An interesting conundrum is the hypothetical instance of a doctor giving an ailing, adolescent Hitler or Stalin some medicine they particularly needed in order for them to survive, with the after-consequences of millions of deaths in World War Two. Extending the horns of the dilemma, from this perspective would it then have been equally "moral" for an obstetrician to have throttled either of them at birth, if, also hypothetically, s/he were to have clairvoyance? Or for their relations to have arranged some sort of a miscarriage to happen, if they themselves were also to have had this precognitive ability?

The answer is, of course, that no one can ever know with true certainty what the true will of another person is, and that, in this example, had miscarriage occured, or had a midwife done the strangulation posited, there would still have been no guarantee that a Himmler or a Trotsky or an Uncle Tom Cobbley might not have done as much damage (or perhaps even more) in their place. As a result, one can have good intentions, naturally, but there can be no act of white magick *per se* other than that involved in one's own alchemy or initiation, which, when truly done, involve a "vertical ascent/descent" of magickal energy "through the planes." This is because any act of altruistic white magick would involve making assumptions about what another person needs, which might not be true, and which it is impossible to know about with 100% accuracy. Furthermore, collective ceremonial "white" magick, properly conceived, is an enclosed operation, defined by the circle, designed to stimulate each one of the participants in a given manner, with a given end in mind, as exactly as with a laboratory experiment, where each is brought closer to the realisation and fulfilment of their own unique true will.

Ipso facto, White Magick does not exist outside of its own boundaried system, where force is **generated internally** rather than **projected externally**. There is also "not" such a thing as an act of Yellow Magick, which would equate with the passive nature of mysticism. Ergo, there are only two types of Magic(k) in the Universe as actual forces of external activity. These are Black (interference) and Blue (coherence).

WHAT IS BLACK MAGIC?

I

When the phrase **Black Magic** is trotted out, the usual associations in the consensus reality formed by the general public are likely to be as follows: Dennis Wheatley. Sacrilege and Blasphemy: more precisely, "Black" Masses. Orgies! Ritual murders, often of children or babies. Gilles de Rais; perhaps even "Jack the Ripper", or "Son of Sam". Kissing goats' buttocks. Sex with a virgin on the High Altar. Desecrating graveyards. Animal and human sacrifices...(I think by now we get the general picture!) The fact of the matter is, that these activities are actually practiced by what, according to the physical evidence, is an extremely miniscule section of the population - with the possible exception of animal sacrifices (commercial vivisection and the abattoir) and orgies (although with the advent of "safe sex" and fear of AIDS, there are likely to be a lot less of them around than there used to be.) In addition, this miniscule sub-section is in all disproportion to the hysterical coverage habitually given by the "news" media. Why is it that all of these diverse goings-on have curiously been blanketed together under the phrase "black" magic - and why does this colour have any meaning in a context where behaviour is unnatural?

According to certain sources, the old Coptic word for Egypt, *Khem*, meant literally black, and the translation of the word *alchemy* meant, in effect, the black art which had its origin in that land. One of the pivotal alchemical processes is known as "the blackening stage" or *The Black Dragon*; occurring just prior to where new life emerges from a state of putrefaction (a stage which is also known by the name Apophis in the Gnostic formula IAO: Isis - Apophis - Osiris.) Also Osiris, the Egyptian God of vegetation, was "lord of the black earth", or to put it another way, the fertilising life-giving alluvial plains of the Nile delta. The "*black* earth" symbolised the energies of intercourse, but specifically the hidden masculine procreative energy, at a time when the full mysteries of conception and childbirth were not widely known. This is the origin of the association of blackness and dirt with sex, and the reason why Osiris was described as a "black God", or to put it another way, the God of generation concealed in the darkness underneath the earth, known to the Egyptians as Amenta (the underworld).

In the moralising usage of the metaphor, white is frequently made preferable to black. It is extremely rare to see "whiteness" described in those terms usually reserved for its opposite, but one exception is to be found in Herman Melville's *Moby Dick*, where the narrator asks why it is that whiteness is sometimes made the intensifying agent in those things which are most appalling to humankind:

"Is it that by its indefiniteness it shadows forth the heartless voids and immensities of the universe, and thus stabs us from behind with the thought of annihilation, when beholding the white depths of the milky way? Or is it, that as in essence whiteness is not so much a colour as the visible absence of colour, and at the same time the concrete of all colours; is it for these reasons that there is such a dumb blankness, full of meaning, in a wide landscape of snows - a colourless, all-colour of atheism from which we shrink? And when we consider that other theory of the natural philosophers, that all other earthly hues - every stately or lovely emblazoning - the sweet tinges of sunset skies and woods; yea, and the gilded velvets of butterflies, and the butterfly cheeks of young girls; all these are but subtile deceits, not actually inherent in substances, but only laid on from without; so that all deified Nature absolutely paints like the harlot, whose allurements cover nothing but the charnel-house within; and when we proceed further, and consider that the mystical cosmetic which produces every one of her hues, the great principle of light, for ever remains white or colourless in itself, and if operating without medium upon matter, would touch all objects, even tulips and roses, with its own blank tinge - pondering all this, the palsied universe lies before us like a leper; and like wilful travellers in Lapland, who refuse to wear coloured and colouring glasses upon their eyes, so the wretched infidel gazes himself blind at the monumental white shroud that wraps all the prospect around him." [3]

In such terms, the traditional colourful metaphors of magick perhaps ought to be "black and blank", rather than "black and white"! However, be that as it may, it is more usual throughout history, and especially during the fearful climate of the Middle Ages, to find **blackness** possessing an enormous range of negative and fearful associations. Lacking a "blue" perception, its colour (or rather lack of it) was seen to symbolise the terrors of Night, when wild animals or shapeless foes could leap out to surprise or attack the lampless unexpectedly. Also,

"Blackness was chaos; it was the sign of death and the tomb, or the ambivalent womb...(it) indicated evil in places as disparate as Europe, Africa, Tibet and Siberia (a prejudice quite separate from any racial attitudes)...It was nonbeing, the void; physically it connoted blindness; psychologically it signified the fearful land of dreams and the unconscious. It was connected with mental depression, with intellectual stupidity, with religious despair, and with moral sin. It was associated with dirt and poison and plague." [4]

This viewpoint was standard for much of the "**old aeon**", by which is meant the long period of history - roughly the last two and a half thousand years - when the cult of "the Dying God" had prominence. This aspect of the Divine, who was invariably a masculine if not patriarchal deity, needed to die and then be either reborn or else resurrected; just as the sun which every day revolved about the Earth sank or "died" every night into the underworld, and needed to be resuscitated by means of prayer, supplication, sacrifice or redemption.

This contrasts with the viewpoint of the "**new aeon**", or cult of "the Ever-Coming Sun", which sees (where appropriate, the so-called) God-Forms of divinities as already immortal, without needing to go through the old formulae of resurrection. The same principle applies also to the human spirit, which can now be seen without obfuscation as perfect and immortal and without sense of shame or sin: the new aeon has no use for the concept of "The Devil", nor for those of hellfire, suffering and sacrifice.

Old and new aeons incorporate the consensus realities at the time of geo-centricity and helio-centricity respectively. The consensus in this new aeon is gradually coming to realize that outer space is eternally filled with the light radiated from trillions upon trillions of suns, and that the only darkness to us is (and ever was) that shadow cast by the rotation of our home, the Earth itself. Looked at cosmically, the Earth (and every other planet, moon and non-stellar object) is a mere mote in this sunlight, the star light of the universe. This truth was known (amongst others) to some of the ancient Egyptians in the time preceeding the old aeon as **Khepra**, "the sun of midnight", or the "**black** and hidden" sun. As the centuries passed, this knowledge gradually became lost, often politically obscured; and in its place an ignorant superstition, craven fear, and even outright terror of the Dark arose. It was no longer recognized as it is in the oriental yin-yang symbol, that the phenomena of darkness and light must out of necessity co-exist and be completely inter-dependent - indeed, must be in a condition of springing forth one from the other - as a condition of there being any perception at all; instead, by contrast they both became frozen, fixed principles of non-fluid opposition: subjectively-imagined absolute concepts of *Good* and *Evil*, locked in "eternal" duel until "Good" wins on the "Day of Judgment."

Along with the old aeon went the belief-system, formalised to its greatest extent in Christianity, of **Guilt** as "original sin", and "unworthiness" as a lack of **Grace**. Into such a stark, dualistic state of affairs, the poor quality of interaction afforded between what were considered mutually exclusive "realms" of light and darkness threw up a large number of phantasms such as, for instance, Paradise, Limbo, Purgatory, Sheol, Gehenna, and Hades. The shadowy realm of Hell-fire-'n'-brimstone was ruled by The Devil, "Prince of Darkness" (also somewhat confusingly known as *Lucifer*, "bringer of light"), who came complete with horns, hoofs, a little pointy-tail, a pitchfork, a goaty beard and a widow's peak. This **cartoon** became a convenient "bogeyman" for keeping the critical faculties and imaginations of men and women shackled for centuries - and, "believe it or not", The Devil *still is* a convenient bogeyman! (William Blatty's film *The Exorcist* (1973) had consider-able publicity, and caused hundreds of people to seek help from priests in the belief that they, too, were possessed by The Devil. Pope Paul VI was moved to declare to a General Vatican Audience in November, 1972: "On the world scene there is **the invisible presence of an obscure agent and demon**...the evil is not only a spiritual deficiency, **but an efficiency, a live being, spiritual, perverted and perverter, a terrible reality, mysterious and fearful.**" And more recently, at Swansea in May 1991, an official Government spokesman declared that all car registration numbers containing "**666**" had been banned as a result of the fact that "under the Driver and Vehicle Licensing Agency, the number 666 is not to be used on any vehicle registra-tion because it is the number of the Devil" - indeed some "revelation", in a supposedly sophisticated society!)

81

Yet in most traditional Tarot packs, *The Devil* card itself is precisely this cartoon image, except that for representational purposes the *bodies* of a man and woman have to be in chains, in place of their more abstract (and therefore harder to pictorially depict) *minds*. Really, could the truth be more plainly stated?!

Interestingly, such an extreme, prejudicial and sinister view of The Devil/ Mephistopheles/Satan/Lucifer/Apollyon/Abaddon/Beelzebub/Belial/"The Adversary"/ "Old Nick"/etc, etc (delete where applicable) only emerged in the early XIVth century. The American philosopher and anthropologist Alan Watts remarked that prior to this time it was "in popular representation, something of a buffoon, and, in theology, a pure spirit, dangerous and tempting but not the direct enemy of man." In mediaeval folk plays and dances, "he" usually appeared in a good-natured humourous role: many were the stories of how easy it was to outwit him, such as those to be found in German folklore, where he was condescendingly labelled *gute dumme Teufel*, or "the good stupid devil." Even the Biblical Satan was far from being the malignant Devil of later Christian doctrine: in the Old Testament Books of *Zechariah* and *Job*, he appears simply as a sort of "counsel for the prosecution" in the Court of Heaven, far remote from being any sort of abysmal or absurd evil image, the emergence of which:

"...is associated with that epidemic of insanity which expressed itself in the persecution of witches and heretics by the Holy Inquisition, whose tortures were quite obviously a pretext for sadistic lust...The Devil's form is, after all, that of lustful Pan, and attendant demons are satyrs; and, as the ministers of punishment in Hell, their images reflect the motivations of their creators. The allure of demonographic literature and art is, to a considerable extent, pornographic. But since the demonographer is very often the same person as the preacher, the pornographic motivation must usually be unconscious or unadmitted. It is concealed under the pretext of righteous wrath and the fear of Hell, and so, at the same time, **it is concealed that the Devil is made in the image of those who imagine him.** The sensation of being threatened, spiritually, by a weirdly alien and incalculable power of malice is, above all, a symptom of unconsciousness - of man's alienation from himself. Furthermore, insasmuch as he is unconscious of the Devil as his own image, he is the more apt to vent upon his fellows his fear of and fury at this disowned aspect of himself. **This is why acceptance of the Devil in and as oneself is a moral obligation...**" [5]

Watts went on to point out that in the mythologies of Africa, India and China, demons never appear devils in our later western sense - hideous as their forms and functions may be (Kali, perhaps), they are always aspects or agents of universal nature. The wrathful figures of Hindu-Buddhist iconography have one hand in the *mudra* (gesture) of "fear not", to indicate that the apparition is yet another form of *maya* (illusion), another one of the million masks of God. Why should this point of view have been so absent from western culture? Could it be possibly that

"When at times any sort of puritanism is dominant, or any fanatical, one-sided view of man, the ignored aspect of our nature appears as an external devil, sometimes as an angel or fallen spirit, and sometimes in the form of other people, as, say, in Anti-Semitism. **In a culture dominated by pleasure-denying forms of Christianity, the Devil will therefore be an external caricature of our erotic, animal, and self-seeking aspects.** The Christian Devil is unique. No other demonic figure has ever been conceived to be so purely malicious, so sinister, and so totally opposed to the universal design." [5]

It therefore seems from the evidence that the ancients knew more about the true meaning of **black**ness than their emotionally superstitious descendants, today literally scared of their own shadow. What enabled this terrible state of affairs, this degeneration into such an awful misunderstanding, to have arisen? The primary cause was the clever and gradual appropriation and absorption, by the early organized Christian Church, of sympathetic elements within the older and more established pagan religions; combined with the turning of those elements which proved abrasive and not to be in alignment into objects of anathema. It was aided in its ascendancy by the sermonising and machinations of corrupt priests, a factor which has caused the original germ of truth in *all* religions to become dogmatic and skew-wise. By tradition, only priests were given the knowledge to read and write: they therefore held an exclusive monopoly, through means of which they were later able to amass a great deal of secular political power so that they became "the power behind the throne", as Popes notably did throughout the Middle Ages in Europe.

"It appeared marvellous to the vulgar that men should be able to communicate at a distance, and they began to attribute other powers, merely invented, to the people who were able to write. The Wand is then nothing but the pen; the Cup, the Inkpot; the Dagger, the knife for sharpening the pen; and the Disk is either the papyrus roll itself; or the weight which keeps it in position, or the sandbox for soaking up the ink. And, of course, the "Papyrus of Ani" is only the Latin for toilet-paper."[1a] (A note for the benefit of newcomers to Crowley: the last sentence is one of his little jokes, which seem to so dreadfully upset some of his critics - the lambs!)

These priests managed to "con"vince ordinary men and women with baseless prejudices and fears such as the possibility of their eternal damnation after death; and by concocting self-serving doctrines and rituals of such a complex nature that people were then forced to seek their professional advice, they were enabled (and only too willing) to exchange such counsel sometimes in return for power and creaturely comforts. By the time of the Renaissance, universities of somewhat more universal learning had come into being, with the result that the monopoly of the Church became broken; but it was not long before printing, the new technological invention, came to be used as a means of extending "the word" - look at Gutenberg's Bible! All works of science and literature found to be **incompatible** were burned, banned, or altogether suppressed prior to circulation: a set of manoeuvres which maybe set human progress back six generations. Within the last century, the overt "churchy" component in the moral "education" or *inculcation* of the masses has become eclipsed. In its place has arisen a substitute, a more secular but nonetheless similarly intentioned and powerful *mass-media*, which has somehow been responsible for deliberately perpetuating misinformation and disinformation and the downright fabrication of facts - the one exception to this general trend being that bizarre hybrid growth of religion and mass-media, *televangelism*, thankfully now in something of a comparative decline due to the rank and patent hypocrisy of its main perpetrators.

The *mass-media* is mainly the (tabloid) 'paper and the "t-v set"; but also included peripherally are radio, advertising, the glossy mag, and the cinema - and, more lately, the sponsored rock concert. *Live Aid* was broadcast internationally, an exercise in fundraising, babyboomers' nostalgia for a lost youth, and almost subliminal and unfortunately expressed missionary sentiments, derived from the chorus of Band Aid's hit single (1984 and 1989), *Feed The World - Do They Know It's Christmas Time At All?* Maladroitly, the highlights of the occasion shown later omitted to show, either from ignorant neglect or calculated censorship, the one potentially controversial speech made throughout the occasion by Udo Lindenberg, a German singer. He expressed his dissatisfaction with mere yuppie conscience-salving, and donations *in lieu of* governmental assistance, rather than tackling *as well* the real social and global economic problems behind the moving scenes of starving babies - such as third world interest debt, militarism, desertification, pollution, less crops for people to eat because of grain for cattle (meat), etc.

The most efficient way that information can come across is by means of a satisfying, energizing, artistic performance of integrity and virtuosity - a participatory construct evolved by the sensibilities of its creators with the audience/spectators/readers in a telepathic (for want of a better word) union. (Conventional science, based on reason and therefore causal relativity, is a lie and cannot share this immediate oneness of artistic "truth"). The artistry of, and information conveyed by, most forms of *mass-media* is geared towards what is reckoned to be a pretty low common denominator of intelligence and wit. The "news", "actual reconstructions" and "docu-dramas" fashion public opinion with condescension and ease. People become accustomed to expect "experts" to do their analysis and synthesis for them; for the most part their minds atrophy and they vegetate, becoming *mentally passive* and too cerebrally lazy to discriminate beyond choosing the next video. The media coverage of the recent "Gulf War", especially on television, was able, if it did nothing else, to highlight the compulsive need to create entertainment and *instant gratification* from what were, for most of the time, non-events. It also gave a one-sided view of the history of the region; and while no sensible person would support the sort of madman who displays his true character by setting six hundred oil wells on fire, why was/is there hardly any discussion of the hi-tech slaughter caused by "Allied" ("United Nations", shurely - did someone mention World War II?) air attacks; the Palestinian question; the former American pro-Iraqi political stance, and so on. Why, oh why, has the mass-media, rather than fostering debate, become a means of spoon-feeding the chattering classes with ready-made beliefs and more and more and "yet more" trivia? It portrays men, women, and (even tragic) events as **stereotypes**, with the result that most viewers' and readers' attitudes - in other words, the attitudes of most of the population - have become standardised and homogenous: *Comment, Opinion, The Voice Of The People, Mirror View, That's Life, The Sun Says.* Etcetera, etcetera, ad nauseam.

Television, although invented in 1926, did not really take off in the mass awareness of the First World until the early 1950s. In Britain, the catalyst proved to be the Queen's Coronation in July 1953; in U.S.A., it was the McCarthy "witch-hunt" hearings of 1954, preceded by a cocktail of variety shows, ball games, *Dragnet* and *I Love Lucy.* Since that time, it has proved to be something of an unstoppable ray-gun, destroying all other less omnipresent forms of culture. Further discussion of the effects of this may have to appear in an accompanying article, *Thelema and T-V* but here the purpose is to concentrate specifically upon the influence and tendencies of the *tabloid*, in the previously indicated sense of an unscrupulously sensationalist or "yellow" press: where the word is used, as in common parlance, as a device to represent more this yellow-journalistic frame of mind rather than a particular newspaper size.

Originally, it had denoted a small newspaper, the size of a bulkier "broadsheet" folded in half. The news presented there was condensed, brisk, and animated, and it devoted a large proportion of its space to photographs, illustration, and advertisements. Consequently, it was associated with being more like a magazine and less concerned with "weighty" matters than a broadsheet. The first tabloid to break surface was Lord Northcliffe's *New York World*, which he correctly prophesised to be the form of "the newspaper of the 20th century", and which appeared fittingly (but a year early) on Jan. 1st, 1900. He pioneered the *Daily Mirror* as the first British tabloid three years later; but the genre did not reach its present recognizable style (of which *The Sport* is possibly the apogee, or maybe that should be perigee) until the dog end of the 1960s, when the Australian entrepreneur Rupert Murdoch took over what was a Labour party paper once called the *Daily Herald* and which had become *The Sun*.

Certain "newspapers" had pandered to the prejudices of the prurient from at least the 19th century onwards in their reporting of crime, trials and public executions - although after Dickens initiated protest about the matter in the 1840s, the latter were no longer allowed to be a voyeur's spectacle. However, the first emergence in the tabloid press of the sophistry with which we are all acquainted began with the putting-out of propaganda in the First World War. This propaganda kept the civilian population from knowing for the duration the sheer scale and horror of trench warfare. In addition, the war was not actually over in a few weeks "by Christmas", as was at first joyfully predicted. It is amazing how history repeats itself. Does anybody recall the hysterically jingoistic reporting of the "almost total victory" over Saddam Hussein's forces in Kuwait after a single day's fighting: itself a parallel of day one of the "Falklands Conflict", which was only called a "War" after it had safely been won?

Once the honour disappeared from the formerly esteemed profession of "journalism", it did not return. The overriding priority began to be to "shift copy" at the expense of truth and the reputation of anybody unfortunate enough to be in the way. This behaviour was ridiculed in Evelyn Waugh's novel *Scoop* (1938) - by Waugh's own admission, a satire on *Sunday Express* newspaper proprietor Lord Beaverbrook - and in Orson Welles' film *Citizen Kane* (1941), widely held to be a portrait of American newspaper magnate and tycoon William Randolph Hearst, the leading exponent of *yellow journalism*. In the film, a correspondent sent to cover a war in Cuba wired through to the office that he had come up with some background material, but unfortunately the war had gone and inconveniently finished early. "You provide the prose poems - *I'll* provide the war" came the memorable rejoinder back from Kane. In *Scoop*, journalist William Boot of the staff of the *Daily Beast* (or, as he was known, *Boot of the Beast*) went one better and, unable to find the particular war he had been sent to cover, made one completely new up from scratch. Probably Mr. Kane and Mr. Boot would have approved of the style of *The Sport*, now Britain's fastest growing paper, most of whose features are widely regarded as humourous invention and are probably written in the same vein. Unhappily, however, the tradition of publishing deliberate and malicious falsehoods is with us today more than ever, as anybody who looks at the libel histories of the *News of the World*, *The Sun*, and *The Star*, for example, can read for themselves.

The phrase "black magic" in the media, along with "devil-worship" and other similar epithets, is always good for a piece of sensationalism, regardless of whether or not it actually means anything. It creates convenient shock-horror, knee-jerk responses of alarm from an unthinking readership. Thankfully in t-v there have been fewer excesses, if only because the printed word affords a certain anonymity which the screen does not. An exception was the recently shown disgraceful *Dispatches* programme on the *Temple of Psychick Youth*, in which - apart from misinformation - cheap studio gimmickry was employed to cultivate an atmosphere of alarm and fearfulness in the viewer.

III

There is a strong case for stating that the growth of **Thelema** was stopped in its tracks for a time by the tactics of the yellow tabloid press. From the Greek word for will, Thelema was the philosophy propounded by Aleister Crowley which states that the discovery of, and fulfilment by, every individual of their own life purpose or **true will** is in alignment with, and an expression of, the Perfect movement of the universal, i.e. divine, will; rather in the way that each separate element of a 3-D hologram contains an impression of the whole. Expressed in the salutation "Do what thou wilt shall be the whole of the Law" ("thou" referring to the second person singular form of "you" once common in English) along with "Love is the law, love under will", this naturally involves everybody else being at liberty to carry out their true will in a reciprocal manner, without meddlesome interferences. One of the principle paradoxes and beauties of Thelema is the way in which Nature generates and guarantees individual freedom through Order and vice versa, instead of being a Chaotic riot of confusion and unbridled hedonistic licence!

The atmosphere in post-World War One Britain was, like so today, one of austerity and restriction. In many ways, it further resembled the spirit of the age almost exactly a century earlier, when the clamour for the democratic right to vote, following on from the hardships endured in the Napoleonic War, was met with brutal reaction. When unarmed citizens were massacred at Peterloo in 1819, it was blamed by the authorities on the demagoguery of a speaker, "Orator" Hunt, rather than the troop of Hussars actually responsible for the shooting. The era, already characterized by underground Radical clubs and corresponding societies, was also the time of Luddite machine-breaking, "Captain Swing", and the Cato Street conspiracy to assassinate the Cabinet. The ultra-repressive legislation passed to deal with the incipient insurrection resulted in the suspension of habeas corpus (which enabled citizens to be imprisoned without trial); the passing of the Combination Acts (which made membership of a trade union illegal and punishable by transportation to Australia); the Seditious Meetings Act (which forbade gatherings of over fifty people); the "Gag" Acts (which introduced censorship of the press for the first time); and the "Acts of Indemnity" (which were tailored to protect magistrates who might have stepped beyond the pale of the law during the period of civil alarm).

The aroma of anarchy in the air was less strong immediately after the Second World War, where in the West, anti-establishment feeling (*Rebel(s) without a Cause, Angry Young Men* and *Teddy Boys, Pop Art, Rock and/'n' roll, Ban the Bomb*, etc) did not materialize until the conservative climate of the early 'Fifties, and even then was restricted to being largely a youthful phenomenon (finely detailed in George Melly's *Revolt Into Style*.) But in the aftermath of the First World War - at the time hopefully labelled "the war to end all wars" - vigorous upheaval and change occured more rapidly. As an indication of how profound the differences were between old and new aeon, these changes often occured simultaneously with the war, occasionally even presaging it. Sometimes it is difficult to know whether a certain pattern of events happened as an inevitable result of the war, or else the war happened as the result of an inevitable pattern of events, so synergetic are the accounts of the times. The so-called "Fall of Eagles" (a fall not so much because of, but in spite of the war) which affected the old imperial dynasties and houses of *Romanov* (Russia), *Hohenzollern* (Germany) and *Habsburg* (Austria-Hungary), had a colossal effect upon the collective psyche of the civilised western world. In many ways, the entire European world order, which had seemed impregnable a generation ago at the turn of the century, collapsed like a mouldy cake as, everywhere, the ancient regimes and traditional forms were challenged and toppled.

In *politics*, there was the sudden 1917 Bolshevik Russian uprising against the status quo; across the countries of Europe a year later, the outbreak of peace brought a wave of desire for nationalistic self-determination; whilst in Britain, enthusiasm for democracy generated "universal suffrage" for men and women for the first time (although the women were presumably judged to be such flibberti-gibbets that they still had to wait until they were nine years maturer than their male counterparts before qualifying). In *economics*, war debts meant that Europe could no longer honour its paper money with gold; instead it became fiduciary, dependent upon *faith*, and led to the Wall Street Crash eleven years later with its repercussions today (see *Thelema and Money* by Rex Monday in the Skoob Occult Review No.1). In *poetry*, T. S. Eliot was one of the first amongst those who, rather too eclectically, perhaps, challenged the rhyming standards of verse which had been around for centuries, with *The Love Song of J. Alfred Prufrock* and *The Waste Land*. In *literature*, James Joyce was on the point of publishing *Ulysses* - abroad, because of interference from the censor. In *art*, the formal innovations of *dada* and *surrealism* arose out of the Zurich cabal of 1916. In *music*, Stravinsky's *Rite of Spring*, along with Diaghileff's choreography and Nijinsky's interpretation of it, created some sort of a furore and outrageous hoo-hah at its first performance in 1913. In *science*, Einstein with his work on Relativity, and Max Planck with his studies in Quantum Physics, were shifting perceptions about what had previously been seen by many to be an absolutely causal and unshiftable ordered mechanistic universe.

The atmosphere was therefore very much a charged one, with the status quo being challenged on every side. Into this smouldering cooking-pot of ideas came the red hot chilli pepper of Aleister Crowley, the most prominent proponent and exponent of some strange mediaeval relic of mumbo-jumbo (such as it was conceived) he would insist upon calling *magick*, which not only challenged the hegemony of the Church of England, at that time, far stronger in influence than today, although in decline; but also bantered with the rigidities of certain types of fixed and dogmatic scientific thinking and philosophy as well. In addition, he was initiated in 1900, aged 25, as a top-ranking (33° Scottish Rite) Freemason, who would have antagonized his fellow Establishment brethren by his effort in 1917 to "**reconstruct**" the whole exclusive privileged system with his masonic Order of the Temple of the Rising Star, or *Ordo Templi Orientis*, which, aside from anything else, unreservedly admitted women, and whose members originally engaged in eastern practices of *tantra* utilising the serpentine, cerebrospinal neural energy of *kundalini*. (Unfortunately the true O.T.O., despite various claimants, cannot be said to exist today.) Lastly, Crowley succeeded in creating a large stir with his attempt to dispel some of the nonsense which was going on in terms of war propaganda, for which a vengeful gutter press branded him with the false label "traitor" - a myth which still persists to this day, but which can be easily dispelled by reading *Humanity First* from *The International*, the supposedly "pro-Hun" periodical which he edited in America from November, 1917 (reprinted in P.R. Stephensen's *The Legend Of Aleister Crowley*) [7.] Still to be resolved is the aspect of his involvement as an undercover agent acting on behalf of British Intelligence, for which he is yet to receive any public recognition or restitution. If, as has been suggested, he was instrumental too in the turning-around of the Second World War in Britain's favour by covert activities, (including the instigation of the "V for Victory" gesture and "Thumbs Up" sign), then the still classified documents pertaining to his secret wartime activities clearly have to be released, and credit apportioned where it is due.

But most importantly of all, more than with science, religion, freemasonry, or patriotism, Crowley questioned the way in which men and women used their minds - which was seen by many to be the most confrontational challenge of them all, far worse than having an electric buzzer "handshake", or indeed their sleep disturbed by some unexpected prank, maybe such as having a sodasyphon discharged at them.

*

The trouble began with the first to be published of two mainstream works of fiction written for popular consumption. Although there had been an earlier favourable investigative essay by him in his journal *The Equinox* called, and about, *The Psychology of Hashish*, this had had a very limited readership. But in 1922, he was commissioned by the firm of Collins to write a novel, which he entitled **The Diary of a Drug Fiend**. This alone was enough to cause eyebrows to be raised (even though it was less than thirty years since the then-acceptable cocaine-toting exploits of Sherlock Holmes) because, as part of the post-war restrictions, under the *Dangerous Drugs Act* of 1920 the publicity about, and use of, narcotics was made much more stringently controlled than previously. At around this time, a lot more propaganda was starting to be produced about the dangers involved in organic and apothecary preparations of plants and herbs, which were beginning to have to compete with the newer concoctions of laboratory-synthesised and commercially packaged products. In today's world, multinational pharmaceutical companies hold an inordinately powerful influence over what is "prescribed" for mental health; meanwhile venerable "home grown" remedies are frowned upon by a brainwashed general public as being quaint, insufficiently medicinal, and - in the case of *cannabis sativa* - plain dangerous. Would it be paranoid to think in terms of a pattern of manipulative control on the part of a vested elite, with an economic and political interest in keeping society as dumb, unquestioning, and ovine as possible? Or would it be, on the other hand, naive not to? Whichever, the combination of radical philosophical ideas and the clarification of ancient mythological (= metaphorical) beliefs expressed by **Crowley, buried** for centuries in the collective unconscious, represented a very grave potential threat to the status quo, a "?" that demanded, and is still demanding (despite attempts since his death at re-internment) to be answered by a "!" of some sort. The flowering of the new aeon.

Although hostile reviewers pounced on the mere mention of the word **drugs,** ironically Crowley's *The Diary Of a Drug Fiend* did not present a rosy view of drugtaking at all, and in fact warns against the horrors of becoming addicted to heroin and cocaine. What actually caused the most disruption, albeit on an unconscious level, was the totally anarchic idea that **Do what thou wilt** could be a functional means of **self-regulation** en masse. The book was a double bluff, a wolf in wolf's clothing, a dramatic manifesto in disguise for a proven means of self regulation *and* living together; an idealised model, to be sure, but the difference between it and 31 other utopias lay in the fact that it was no pipe-dream but was actually going on that very moment at somewhere called "the Abbey of Thelema", near Cefalu in Sicily. The magickal and social life of the thelemic community there was described in some detail. For example, no newspapers were allowed - not only because their integrity had deteriorated, but also because a wealth of classical and top quality contemporary literature could be read from Crowley's collection. "...Having a library of first-class books," he ventured, "we should not spoil our appetites by eating between meals, especially the dirt of the streets..." [8a]

Finally, as if to add icing to their cake of celebration, the book had the absolute effrontery to openly advertise for readers to come forth and join the beautiful people - a clarion calling them to rise up and awake:

"The Abbey of Thelema at "Telepylus" is a real place. It and its customs and members, with the surrounding scenery, are accurately described. The training there given is suited to all conditions of spiritual distress, and for the discovery and development of the "True Will" of any person. Those interested are invited to communicate with the author of this book." [6]

"We are stardust" was rhapsodised about "the Woodstock nation", the three-day flower-power would-be utopia of the late 'Sixties, but did anyone write anything similar about the Cefalu experience? James Douglas, who reviewed *The Diary* for the *Sunday Express* dated November 19th, 1922, did not appear to like what he learned of the Abbey of Thelema (or, indeed, his own subconscious):

"A large number of his [Crowley's] books are privately printed - some of them in Paris. They are either incomprehensible or disgusting - generally both. His language is the language of a pervert and his ideas are negligible...Although there is an attempt to pretend that the book is merely a study of the deprivation caused by cocaine, in reality it is an ecstatic eulogy of the drug and of its effects on the body and the mind. A cocaine trafficker would welcome it as a recruiting agent which would bring him thousands of new victims...At the baser and more bestial horrors of the book it is impossible, even were it desirable, to hint...I imagine that this book secured publication in the guise of an exposure of the evils wrought by drugs. But its true character is stamped on it in spite of its ingenious use of innuendo and artifice. It is a book that ought to be burned." [7]

Once the spotlight of publicity was directed, it began to glare down ever more harshly upon the activities of **To Mega Therion 666**, and those who were termed by it his "disciples". Crowley metaphorically styled himself in this way - the Greek for *Great Wild Beast* - as an unabashed and unashamed human acknowledgement of his natural (that is, divine) animal desires. It won him few friends in a Christianized society. The following Sunday, an in-depth exposé purported to **reveal all** about the allegedly seamy and sordid goings on at the abbey, under this dramatic banner headline:

"COMPLETE EXPOSURE OF DRUG FIEND AUTHOR - THE BLACK RECORD OF ALEISTER CROWLEY - PREYING ON THE DEBASED - HIS ABBEY - PROFLIGACY AND VICE IN SICILY."

Crowley's attitude to it was, at first, understandably philosophical and bemused:

"At the end of November I received a telegram from Hammond which I took as a sort of joke. He said: "English press states you are guilty of sending girls on streets in Palermo or Naples and that you served prison sentence in America for procuration - wire immediately." I replied "Allegations utterly absurd." My only annoyance was having to pay for the telegram. Presently copies of the Sunday papers for November 26th arrived. I read them with tireless amusement. I had read in my time a great deal of utter balderdash, but nothing quite so comprehensively ridiculous. It gave me the greatest joy to notice that practically every single detail was false. There was, for instance, a description of the abbey, without a single failure to misstate the facts. If a thing was white, they called it red, if square, circular, if stone, brick; and so for everything. I saw no reason for taking any action. I was content to enjoy the absurdity and profit by the publicity. Unfortunately the sense of humour is rare in England...The only misfortune in the matter was that my publishers reflected that doing as they did a large business in bibles and similar pious publications they could not profit by the publicity as their clear duty was to do. They professed all sympathy with my position, but insisted on some form of vindication before proceeding to carry out their contracts. I find their attitude inexcusable. They live in a country which boasts of sportsmanship and fair play as their copyright, but refuse to apply their principles, to say nothing of elementary justice, to cases which involve the suspicion of sexual irregularity...What struck us as the best joke in the whole article was the description of the abbey as a focus of all possible vices. We were all drug fiends devoting ourselves uninterruptedly to indulgence in all conceivable sexual abominations...By this particular period, our conduct was so moral by the strictest standards that it would not be matched by any community of equal numbers in the world. [8a]

Before the situation settled and had a chance to lie like a sleeping dog down of its own accord, the unfortunate death of Crowley's young protégé, Raoul Loveday, by illness in the following February became the signal for the damwaters of resentment to break. No longer "tirelessly" amused, Crowley instead became full of contempt for the way in which things about him were appearing in the press:

"The reporters of the gutter press got after her (Betty May, Raoul Loveday's widow, whom Crowley once ejected from the abbey on account of her reading a newspaper), made her drunk and prompted her to give them a sensation story which was one long series of falsehoods. The rabble resumed their chorus of calumny. They completely lost touch with reason. Each fresh article was crazier than the last. I was accused of the most fantastic crimes up to cannibalism...In one way or another, I achieved an enormous amount of work in the three years (at the abbey). But my most important labours have been definitely magickal...(However), the enemies of mankind, seeing that **despite everything my work was nearing manifest success**, redoubled their malice." [8a]

The situation had got out of hand, and soon proved irrevocable. The hateful and hurtful attacks that followed in the *Sunday Express* and *John Bull* were unprecedented - nor have they been surpassed since, with the possible exception of coverage of Hitler and Charles Manson. A short parade of some headlines, whose style, if not   the extent of malignity, is now commonplace and must now be recognisable by everyone who looks at a tabloid, gives a short indication of the invective of the era -

"DRIVEN TO SUICIDE BY THE DEVIL-WORSHIPPERS"
"THE KING OF DEPRAVITY"
"A HUMAN BEAST RETURNS"
"A CANNIBAL AT LARGE"
"THE WICKEDEST MAN IN THE WORLD"
"A MAN WE'D LIKE TO HANG."

Anybody interested in a fuller documentation of these articles together with a sober analysis of the background surrounding the journalistic events should again consult P.R. Stephensen's *The Legend of Aleister Crowley*. These days, such head-lines tend to cause the reverse of their intention, if only because people are now so familiar with the ludicrous "style" of tabloids and their mechanics of hype. That is the reason why they are again reproduced above: because they are so obviously ridiculous - and quite hilarious too, viewed a certain way. It is natural for the level-headed reader to ask why on earth such a superlative fuss was made, and why so much was fabricated, when there was so little actual evidence to show for itself; and then to arrive at the conclusion that there must be more to the business after all than a first glance would suggest. Stephensen's own penetrating explanation as to why   this campaign against Crowley happened carries the ring of truthfulness about it:

"During the First World War Fleet Street had been trained in the technique of scientific propaganda which may be defined as personal vituperation based on moral horror; after Versailles, it was no longer necessary to vituperate the Kaiser, but Lenin and Trotsky were easily to hand as substitutes, and the vituperative weapon was sharpened still further upon their bodies; but after the failure of the Allied intervention in Russia, and after the Triple Alliance strike of British workmen against intervention in Russia, the "Bolshevik menace" propaganda began to lose its point; nevertheless a whole generation of specialist vituperative writers had to "carry on" in Fleet Street somehow. Not only were the copywriters of Fleet Street trained in the School of Propagandist Abuse, but their **millions of readers had also become accustomed to expect this kind of thing**. Crowley came into the news opportunely for journalists confronted with a dearth of "horrors". The rusting weapons of vituperation were polished and brought into play." [7]

He then wondered, "did the journalist capable of writing such pieces have his tongue in his cheek, or was he sincere and a moron?" and, in the course of examining his own question, wrote that he was inclined to believe that it was "merely" the case of clever journalism, extremely capable in extracting the utmost possible excitation from a story:

"...Given the task of "writing up" Aleister Crowley in a sensational manner, the journalists carried out their task ruthlessly. The morality of the procedure is another question, if we remember always that the whole concoction was brewed about a private individual, whose private life was "investigated". How many of us could survive a similar investigation, carried out by journalists trained in denunciation and in the colourful phrase?...How would the "Sunday Express" have exposed Byron? In what terms would they have described "Don Juan", and with what phrases would they have gloated over his amours? What would have been the results if the private life of Shelley and Keats had been dragged into the front page of a Sunday newspaper specializing in moral indignation and invective?...(Yet) **the treatment accorded to Crowley by his contemporaries may be of some use if it serves us as a warning against the dangers peculiar to the age in which we live..."** [7]

The upshot of all of the unwanted and unwarranted publicity was that the attention of the Italian authorities came to be turned on the Abbey and, five months after the initial catalytic Douglas review, it was forced to close down.

"...Two Oxford men arrived at the abbey (and) were flabberghasted to find us perfectly normal decent people. The morning after their arrival, I was summoned to the police, who showed me an order from the Minister of the Interior expelling me from Italy. No reason was given, no accusation made. **The policy of backstairs intrigue and foul strokes, whenever they felt sure that I could not defend myself or hit back, was still the order of the day.** The Commissary of Police was staggered by the smiling calm with which I received this stab in the back. I did not even protest or ask for the reason of this outrage. I courteously requested a week's grace to arrange my affairs, which he, with equal politeness, granted. He tried one dirty police trick. These people seemed unable to help themselves. He tried to persuade me that the order included the whole community. The injustice and tyranny of this order excited the utmost sympathy and indignation of our guests, who promised to do all they could to secure fair treatment. My behaviour in this ordeal aroused their admiration. It became abundantly manifest that my conscience was clear. Such calm courage, not only on my part, but on that of the others, who were really much more deeply injured than I was myself, showed that we possessed the secret of sailing triumphantly above the clouds of circumstances in the pure air of freedom in the sunlight of happiness." [8a]

Its members dispersed, and Crowley never really found a proper base since - he truly became that which he identified with, the "Wanderer in the Waste" land. His review of all of the above incidents in his autobiographical *Confessions* tries to set them to rights, and in retrospect acts almost in the form of a "plea for the defence":

"The most trivial and commonplace incident must be cooked up with all possible spice of sensationalism...(but) the ultimate effect...will be to familiarize the public with my name and interest them in my career sufficiently to induce the few intelligent individuals who have read it to inquire independently into the facts of the case. The strong point of my position is that there is nothing in my life of which I need be ashamed. Inquiry must inevitably result in clearing my character, and any person whose attitude is worth a moment's consideration should experience a reaction of indignation and disgust. The stench of the cesspool of calumny will offend his nostrils and he will insist on restoring equilibrium by long reviving inhalations of the perfume of my personality." [8a] (Again for newcomers: another self-deprecating little joke from Crowley. Try not to laugh or snort too hard!)

In many ways, the downfall of Crowley in terms of his being able to put across the message of Thelema in person, directly and effectively, and on a wide scale, dates from that time. He would continue to receive queries from interested students, but any widespread popular credibility was now lost for ever to him in his lifetime. The affair also tainted for a time the propagation of the philosophy of Thelema by association, since in the public eye, with the exception of a few discerning individuals, it was almost impossible to disassociate the two. What revolutionary course Thelema, Aleister Crowley, and indeed world events would have taken had the magickal community at the Abbey of Thelema been allowed to continue to naturally evolve and thrive, is something at which we can now only wonder.

IV

But the reason it did not do this was because of the widespread interference and influence of the "black magical" attacks by the tabloids at the time. The purpose of the cynical thinking behind these attacks existed not in voicing truth, but in the deliberate spread of lies and the perversion of information. Once perverted, this may carry on breeding mischief of its own momentum like an unchecked cancer. Metaphorically, this "disease of language" is known in magick as the function of the chattering "Ape" of Thoth, the mocking *Cynocephalus* who distorts sense and meaning - or sometimes at its most debased, *Qlipoth of Hod* : unbalanced energy on the reversed Cabbalistic Tree of Life, relating to verbal intelligence and the densest form of mentation.

It is commonly held to be the case that the magickal thought or intention precedes the magickal deed or act. If so, then the unthinking conception and propagation of black magic by some reporters, social workers, and evangelists, goes forward to create a reality wherein innocent people are hounded, citizens lose their jobs, children are separated from their parents, and so on. If the situation of not so very long ago were to be described, to that list would also need to be added that cat-owners would be ostracised by the community and blamed for bad luck; pagans believed to be "in league with" the Devil would be pricked all over their bodies for "his mark", then tortured for incriminating confessions on rack and strappado; and men and women of every description would be drowned or hung or burnt at the stake. Between 1603 and 1683, an estimated 70,000 were put to death for witchcraft, although it never reached the same intensity here as it did on the Continent. The number of heretics murdered by the Christian Church altogether in the combined purges of mediaeval inquisition and witchcraft slaughters has been put as high as 10,000,000 - proportionately greater, using today's population standards, than the total of those murdered in either one of the two World Wars. Praise The Lord! (?)

The process can also thankfully create a reverse situation where a backlash can occur, which is beginning to happen as the 1990s progress. This is despite attempts made to scupper these developments by a few poor misguided souls who, like their predecessors who four centuries ago saw a "sorceror" behind every heathen, or who four decades ago saw a "red" under every bed, now see a "satanist" around every corner. It is evident to people who follow current affairs, for example, that the mental image formed by the West of the Soviet Republics as "The Evil Empire" in the early 'Eighties, and previously as a savage grizzly bear is, as a result of *glasnost* and *perestroika*, in the stages of being dismantled and rehabilitated in favour of something more humane and terrestrially constructive - rampant nationalism permitting.

There is a useful way to work constructively with the metaphor, and resultant reality, of black magic; and for each person, as the **individual representative and foundation** of consensus reality, to be able to neutralise the misinformed mental construct attached with it. This is by using the same technique which "punk rock" did with the *swastika* (venerated as a holy Sanskrit symbol (= non-literal metaphor) for whirling creativity and well-being before its adoption by the Nazis; now transformed into a device to confront people's misconceptions), and Madonna has done with the *crucifix* (always a symbol of "man's inhumanity to man", unworthy of worship; now transformed into an item of kitsch jewellery.) Black magic can, instead, be regarded as something which is not done in accordance with one's inmost nature - or one's true will, to put it another way - and which must therefore be against the natural developmental process of the whole cosmic "continuity":

"The Magickal Will is in its essence twofold, for it presupposes a beginning and an end; to will to be a thing is to admit that you are not that thing. Hence to will anything but the supreme thing, is to wander still further from it - any will but that to give up the self to the Beloved (i.e., the universe) is **Black magic - yet this surrender is so simple an act that to our complex minds it is the most difficult of all acts**; and hence training is necessary. Further, the Self surrendered must not be less than the All-Self; one must not come before the altar of the Most High with an impure or imperfect offering...this training may lead through all sorts of complications, varying according to the nature of the student, and hence it may be necessary for him at any moment to will all sorts of things which to others might seem unconnected with the goal...The majority of people in this world are ataxic; they cannot co-ordinate their mental muscles to make a purposed movement. They have no real will, only a set of wishes, many of which contradict others. The victim wobbles from one to the other (and it is no less wobbling because the movements may occasionally be very violent) and at the end of life the movements cancel each other out. Nothing has been achieved; except the one thing of which the victim is not conscious: the destruction of his own character, the confirming of indecision." [1b]

The interested reader is urged to consult *Magick in Theory and Practice* further if s/he wishes to find an example of a comprehensive training syllabus for attaining the all-important one-pointedness of will. In it, the attainment of what is metaphorically called **The Knowledge and Conversation of The Holy Guardian Angel** - the full realization by the (elementally) balanced ego of a transpersonal self - is given as the single worthwhile objective of all magickal activity: all else is seen as "black" - that is, "a process of disconnected fatuity", as Crowley once remarked; from the activity of anybody who attempts to divert spiritual force for material ends, such as "professional" healers, divinators and false gurus; to anybody who knowingly and wilfully rejects truth because it does not pander to the expectations of their petty egos.

"The Holy Guardian Angel" is known as a figure of speech. When conversant with it, the single worthwhile magickal attainment then becomes to give all of one's blood "unto the Cup of Babalon" in **The Communion of Saints** - in other words, to go totally beyond altogether the ego into a mystic state of unity - or nothingness - with the universe. Once more, everything else is seen as "black" magic.

These two magickal operations are identifiable with the *internal spiritual alchemy* mentioned earlier, which alongside *initiation*, remain the only accurate description of "white" magick: the Double Wand of Power. The only reason why aberrant phenomena are best labelled "black" any more than, for instance, red, green or amber, is because of the deliberate contrast of metaphors afforded by *The Book of the Law*, which reveals: "There is a veil; that veil is black. It is the veil of sorrow. Tear down that lying spectre of the centuries..." (2:52), and concomitantly, "...my colour is black to the blind, but the blue and gold are seen of the seeing. Also I have a secret glory for them that love me." (1:60).

The Book of the Law, the word of which is Thelema, is the mystical text published by Crowley under the imprint of Ankh-af-na-khonsu, "the priest of the princes", along with a Comment which, somewhat in the manner of a zen koan, forbids the study of it. The text contains some of the most sublime metaphors to be found anywhere in literature, and I direct the reader's attention towards it if his or her acquaintance has not already been made. Yet such is the challenging nature of the book that it is not without the odd red herring whose purpose is, without beating about the bush, to take the bull by the horns: to put noses to the grindstone and to winnow out the wheat from the chaff. The Comment is an interesting coda: it consists of a series of stern commandments, at odds with the thelemic message of the book itself. The unwritten assumption is that the reader should make up his or her own mind, rather than be told what to do or threatened in an old aeon fashion. Crowley, pre-empting the reaction of the book burners, considered it "wise" to destroy the book after the first reading. Yet at least one fool has blindly "followed orders" and obliged, consigning, along with his discriminatory faculty of reason, the loathsome *bible of hell* to oblivion in the flames.

If something is "black", it is regarded as being an impediment to a state of clear vision - such as the acute eye-sight of a hawk, for example, which sees everything keenly and accurately. The nature of that which remains beyond, or rather behind, the blackness is blue and gold. The gold serves as a metaphor for the alchemical Sun, the star which burns in the heart of every wo/man, with its unknowable core of inmost divinity hidden behind the black veils of accreted psychological complexes. All around every star and system is shed the blue light of manifestation: as the unclouded daylight sky, as "the blue lidded daughter of sunset", and as "the untravelled, the unthinkable immensity of space; night, the impermeable blue."

In his experiments, the psychologist and scientist Wilhelm Reich was able to isolate and photograph a strong brilliant field of blue "orgone energy", reproduced as a colour plate in the hardcover (Farrar, Strauss & Giroux) edition of *Cosmic Superimposition/Ether, God and Devil*. He saw what he called **orgone** to be similar to that which the ancients recognised as the aether (and which *The Book of the Law* also reveals **Nuit**, the Egyptian star-goddess): a universal, i.e. continuous, life-force which contains, and is simultaneously an expression of, all (sub)atomic things.

V

Why is it that people sometimes act in such a way as to interfere with and restrict the will of another? And why do social interactions and communications in our little world become so frequently characterized by what has been called this metaphor of black magic? One possible answer is that most human responses are still stuck in the old grooves of amphibian or reptilian or mammalian patterns of atavisitic behaviour. These were pretty much indelibly programmed from the time of our prehistoric ancestors long ago, when they were ingrained into our genes and cellular memory of the brain and central nervous system. Overloaded on top of this is what, at present for the majority of human organisms, is a tendency of entropic inertia to eschew any form of radical departure from the cosy and the habitual, the familiar and the traditional.

"With many people custom and habit - of which ethics is but the social expression - are the things most difficult to give up: and **it is a useful practice to break any habit just to get into the way of being free from that form of slavery.** Hence we have practices for breaking up sleep, for putting our bodies into strained and unnatural positions, for doing difficult exercises of breathing - all these, apart from any special merit they may have in themselves for any particular purpose, have the main merit that man forces himself to do them **despite any conditions that may exist. Having conquered internal resistance one may conquer external resistance more easily.**" [1b]

When entropic inertia is challenged, all sorts of defence mechanisms spring into action. The human being, who is also a human animal, may become armoured and agitated; perhaps even violent. Like other primates, we seem to be widely equipped with a variety of inborn behavioural patterns which have been shaped by tens of thousands of years of our predecessors having to defend themselves against wild and predatory animals. Along with living in primitive settlements and societies, where there is an emphasis on pack hierarchy, and where a dominant position in it has had to be asserted and then maintained from challenges by others, this has led to a modern social system which, although in one sense is "natural", is nonethless inappropriate for our future evolution. Repressed people have a pathological tendency to either feel inadequate, inferior and submissive, or else to over-compensate for this by unduly trying to be "one up". They may also resort to crime or be excessively suspicious or paranoid of the motives of strangers. For evidence of this, just take a look round at the number of "Beware of Pickpockets" and "Do not leave any bags unattended" signs there are! - sometimes, it is sadly true, for sound reasons. Honour and self-worth are, by definition, in short supply amongst thieves, who are far more likely to be people with some expensive *habit* to support (gambling, drinking, narcotics, collecting "limited" editions or special objects, or staying "in" with the in-crowd through the acquisition of the latest fashionable designer clothing, trainers, and accessories, etc), than starving or specifically suffering from the psychological disorder of clinical kleptomania.

The nearer someone gets to penetrating such defence barriers, "invading the territorial space" of another person, the more opposition will occur. Even when an attempt is made with the best motives in the world to help somebody with a problem about personal (in)security, on one level that person will be hated for it. This is because the one showing compassion, unless they happen to be some sort of a yogi in a highly-developed state of being, is not only likely to suffer from the malaise to a degree themselves, and is thereby putting the other one into what s/he may feel to be an inferior pack position; but s/he is also making that other person more and more aware of, and afraid and annoyed by, what it is s/he has spent a lifetime trying to keep away from - namely, their own subconscious. As Crowley phrased it in *The Heart of the Master*:

"Note also that many men, feeling in themselves the bitterness of Restriction, seek to relieve their own pain by imposing a like burden upon their fellows: as it were a cripple who should seek ease by mutilating the bearers of his carriage. Also, to deny the Law of Thelema is a restriction in itself, affirming conflict in the Universe as necessary. It is blasphemy against the Self, assuming that its Will is not a necessary (and therefore a noble) part of the Whole. In a word, he who does not accepts the Law of Thelema is **divided** against himself: that is, he is insane (schizophrenic), and the upshot shall be the ruin of the Unity of his Godhead." [9]

Wilhelm Reich, like Crowley, was obliged by a conspiracy of the authorities to leave several countries. He ended up dying in an American prison and having his books burned in an American incinerator - an ironic indictment on the hollowness of the First Amendment and its undertaking to guarantee "freedom of religion, expression, and assembly". In the protected sphere of the medical and psychiatric profession, he committed the unspoken crime of being a loose cannon; a rogue activist, daring to speak the truth about the nature of the interaction between sexual politics, repression, and the authoritarian state (for further information, see his *The Mass Psychology of Fascism* (1933), amongst others). This he did somewhat too loudly for the comfort of society's pack leaders - or maybe herd, or flock leaders would be the more appropriate description, judging from the level of support he was given. Among his other notable achievements was the fact that he was the first to psychoanalytically isolate the suppressive behavioural tendency in our neurotic society, calling it "**emotional plague.**" This (what is now classified as) **sociopathy** was summarised concisely by his biographer David Boadella as follows:

"The term "emotional plague" was introduced to describe a disturbing phenomenon: the presence of group-irrationalism and group-destructivity. When Reich had studied the character-neuroses, he had described the layering of the personality in terms of the superficial controlled layer, paying lip-service to moral values and aims; a destructive and pathological middle layer, the "repressed Freudian unconscious"; and a primary source of undistorted biological impulses. In the neurotic these layers were normally in conflict with each other. **Under certain social conditions, however, pathological secondary drives could become socially infectious and heavily rationalised, so that they could be acted out much more fully than the average neurotic is able to act out his perverse impulses...**The emotional plague character is a person who has **entered a mutually reinforcing situation with a number of other people, all of whom have in common that they have a lot of destructive impulses that they are not aware of and who create together a *social alibi* for acting out these impulses in concert, and with the rationalisation of some group ideology.** Thus, in the Salem Witch trials it was possible for a whole community of allegedly Christian people to collude together in such a way as to persecute by torture and execution anyone who dissented from the group ethos and who did not join in with the ritualistic process of condemnation and self-condemnation." [10]

Anybody who likewise speaks out in the manner of Crowley or Reich inevitably swims upstream against the prevailing current of ignorance, stupidity and superstition. That is why among the metaphors attributed to the A∴ A∴ system, the grade of

Magus is said to be "cursed" - because he has no choice but to speak out: interpreting, in an unavoidably direct fashion, each single phenomenon on every occasion as a particular dealing of the universe (as a superconscious entity) with his soul.

The "ladies" and "gentlemen" of the yellow tabloid press serve, often without realizing the repercussive impact of their own words, as a powerful medium for evoking the emotional plague, which is the exteriorization in tangible form of black magic. Yet it can also be evoked in the form of any communication between two or more people which involves a malicious "bad-mouthing" defamation of character; malignant gossip; a deliberate and vampiric draining atmosphere of negativity; or an intentional spread of slanderous misinformation.

Why is it then that black magic and its harbinger, emotional plague/sociopathy, arises? No one exactly knows. It seems very probable that the bottom line is personal insecurity, which manifests in its lighter side as embarrassment, but which, when pronounced, has its immediate defensive expression (or counter-attack) in a mean and vicious *schadenfreude*. This is when somebody feels worthwhile at the expense of somebody else being made to feel worthless: the attitude of bullies towards victims; the feelings of Nazis towards non-Aryan minority groups or rednecks against negroes; the snobbery engrained in the worst aspects of the caste system and the class system, and so on. The "blame" for why this happens in turn must rest with a lack of **fluidity** and a lack of **self-regulation** in the experiential growth of the individual. Cultural brainwashing from the wrong mental-constructs is also responsible to an enormous extent. These are assembled by an unspoken sub-conscious general consensus in order to keep innovators in line, to prevent unwanted challenging and unconventional ideas and metaphors from rocking the boat, and to ensure that the message from people like Crowley remains buried.

The solution to the problem is outrageously simple in theory, and extremely difficult to bring about in practice. Coming to the superconscious entity of the Universe as a whole ("Nuit", or "Nu" for short) with an inner red gleam of spirit (to be metaphorical once again), we have to explore and exceed the outermost limits of the white (the mind); to flow along with the course of the yellow (the middle way); to be at one with the blue (in diminishing internal friction and restoring a coherent unity); and to dispense with the black (that stubborn and interferesome blind refusal to accept the reality of the continuity of existence). Fixed perceptions of things have to be changed, or become open to change; society (the individual) needs to become more fluid and receptive to foreign ideas; we need to question and challenge every thing we are told, and to keep (if not expand!) our sense of humour; and finally, from a mental position of being metaphorically boxed in, we need to get out of our boxes. We need to get out of our Tree!

BLUE MAGICK

"He that riseth up against thee shall be thrown down, though thou raise not so much as the little finger against him. And he that speaketh evil against thee shall be put to shame, though thy lips utter not the littlest syllable against him. And he that thinketh evil concerning thee shall be confounded in his thought, although in thy mind arise not the least thought of him. And they shall be brought unto subjection unto thee, and serve thee, though thou willest it not. And shall be unto them a grace and a sacrament, and ye shall all sit down together at the supernal banquet, and ye shall feast upon the honey of the gods, and be drunk upon the dew of immortality. For I am Horus, the crowned and conquering child, whom thou knewest not!" From *The Vision and the Voice* (The First Aethyr) by Aleister Crowley (1909).

I

Why should a metaphor concerning **blue** magick exist? What real foundation will it have, if any? And how much bearing does it have in the way of the price of milk? (the sceptic rightly asked).

Outer space is often spoken of as being "inky" black; but visual evidence shows it to be really a very dark shade of **blue**. Once night falls here on Earth, the sky does not become black, but turns deep indigo (city smog permitting.) As far as can be ascertained, "space" in the infancy of the universe was brilliantly illuminated, but as its expanding fabric continued to cool, it became gradually darker in visible light. This process continued until it appears as it is does today to us carbon-based life-forms breathing nitrogen and oxygen on the surface of an iron-based planet: the elemental products of a second or third generation (super)nova cycle. Due to atmospheric effects and starlight radiations from what is, erroneously, called the void, there is always some trace of a blue sky left at night - it never becomes entirely black. This blackness is a fallacy, an illusion, a veil. A useful imaginative and meditative exercise, relating to *Ain Soph (Aur)* or *Limitless (Light)* on the Cabbalistic Tree of Life, which results in some very powerful and pleasant changes in consciousness after a very short time, is to see and hold the image of outer space as stretching into infinity with the azure colour of a cloudless and sparkling sky on a clear and sunny day. (Once successful, "one" may then "concentrate" in it various forms of matter to endless degrees of complexity until the train of this "imagi(ni)ng" is broken. By such means is the process of creation mimicked.)

Into the blue are studded an "approximately infinite" number of stars, the hottest (most energetic) of which are actually **blue** stars. Rigel, 850 light years distant in the constellation of Orion, is an example of such a blue star, with a surface temperature of 25,000 °C, compared with the 5,700°C of Sol/ Ra, our own yellow sun, and the 10,000°C of Sirius A, a star which is "white hot" and a little over eight light years away.

In the science of spectroscopy, the speed at which stars or galaxies are travelling towards or away from us can be determined by examining the exact wavelength of lines in its spectra. If a stellar object - by which is meant those objects engaged in a nuclear fusion process of converting hydrogen into helium - is receding, its radiation is "stretched" and the wavelengths are slightly longer than they should be. If it is approaching, the wavelengths become compressed and shortened. This distortion of the wavelengths is known as the **Doppler effect**, and where they are lengthened or shortened is calculated in terms of "red shift" and "blue shift" respectively. The effect is exactly the same as when, acoustically, the pitch of an ambulance siren rises (blue) as it speeds towards a listener, and then abruptly falls (red) as it passes away. It is possible to view the "**blue**" shift, where the wavelengths are bunched together towards the blue end, as a metaphorical embodiment of the loving desire between stars and galaxies to come together *for the chance of union.* The reverse would be a "chaotic" dispersion evermore into the four (or even eight) points of the compass, where all coherence is dissipated and lost - at least until it begins to turn blue, and then pulls itself together again.

In the rainbow of the visible spectrum, the wavelengths of the highest energy radiated are in the **blue** primary colour, away from the yellow and red. The blue wavelengths go from azure to indigo to violet, then on to ultra-violet A, B and extreme ultra-violet (EUV), before turning into radioactive x-rays, gamma rays, and cosmic rays - ever more rareified and darker shades of blue. At the extreme end of the known waveband resides cosmic radiation, the most intense and powerful form of radiation which can possibly exist, because the particles of which it is composed are moving almost at the speed of light which nothing has yet been known to be able to exceed. The major evolutionary quantum leaps, such as humanity's development from the apes, the emergence of civilisation, etc - as well as the death of the dinosaurs - might have been attributable to the mutative effects of a sudden large influx of cosmic rays, which are normally shielded from us by our sentient terrestrial magnetosphere and the movement of the solar wind coming from Sol/Ra.

Even though radiation measured from the blue end of the spectrum is the most energetic, the whole universe is completely composed of all manner of light "in extension". In his *Star Sponge Vision*, Crowley noted that each star is connected by many rays of light with every other star, and that:

"In the world of ideas each thought possessed a necessary relation with each other thought; each such relation is of course a thought in itself; each such ray is itself a star. It is here that logical difficulty first presents itself. **The seer has a direct perception of infinite series.** Logically, therefore, it would appear as if the entire space must be filled up with a homogeneous blaze of light. This however is not the case. **The space is completely full** (*i.e., blue*) **and yet the monads which fill it** (*i.e., gold*) **are perfectly distinct.** A further development of the vision brought to the consciousness that the structure of the universe was highly organized, that certain stars were of greater magnitude and brilliance than the rest...This meditation developed in the course of time into such importance that I feel almost justified in calling it the radix of my whole philosophical outlook..." [8b]

A practical method for the simple realisation of this blue (and gold) state of consciousness can be found in *Liber Nu*, for example, which appears in the anthology *Gems from the Equinox*, published by Llewelyn Press.

II

So what then is blue **magick**? It is, for one thing, the philosophical practice of a School, which for convenience, and in line with the other three colourful metaphors, could be labelled the "Blue School". At the *Black and Blue Magick* talk given in May 1991 where these labels were originally put forward in public, there was a degree of worried concern as to whether the act of cursing had any part to play in blue magick. Before dealing with this, it would prove useful background material to look first at the prevailing religions worldwide, to see if there may be any other precedent for the cursing act.

Islam deals with cursing in a very real and direct fashion with the *fatwa* and Salman Rushdie. To Buddhism, life is a curse of sorrow anyway. In Judaism, a whole arsenal of maledictory curses can be found in the Old Testament (Chapters 27 (vv. 13-26) and 28 (vv. 15-68) of the Book of *Deuteronomy*) directed against those who could not be bothered to obey the tyrannical pronouncements of Jehovah. In applied Christianity, the propagation of the gospel of the New Testament was assisted by a solemn ritual of cursing that was extremely efficient in the Middle Ages at removing political troublemakers from their sphere of influence.

Excommunication was described by Henry Lea in his *History of the Inquisition* (1956) as follows: "To the public (the excommunicated person) was an outlaw, **without even the right of self-defence against the first-comer, for his very defence was rated among his crimes;** in the popular faith of the age **he was an accursed thing, without hope here or hereafter.** The only way of readmission into human fellowship, the only hope of salvation, lay in reconciliation with the Church through the removal of the awful ban." The *Catholic Encyclopaedia* establishes that the excommunicated outcast can be "considered as **an exile from Christian society and as completely non-existent,** for a time at least, in the sight of ecclesiastical authority." In the Catholic Church, the most widely familiar form of excommunication is the ceremony known as *bell, book and candle,* so-called because "the officiating cleric reads and solemnly closes the book from which he has read the curse; a bell is tolled as for a dead man, and candles are extinguished as a sign that the soul of the offender has been removed from the sight of God." A procedure for pontifical denouncement was also devised by Pope Zacharias as follows: "The pope was to wear violet vestments and his mitre, and to be assisted by 12 priests carrying lighted candles. He formally deprived the offender of the Mass and separated him from the society of all Christians in the words: **"we exclude him from the bosom of our Holy Mother the Church in heaven and on earth...and we judge him condemned to eternal fire with satan and his angels and all the reprobate, so long as he will not burst the fetters of the demon, do penance and satisfy the Church."** Finally the pope and 12 priests threw their lighted candles to the ground." Er, nice people, these Christians! So much, it seems, for their renowned "Charity" and the business about "forgiving thine enemies"! Nor is the otherwise sheepish Church of England exempt from indulging in a spot of cursing: still printed in *The Book of Common Prayer* is a service known as *A Commination or Denouncing of God's Anger Against Sinners* containing "...the general sentences of God's cursing against impenitent sinners..." Again, something of a big deal for "love thy neighbour" and turning the other cheek!

It is a good idea at this point for us to once again "exorcise" the consensus reality of what a word has come to represent. By examining its earliest meaning (in connection with its etymological origin), any superstructure of knee-jerk emotional response can be quickly removed from it, using the same purification process with which the word "black", and the phrase "black magic", were dealt with earlier.

The word "curse" is related to the idea of suffering, of having, or being made, a cross to bear. It is of Scandinavian origin, from the Swedish *korsa* and Danish *korse,* meaning "to make the sign of the cross" (from the Swedish and Danish noun *kors,* a corruption of the Icelandic *kross,* meaning "cross", which is itself derived, via the Old Irish *cros,* from the Latin *crux*). The **cross**, an ancient symbol signifying the four elements (the fifth element of Spirit is sometimes shown upon it as a rose), is in its most basic form **balanced horizontally and vertically**. In white magick, this is affirmed in the Gesture of the "Cabbalistic Cross", which starts and finishes the classical "Lesser Banishing Ritual of the Pentagram of Earth" (as practiced for instance by the "white" magickal order of the Golden Dawn), whose purpose itself is one of establishing neutrality and equilibrium.

In a blue magickal context, to curse simply has the original meaning to "*rectify balance*". The word can be encountered in this sense in several places throughout *The Book of the Law*, which also has as one of its central keys the formula:

$$0 = (+1) + (-1), \text{ or } 2.$$

As such, it is directed towards the entropic degeneration of institutionalized religion, as anticipated by the Yellow School (3:49-54); towards those foolish enough to deny the fact that *there is no bond that can unite the divided but love* (1:41); towards the pitfalls of placing too much emphasis upon reason and the dualism of causality "*Because and his kin*" (2:28) - and towards the actual reader, who is advised "*deem not too eagerly to catch the promises; fear not to undergo the curses*" (3:16). But since the motivation for cursing in this way stems from the whole universe as one single entity, the power obtaining from it is infinitely greater than a malefic *schadenfreude* curse to wish misfortune on others, emanating from any mere individual and black magical source.

III

As perhaps has been intuitively gleaned, the starting-point, and also perceived means of operation of blue magick, is Nothing (   ), other than that commonly regarded as "black magic", as was discussed previously in terms of the emotional plague, sociopathy, etc. From the point-of-view of its blind slaves, the appearance of somebody working blue would be indistinguishable from "black magic", rather like the aborigine who was taken to Paris and mistook the Eiffel Tower for a type of unfamiliar and gigantic tree. An obvious danger here is that of a misconstruction by all those unaware of blue magick's hidden motive - yet since so large a part of its Success against black magic revolves around just this very concealment, there does not seem to be any way that this particular aspect can be resolved. Rather like the effect of nitroglycerine, its very hazard also ensures its efficacy in moving away an obstacle.

Blue magick is similar to yellow magick (not that there is any such thing, of course!) in that it is an **absorbent** type; i.e., it works "in reverse", according to what is being done by the environment to the magician, rather than the magician working any magick on the environment. The difference is that in blue, the magician is a conscious + willing tool of events; whereas in yellow s/he "let's be." The moment yellow starts to *react*, because of its own nature, it becomes blue. White alone, since it is based on one individual's assessment as emphasised earlier, can never know if the actions it is doing beyond itself are "true". But when white is motivated to change things through the worship of Nu, the reaction becomes blue if and when its repercussions percolate beyond an immediate subjective environment. Yellow can and does, become blue; white can, and does, become blue; but the interesting thing is, that black too will evolve to become blue, and in spite of itself.

Blue magick is in alignment with the neutrality of Tao - Teh, and yet its visible manifestation to others with a veiled, black "out-look", will be that of the blue magician trying to mould the universe to his or her (lower) will. It flows along seamlessly with the perception of other peoples' unbalanced mental constructs as a thoroughly invisible nemesis. Antagonistic people who project, using *transference*, that a blue magician is employing "black magic" would actually be encouraged in their belief by his/her behaviour. This behaviour would not seek to rectify these erroneous assumptions by means of reflexively fighting fire with fire, because by engaging in direct confrontation, it would give them an acknowledgement of a power which they did not own. Such acknowledgement would in turn only detract strength away from the blue magician, and give it to them instead in equal degree.

Rather, a blue magician would seek to **maintain** and not alter that impression, making the way extremely simple for it to become rock hard - like the Tarot trump *The Tower*, for example, which is then Changed by Lightning. A contest involving blue magick is one which takes place without any imbalance of passion, emotion or violence, but with an inner truth and resolve that knows of no defeat. This is possibly what "The Great Beast 666" did when he revelled/reviled in being *The Wickedest Man in the World*. (Or, as Crowley put it at the *Laughing Torso* libel trial when asked what a "fair expression" of "The Beast 666" might be: "It only means sunlight. If you prefer, you can call me *Little Sunshine*.")

Such behaviour as described will, once set in motion, necessitate the perpetrators having to increase the strength of their black magical attacks in order just to maintain their pack position - rather as an addict, once gaining tolerance, might need an increasing dose of a drug in order to remain "normal". The effect of this will mean that there is no alternative but to *go on* increasing the projected force of those disordered perceptions which constitute the awry mental construct of the[ir] universe. This will sooner or later result in one or more of the following:

(a) some degree of **catharsis** on their part. For example, anything from a realization that they have been acting blindly and stupidly, to (if they are particularly obstinate) a complete and total nervous breakdown, or worse - the upshot of this being, as was remarked earlier in the excerpt from *The Heart of the Master*, schizophrenia and the ruin of the unity of his or her divine nature;

(b) it being made apparent, in stages, to all in their environment that they had not been speaking honourably and with **mayat** (the ancient Egyptian principle of truth, symbolised by a feather) because of the increasing absurdity and disconnectedness of their behaviour;

c) the practitioner of blue magick experiencing more than one level of **awareness**: he opportunity of "taking a step back" into the witness consciousness of being able o observe his/her mental constructs or levels of programming;

d) the practitioner of blue magick experiencing knowledge in how to **deal** (and how not to deal!) with various levels of his or her ego vehicle energies, especially those of *subconscious* atavisms (symbolised by fangsome "monsters" or "creatures of the deep" which are motivated by seemingly "alien" primal drives such as eating or devouring); and the *id*, the potentially tempestuous repository of natural animal desires (symbolised by the lion, "king of the beasts"); and finally

(e) in terms of a sense of **games(wo)manship** in the lila, for the blue magician, a psychological advantage such as a master has over his/her opponents (who are also all masters, were they but to realise it, and kings and queens forever.)

Here is an example of the way in which a phenomenon (in this case, an instruction) can have the same appearance, but a different interpretation - according to the mental construct of the beholder - as to whether it is black or blue:

"Let the magician bearing himself as a great king root out and destroy without pity all things in himself and his surroundings which are weak, dirty, diseased, or otherwise unworthy..."

Black? or Blue? Your perception!(!) Many of the writings from *The Beast 666* challenge in this way. This extract comes from the first recommended practice of Ethics, Part 8 of *Liber Had*, which can also be found in the *Gems from the Equinox*.

Crowley's **Liber Oz**, or *The Book of Strength*, is another sterling example. Written four years prior to his death in 1947, this short document consists of a series of simple declarations with regard to the rights of man - *man has the right to think what he will, speak what he will, write what he will* - and so on - finishing with the statement: *man has the right to kill those who would thwart these rights. The slaves shall serve.*

Now, what exactly is to be understood here by the word "kill"? It is hardly likely that murder is being proposed - just as the meaning of the card **Death** in the Tarot, rather than suggesting non-existence, indicates "change". Similarly, when Crowley writes of "child sacrifice", it is simply a (teasing, to be sure) metaphorical device relating to the spending of semen in a sexual act which fails to result in pregnancy. The act of killing can therefore be here equated with the causing of a death to occur, in the sense of a shift or change in perception. The black interpretation of this line is: "man has the right to murder those who would thwart these rights". The blue would be: "man has the right to alter the consciousness of those who would thwart these rights, in alignment with his/her true will." As for the idea of slavery, the universe allows anybody the freedom to be as slavish as they desire! The man Aleister Crowley was described in *The Book of the Law* (1:26) as being the "slave" of infinite space. And in (1:10), we are told that the servants of infinite space are "few and secret". But it is useful to remember that the *service* done by such *slaves* must always be in accordance with true will - "Do that, and no other shall say nay." Then, of course, they are no longer slaves, but kings. Any slaves that fail to rise to this wealth of sovereignty become poor, sad folk: *beggars*, dependent upon the compassion of others, unable to hide their lack of wealth and spiritual poverty.

One more example occurs as follows. *The Book of the Law* mentions (3:15) "...kill and *torture*..." "Kill" has been discussed above. Torture, in the unexorcised consensual understanding, is rightly an ugly word, full of reference to humanity's cruelty towards its own kind. But since *The Book of the Law* deals with evolution rather than de-evolution, and with regeneration rather than degeneration, the meaning must therefore refer to something else. It could, for instance, be meant as a noun in the sense of *ordeal* - such as running a marathon, solving a rubik's cube, or going through the "dark night of the soul" - all of which could be described as "torture" for a person undergoing them before s/he arrives at the liberating exhilaration of accomplishment. Elsewhere, a further clue indicates that "the tribulation of ordeal is bliss" (3:62) - of which Crowley comments: "the solution of each complex by tribulation (or rubbing away) is the spasm of joy which is the physiological accompaniment of any relief from strain and congestion." This is paralled in the practice of *vegetotherapy*, pioneered by Reich, where one's physical and mental "character armour" is erased by massage, allowing mental and bio-energies to "stream" freely once again.

A key application of blue magick is in a sense very like those old folk sayings - pithy old saws o' yore such as: "give 'em enough rope to hang themselves", "they're digging their own graves", and that *magic potion* for schadenfreude, "evil comes to those who think ill of others" (*honi soit qui mal y pense*). In terms of its reaction, the approach of blue magick is in one sense perfectly identical with all true branches of martial arts, and in another with Simon Iff's handling of "the Thing in the Garden" in Crowley's other novel, *Moonchild*:

> "For my part, I prefer the way of the Tao, and to do everything by doing nothing...If everybody did his Will, there would be no collision. Every man and every woman is a star. It is when we get off our orbits that the clashes come. Now if something gets off its orbit, and comes into my sphere of attraction, I absorb it as quietly as possible, and the stars sing together again...The secret is to have assimilated all things so perfectly that there is no longer any possibility of struggle. To have destroyed the idea of duality. To have achieved Love and Will so that there is no longer any object to Love, or any aim for Will. To have killed desire at its root; to be one with every thing and with Nothing...Why does a man die when he is struck by lightning? Because he has a gate open to lightning; he insists on being an electrical substance by possessing the quality of resistance to the passage of the electric current. If we could diminish that resistance to zero, lightning would no longer take notice of him. Also, there are two ways of preventing a rise of temperature from the sun's heat. One is to oppose a shield of non-conducting and opaque material: at the best it is imperfect; some heat will always get through. The other is to remove every particle of matter from the space which you wish to be cold; then there is nothing there to become hot; and that is the way of the Tao...**Where Nature has been outraged, an attempt made to interfere violently with her laws, it is permissible to act - or rather, to counteract just so much as is necessary to restore equilibrium.**" [11]

Simply put, in essence **blue** magick has the appearance of **black** with the normal tactical strategy of **yellow** and the aims of **white**. It also partakes of the nature of the Egyptian God Horus in his aspect of Avenger, in that it aligns with the principle of vengeance (or adjustment), and it can only work with what has already been acted upon (that is, adversely interfered with) the magician from outside. One way or another, a "heavenly" order is restored on Earth through the agent of blue magick, in which the Magician and the Exorcist are one. Again, it is not that (the general consensus view of) black magic would be practiced by the magician here. Just that to all appearances it will seem so to the eyes of the blind accuser, which simply project inner delusions! But with the passage of time, the black to the blind becomes blue to the **seer**; meanwhile all remains lawful within and unto the continuity of Nuit, "the darkness of blue light", which is none indeed. Aum. Ha.

Love is the law, love under will.

"Conquest."

References

1. Aleister Crowley, *Magick in Theory and Practice* (1929); (a) "Magick", Chapter 8: "Of Equilibrium" (footnote); (b) "Book Four", Chapter 6: "The Wand".
2. Aleister Crowley, *Magick Without Tears* (c.1943), (a) Letter 68 (b) Letters 6-8 inclusive.
3. Herman Melville, *Moby Dick* (1851), Chapter 42.
4. Jeffrey B. Russell, *The Devil: Perceptions of Evil from Antiquity to Primitive Christianity* (1977), p.66.
5. Alan Watts, *The Two Hands Of God: the oneness of opposites* (1963), pp. 36-39.
6. Aleister Crowley, *The Diary Of A Drug Fiend* (1922), note at start of Book III.
7. P.R. Stephensen, *The Legend Of Aleister Crowley* (1930), Chapter VII.
8. Aleister Crowley, *Confessions* (1929), (a) Chapter 96 (b) Chapter 82.
9. Aleister Crowley, *The Heart of the Master* (1924), p.38.
10. David Boadella, *Wilhelm Reich: The Evolution of His Work* (1973), pp.214-215.
11. Aleister Crowley, *Moonchild* (1917), Chapter 5

ARTICLES OF ASSOCIATION FOR THE COMPANY OF HEAVEN
A Manifesto

Do what thou wilt shall be the whole of the Law.

1) The company of heaven is unreservedly open to Thelemites. There is no exclusion whatseover based upon grounds of sex, race, age, religion, social or economic status, national origin, tradition, or culture. The organization is democratic rather than hierarchical in accordance with the principle, "Every man and every woman is a star", and there is no leadership as such.

2) The company of heaven respects the sovereign true will of every member. There is a strong emphasis on Tolerance of the equal rights of all members.

3) The company of heaven is a non-religious and non-profit-making federation which does not ask for money. When numbers allow, an information service or newsletter may be produced for the benefit of members, which will then be offered for voluntary subscription at a reasonable rate in order to recover costs.

4) The signature of each member accepting the law of Thelema does not commit him or her to anything else at all. No other oaths or vows are required. If they wish, individuals are also free to revoke their membership and to be responsible for the act to no one but themselves.

5) Optional *ad hoc* activities amongst members remain the responsibility solely of the participants at any such meetings.

6) Unnecessary secrecy without good cause is frowned upon; therefore members of the company of heaven should not object if their Names (although not their personal details, such as address, phone numbers, etc, unless confirmed) are "unveiled".

7) Members can worship the universe within us and without us with Beauty and Love, in an infinite variety of ways.

8) The members of the company of heaven encourage one another in the accomplishment of the Great Work: the balanced discovery within themselves of their own true will and identity; the nature and meaning of "external" existence.

9) The company of heaven encourages a more ecologically responsible use of the Earth's natural resources and the evolution of a collective global awareness in preparation for a future period of Truth and Justice.

10) The company of heaven also seeks to cultivate the consciousness of the continuity of existence: the intricate and holistic inter-relationship of members with other human beings, life forms, and energies; the Earth; the Sun; other planets, stars, galaxies; and the universe as a whole, including *extra-* or *praeter-* human intelligences.

11) The company of heaven is affiliated to the A∴A∴

Love is the law, love under will.

the company of heaven

I, being of sound mind, freely declare that I accept the Law of Thelema, which is:

....
[Do what thou wilt

....
shall be the whole of the Law:

....
Love is the law,

....
love under will.]

Own True Name

Signature

Chosen Name or Motto (if any)

Date and place

I understand that this makes me a member of the company of heaven. [No. 0,000,   ,
. . .]

Every man and every woman is a star:
The unveiling of the company of heaven.

ILEL
by
Gareth J. Medway

In the stone schoolhouse,
Its walls washed by the sun,
The teacher said: "Wisdom may find you in your old age."
Adolescent Ilel thought:
"Why wait?
Why not seek Wisdom, and find her young?"
He left school that day never to return;
Instead he walked the streets, and asked passers-by where Wisdom lived.
Some knew not; others gave false directions.
One man said: "I am going that way now; follow me."
He led Ilel to a wine-house,
Where decayed men sprawled in the sawdust,
While others snarled at each other like disgruntled dogs,
Or sat all oblivious of the rest.
On a crude stage,
A painted harlot danced disgustingly.
She smiled at Ilel, and beckoned,
But he ran outside.
"Surely that is not the place", he thought,
"They have not found Wisdom, merely forgotten her absence."
Another day,
A man approached him without his asking,
And said: "We have built a palace for Wisdom, and she dwells with us."
He took him by the hand,
And brought him to this exceptional residence.
It was a gold-roofed building on a hill,
Fenced off by outer courts,
And guards,
And warnings.
Ilel was told: "For fifty pieces of silver
You may become a servant here,
And one day, with obedient behaviour
You might be admitted to Wisdom's presence."
Ilel had not such coinage,
But for a while he hung about.
Eventually he asked an old man amongst them what Wisdom looked like.

He replied: "I have not seen her all these years,
From her inner acolytes we get reports,
And hard instructions which they say emanate from her.
But who knows?"
Ilel thought the people of the city fools and liars,
And forsook the populous places,
But frequented the wilderness,
And only kept contact with people as was necessary for a bare livelihood.
A long time later,
He was walking through a desert,
Parched,
Hungry,
Exhausted,
When a blue something appeared in the distance.
He began to run,
Though his tired limbs could barely sustain such effort.
It was no mirage,
But a real fountain and pool,
With palms and bright flowers all about it.
He hardly cared about the figure beneath the tree,
But splashed the cool nectar over his head,
Then drank mouthful after mouthful, crystal-like from his cupped hands.
Only when his thirst was quenched,
Did he take notice that he was not alone:
A woman sat, cross-legged, watching him.
Richly robed she was in shimmering silk,
A blue-green globe revolved beneath her hand,
Her hair was black and wavy and long,
And her face shone with inner light.
He did not need to ask,
He knew,
It was her whom he had so long sought.
She smiled,
And raised her arms in welcome.
He knelt,
And kissed the ground before her feet.
But as he gazed on her smoothly-formed countenance,
An uneasy recognition gripped him.
"You were the whore in the tavern," he cried.
Her voice was melodious but firm:
"I was in the palace too,
You looked towards the select circle,

And never noticed me among the menial acolytes.
You have passed me by many times,
For I can be found in many places,
But always unnoticed,
Despised,
Revered for the wrong reasons,
Or sought to be captured and abused."
Ilel continued his journey,
But now he could go where he wished,
And cared little for discomfort or danger,
For he knew that wherever he went,
A kind woman would give him shelter,
Tend his injuries,
Refill his purse,
Share his happiness,
And nurse him in his final days on earth.

LUNAR ECLIPSE
by
Mouse

Lady,
bring out the beasts through this moonskin full.
When you're hidden within the shadow of Earth,
inside a girdle of fire,
the sun's black seed speaks through your circle,
mouthing your secret myths.
Fire-snakes slide, greeting ground-spinner shades -
nothing there, in angel veils,
in earth's warm glow of secret fire.
Sister seeping through moonskin full -
a touch of cool kisses, a glimmering of pearlsofts,
met within earth's secret fire.

THE CONVERSION OF ANTARES
A True Love Story

Antares Numi*ON
Magick River
44000 Kuala Kubu Bharu
Malaysia
25.IV.93

Dearest One:

Please don't be disappointed that this is a general bulletin and not a personal letter. Ten days ago I returned from the greatest adventure - and the most important initiation - in my experience so far (so fa mi re do?): there's much to tell and many to touch feelers with and it seems the only way is to try and put it all down in words and trust that the profound joy and delicious sense of perfection I feel will be magically transmitted to you.

The alternative would be to remain in blissful Silence for another Eternity...but let's keep the postman in work. And now I take a very deep breath (I hope you're comfortable and totally relaxed) and may each word that issues forth be impregnated with the essence of True Love.

Between the 13th and 21st March I attended STAR-BORNE REUNION #8 at Falls Creek (a ski resort in Victoria, Australia) and was completely reintegrated. It was a close encounter with beings from a dazzling diversity of worlds - and yet there was an instant recognition and remembrance of our total unity of purpose; no personal biographies were exchanged but on the transpersonal level it seemed impossible that we had never been aware of one another's existence. Elven kings and queens, fairy-tale princesses and princes, veterans of intergalactic battles, wayward priestesses from the Temple of Isis, Atlantean technocrats and Mayan sorcerers, gnomes and whales and turtles and dolphins and used flying-saucer salesmen... Gods and Goddesses from every pantheon sat together at breakfast. Sirians smiled at Pleiadian jokes; randy cherubs and retired dark lords, paranoid androids and conscientious coneheads, overweight angels and pandimensional tricksters, hierophants and elephants and mutant ninja Nubian nuns...we were all ONE and always had been! And of course the totally irresistible Solara was there in her full undeniable Presence: the moment I made eye contact with her I knew we had waited aeons for this meeting. At the very beginning of our long and terrifying adventure into physical form we had agreed to reconnect at the End of Time - and there she was, magnificent as ever, and there I was, and this was definitely IT!

Each day, each moment of the Reunion brought forth indescribable feelings and epiphanies. My emotional body was thoroughly cleansed by the spontaneous outpourings of joyous tears; my heart expanded like a balloon - no, like a planet and fused ecstatically into the One Heart. Love at its purest, in its full-spectrum

114

Totality, shone forth like the Sun of Suns, the Source of All Being. Layers of congealed experience peeled off like so much ancient snake skin and I was left shining, beaming and bouncing in the Beam. Details of what we actually *did* are irrelevant: the rituals were sacred, inspiring and altogether REAL. I was completely myself, absolutely relaxed, and blissed out beyond words from start to finish. Finish? But this will never end. I know for sure now how Eternity feels - and how spectacularly vast and glorious we are in our Essential Oneness.

Subjectively speaking, I was finally transmuted from a being frustrated by limitations to a Divine Limitlessness. All myths were satisfactorily resolved within me: I experienced the alchemical wedding of Isis and Osiris, Jesus and Mary, Tammuz and Inanna, Rama and Sita; the vindication of Set and Lucifer; the rejuvenation of Sanat Kumara, the Ancient of Days; the magickal birthing of the Star Child. In seven days God created the world - and in seven days the entire universe was reborn and transfigured. My molecules expanded, my chromosomes repatterned themselves, and I took my first steps on the New Road, having jumped the Abyss beyond the Doorway of the 11:11.

A few years ago I read an excerpt from Josè Argüelles' book, *THE MAYAN FACTOR*, in which he announced the arrival of an "extraterrestrial technical team" on Earth in 1992. Naturally I had been very curious and excited to see how this epochal event would unfold. On the second day of the Star-Borne Reunion at Falls Creek, I suddenly realised that the "technical team" Argüelles mentioned was right here - and that WE WERE IT! All it took was a fearless and indefatigable Messenger named Solara Antara Amaa-Ra to shake us all out of our deep sleep.

AN-NUT-TA-RA-HU! Total Surrender to our Divine Mission on Earth, the Completion of our Evolutionary Efforts, the Unification of our Polarities, the Transcendence of Duality, the Realisation of a New Heaven and a New Earth, the Ushering In of the Golden Dawn in the Long-Awaited Aeon of Horus...and at last, at long and weary last, the Crystal Vision of HOME!

It's only a matter of Time; but considering that both the Mayan and the Egyptian Calendars end on 31st December 2011, it's really NO-TIME at all. Anchored in the Template of Oneness, Giddy in the Heights of True Love, Floating on Rainbow Clouds of No-Mind, No-Problem, No-Worries, Mate...and transported by Gleaming Sparspangled Trekset Magical Mystery Tour Bus, I arrived back in Melbourne on the 21st March high on Soluntra's marvellous Star Essence.

And that's when the Loony Lords of the Labyrinth took over.

Bear in mind it was the Fall Equinox in the Wonderful Land of Oz, and the Wizard was ready for some Real Fun. I took a cab with Aku Ek Tara back to her little house in St Kilda (where I'd left the rest of my 3D baggage). As soon as we entered I sensed a powerful magnetic field of despair and isolation: it was emanating from Aku's nomadic house guest, a Swiss visionary painter, musician and mystic named Christian Camenzind. Aku announced that she needed some head space and disappeared into her room. I made tea and had it in the garden with Christian, who began to unburden his soul to me. After a while it dawned on me that I was face-to-face with the Phantom of the Unfinished Opera of Duality. Christian had taken on my own former experience of Unrequited Love and Tragic

Romance - which was the meaning of my earlier name "Tamaares" and on the last day of the Falls Creek Reunion I had edited out that name, having played out the painful cycle of separation and loneliness that has been the lot of all passionate lovers during the Time of Duality.

Christian finally let me in on a "secret": he was actually St. Germain. Well, he could have been Count Dracula for all I cared. I felt compelled to try and heal him, to fill the vacuum in his heart; and so we went out and had a Chinese meal together. Afterwards we walked along the esplanade and sat for a long time in silence under the Sentinel Palms near Luna Park. A couple of new stars appeared in the clear sky; there was a tangible atmosphere of transformation, of the swirling together of realities; all the kingdoms were alive and alert to the impending change of Evolutionary Spirals. Inexplicably I knew the Antarion Conversion would activate for me on the 22nd March - and it was now nearly 11 p.m. on the 21st.

A shadowy figure staggered out of the darkness and approached us. It was a battered-looking slip of a girl who seemed to me a Starchild who had crashlanded. She had just been punched in the face and blood was drying on her nose. I offered her my place on the bench and asked what had happened. She said she was in agony from heroin withdrawal; she needed money to score a fix, just for the night, because she was going to undergo rehab the next day; her name was Michelle, she was 15 years old, and she was willing to offer her sexual services in exchange for some cash. I told her to calm down and I'd try and help. "I don't need love," she said, "All I need is money." I looked into her eyes and said: "You need both money and love." She planted a kiss on my lips and started telling us she was a good person, but someone had stolen her crystal and now she couldn't believe in anything. She needed $50, she said. I checked my wallet and found $30 in it. "All right, you can have this, Michelle." Christian took out $20 from his wallet and added it to my donation. Michelle shivered and nearly burst into tears: "I don't believe there are people like you! This isn't happening!" she sobbed. Then she wrote her phone number on a piece of card and thrust it at me, beseeching me to call her the next day, because she really wanted to be my friend. "Well, tell your friends you met a couple of angels." Michelle hugged us both and disappeared towards the sleazy part of St Kilda.

I asked Christian to follow me through the Antarion Conversion, and we walked briskly to a lighted pavilion in the middle of a park where we found two parallel benches. Nearby a group of pilgrims were gathered: they looked like Jehovah's Witnesses, and possums were running about, very much alive. At 11:11 p.m. I felt a change of frequencies in the night sounds and thought for a moment that the pavilion was a concealed time machine or maybe a flying saucer! We sat in silence for what might have been 11 minutes and then I felt the urge to walk out of the pavilion in the opposite direction. Reality felt different. Christian came slowly towards me and stared at me for a long time. Then he smiled and said: "Akhnaton, you are Akhnaton." I returned his smile and nodded. "That was another story a long time ago." Perhaps Christian had recognised me when I did the Annuttara-hu mudra (which has now been integrated into my own).

I led Christian towards the sea. It was the fulfilment of every promise. Quetzalcoat stood on the ramparts and surveyed the gentle surf; he went to the water's edge and addressed the elements; bade farewell to the past and greeted the future on this brand new midnight before the Golden Dawn. A streetlight flashed on and off, keeping pace with Christian's internal struggle between doubt and certainty. "Hello, Iaoh!" I said, smiling at the thought that good old Metatron was such a wonderful pinion holding all the realities aligned. Christian wanted to head back to Aku's and so I obliged, though I really felt like swapping stories with every stone and every bush and every tree and lamppost and garbage bin in sight. Everything spoke to me, every atom, every molecule sang its remembrance of the Source. I wanted to dance forever through the streets of paradise. But I let Christian lead me back to the confines of 42 Fawkner Street, where he showed me his visionary paintings. They were brilliant, truly inspired works, but they belonged in a different universe: nothing connected in Christian's images, all forms existed in a perpetual limbo, devoid of continuity; I recognised him as a messiah of Oblivion, of *hedawa*, of the Pause between Creations. Then he showed me a bracelet he had bought recently: it was the Zunni map of the Universe and it corresponded with the shape of the Starburst on the Star-Borne Unlimited logo - instead of a Central Sun it featured an abstract face in blue and brown with eight turquoise feathers radiating from each side. I knew by this sign that Christian was himself a Manu - an Adamic manifestation - but of which Cycle? This one, the next, or the one beyond? Was I being shown an Alternate Universe, a parallel reality? Was this a vision of an Antimatter Probability? I was spaced out (and in) enough already and bade Christian sweet rest.

I felt wide awake. Glancing at the blanket on my bed I realised that the colourful "ethnic" patterns on the printed fabric made perfect sense: they were in fact the hieroglyphic chronicle of the evolution of Consciousness through all the dimensions! So this is the Fabric of Oneness, I thought...and it shall be keeping me warm! Everything made perfect sense, everything was perfect and had always been so. Mistakes did not really exist as such - but were programmed into our histories to produce the necessary aberrations leading to complexity - and the eternal possibility of regeneration and spontaneous creation. How could I sleep? I found myself travelling at the speed of thought through the strands of my DNA, as all genetic memories became accessible. The Mystery of Being revealed herself to me and I relived the First Moment of Creation. Parthenon smiled and quivered and gave birth to me and the Male Principle wriggled into being in all its serpentine virility. The Adventure of Immaculate Conception, starring the Original Cosmic Sperm!

A wise woman and healer living in Chelsea had presented me with a seven sided quartz crystal the day before I left for Falls Creek. She said it was given to her - but she knew it wasn't meant for her and when she saw me, she suddenly felt compelled to pass it on. A tiny equilateral triangle marked one facet of the quartz - and I knew it was the key to the crystal's teachings. Now I held the mineral being in my hands and was given the information that it had been awaiting my arrival since Hyperborean times. The Crystal...Kristos! Pleiadian memories activated.

The Tribe of Benjamin, expelled from Palestine, had resettled in Greece, in Arcadia, sometimes called Elysium. One of the "lost tribes of Israel": was I Benjamin? Now it reconnected: all Mystery Plays and Rites of Initiation had been designed to screen candidates for divine rulership. The Perfect One was the Master Genetic Coding from which all subsequent life-forms were generated - and through the Ages of Devolution Into Form, the Original Essence had maintained its absolute integrity by losing itself in the stormy seas of Relativity. The Creator was the Spirit of Innovation, activated by Total Love (not merely "Pure Love" but TOTAL LOVE!) But what about Benjamin? Yes, the Arcadians had perpetuated the worship of Pan - the All-in-One, the Everything-Out-of-Nothing - which subsequently devolved into the veneration of Priapus, symbol of Fertility and Resurrection. During the darkest phase of Kali yuga, at the height of the Patriarchal Era (which began approximately 7,200 years ago), Pan had vanished into the Unseen - become one with Mother Nature, the Goddess Gaia, who took on the role of Scapegoat for the Fall. The Spirit of Civilisation, of patriarchal control, equated the Female with Darkness and Sin, and Pan became the Devil Incarnate. Gilgamesh ruled the Cities while Enkidu roamed the Wilderness. Having contrived to kidnap Enkidu through the services of a temple prostitute, Gilgamesh developed a fear and loathing of the Goddess, blaming her for the enfeeblement of Manhood.

Duality produced the concept of the Shadow Self, the Doppelgänger, the Jekyll and Hyde Syndrome. In Palestine it resulted in the confusion of the Jewish tribes, torn between Spiritual and Secular polarities. The Jesus Mythos left a legacy of schizophrenia dividing Christian aspirations down the middle: Redemption or Punishment of the Wicked? Satan was set against Jesus in an adversarial role: Benjamin versus Joshua, Loki versus Thor, Cain versus Abel, and so on. Now in the Advent of Oneness, the polarities unified, the Mystery of the Ages can be revealed. We are One. The Great Beast 666, Panthera, To Mega Therion, Baphomet, Prometheus, Ahriman, Set...redeemed and honoured as the Male Aspect of the Female; the Aboriginal Wisdom long suppressed by the Colonisers of the Earth.

My phallus rose from the dead like Osiris - and was reverently attended to by the priestess power in my left hand. The One Eye twinkled at me and I beheld the Holy of Holies, the vesica piscis: the Female Within the Male, the Male Within the Female, hosanna! The Hole in One.

THE WHOLE IN ONE!

Serpent energy coursed through Creation, through the Body of Christ, and the Aeon of Horus dawned like the blush of a Virgin. Not since 1969 had I felt so completely AWAKE, so AWARE, so ALIVE, so COMPLETE. Solara and I were fused and I could locate her in the left half of my physical being - but she was no longer Solara, she was my adventurous anima made flesh, the Isis of my Isness, the Perfect Wisdom of my cells.

Happy Birthday! sang Creation - and I felt like the bubbliest one-day-old in the entire Universe.

Christian burst into the room pulsating with pain and anger; Aku had just woken up and requested that he move his gear and himself out of the house. She wanted time and space alone, with her ex-lover, Mr Love, and he had trouble dealing with Christian's powerful energy field. I felt Christian's distress like a hammer blow in the heart and tried to calm him - but he snarled spitefully at me and I felt a surge of irritation rise. Oh no, not on the first Morning of the New Reality! Not a slap in the face from the last vestiges of Duality! I offered him a tremendous hug to try and heal his heart chakra - but it was useless, or so it seemed at the time. Christian fled from the scene like Eternal Despair. It was then that I noticed the polystyrene surfboard leaning against one wall of the bedroom. "Ah, surf's up!" I remembered the advice we'd all been given at the end of the Reunion: Go out there and Ride That Surf! Okay, I shall...but where's my magic crystal!? Gone...surely Christian wouldn't... no, no suspicious thoughts, no unkind feelings! The other possibility was that the crystal had gone through the Doorway back into the Unseen...or maybe I was now the Crystal?

Into my shoulder bag went my flutes, the Essence of Betelgeuse, Canes Venatici and Wega, Solara's 11:11 book - and a rock I'd picked up from Falls Creek. I floated around St Kilda, relishing the vastness of my new expanded starry body. I stopped at a bookshop and rejoiced at the greater truths now available to all who can read. Antarion Conversion symbols appeared everywhere: on manhole covers, on the sides of old buildings, on sidewalks. The Mind of God has always been expressed through the works of Man - but remains invisible until one is awake! The 11:11 was everywhere I looked - in the tramlines, represented by pillars, depicted by trees. I blew on my flute and wind vortices swirled, arresting seagulls in midflight. Faces on the street were sometimes bewildered, sometimes jubilant, sometimes sphinxlike. I met a council of ancient kings sitting in a circle in a park. One introduced himself as Montezuma. They were the reincarnations of ancient brigand chiefs and aboriginal sages. I offered them all cigarettes and told them the long wait was over.

All day long I walked and danced through Melbourne, glorying in the new freedom of my multidimensional being. A barefoot puck, pilgrim, Prince of Peace. I walked up to church doors and was turned away without so much as a welcome or a cup of tea. Deformities scurried along the pavement, creatures out of the fevered imagination of Hieronymus Bosch. Angels waved at me and held up the victory sign. Starbabies and children flashed joyous greetings at me, fully cognisant of my presence. I walked through residential streets, stopping to peer through closed gates, hoping to be invited in for a drink or snack. Doors stayed fearfully shut - except where youth played. A kind stranger gave me a bottle of water: I drank deeply and the half empty bottle turned into a spirit compass, tilting merrily up each time it detected love and lightness in a passing body - and dipping leadenly when confronted with the gravity of humourless, dehydrated souls. I felt like the Assessor of Souls on Judgement Day - yet wherefore judge? It was merely a game - albeit an educational game - to demonstrate the profound importance of love and laughter as the keys to the Kingdom and Queendom of Heaven on Earth.

The shirt of many colours I was wearing had been a gift from the saucer-eyed goddess Marilia: it showed the Empress, the King of Pentacles, the Knight of Swords, the Ace of Swords, the Ace of Cups, Temperance and the Fleur-de-lis amidst a field of 8-pointed stars. For those familiar with the tarot, I was the embodiment of the Hermit and the Fool, the 22 and the O - the perfect marriage of Wisdom and Folly!

I needed no food, only water and star essence. Essence sustained me: the essence of trees and flowers and animals and humans with a lively sense of humour. I was aware of the mineral kingdom as I had never been before - buildings were awake in a way I had hitherto never experienced. Everything acknowledged me even as I acknowledged it: electrical entities hummed in heightened consciousness; inanimate structures suddenly seemed more alive than many humans I passed in the street! The principle of the Seven was in full operation: indeed all numbers conspired towards mathematical perfection, I was the living Kabbalah. I saw the Unseen in the Spaces In Between: the ghosts of yesteryear gawped at me from every window and those that recognised me were released from limbo. Sitting on a rock on a quiet street corner, I remembered the rock I was carrying in my pouch and placed it on one of the larger stones whereupon word quickly spread about the mass awakening Star-Borne had engineered at Falls Creek.

By now I had no idea where I was. I only knew I needed rest and shelter; twilight was approaching and the photon supply was swiftly decreasing. But I had not money on me and felt no desire to contact Aku Ektara. All I wanted was for a stranger to approach me and offer friendship or help; and the faces I saw were mostly locked in the habit of suspicion and wariness - ah, the curse of Machinetime and Survival in the Modern City! My address book was not on me, so I couldn't call Azuriel for advice; besides, I knew this was an adventure I had to see through on my own. In the growing darkness I found myself walking along Alma Road. I needed a bath to cleanse my etheric body - but the best I could manage was to wash my feet at a standpipe below an apartment block. I was attracted to the garden next door - it felt hospitable. So I rang the doorbell.

A well-groomed man in his 50s opened the door. I asked for a glass of water and the use of his telephone. He was gracious enough to let me in but said I had to hurry because he was about to have dinner with some friends. He asked me what was happening to me and I said I wasn't quite sure; I had been reborn only a few hours ago and was finding it hard to feel at home in Melbourne. Then he asked me if I knew the names of the Magi who witnessed the birth of the Infant Christ. I said I'd recognise them if I saw but I didn't know their names. Then he said if I were genuine I could tell him the names of the Magi. Never mind, I said, just let me use the phone. I managed to get through to Yvonne Bource Teoh, the healer who had given me the magic crystal. I told her where I was and she said to wait there and she'd drive over and pick me up.

I sat under a tree and waited by the kerb. Shadowy beings shuffled about in a macabre pageant of the lost and lonely. I felt like one of them. Nothing around me seemed familiar or welcoming. This was not the same reality I had stepped into this morning! I've lost my way home, I thought. I tried playing my flute; it sounded feeble. I softly sang the starry song we had learned at the Reunion: "Ina kevoke, ina ke vive..." At least the tune was intact but it felt remote - it didn't belong in this immediate reality, which was definitely some sort of dead-end in this labyrinth. What happened to Oneness? I was back in Duality - and this was a lot more like Hell than Heaven. Paranoid notions crept into my mind: Christian was a Black Mentalist, a vampire! My starry essence had been siphoned away through treachery! It was with tremendous effort that I forced myself to let go of these negative fantasies. Finally a car pulled up in front of the kerb. Yvonne was resplendent in her Star Commander's outfit which bore the insignia of Neptune and the Pleiades. I got into her car with tremendous relief, feeling like the minutest fragment of my being. She didn't say much; but the tape she was playing sounded like one of Christian's paintings, the ghostly sighs and grumbles of pulsars in transit. "If you don't mind,

Yvonne, that music doesn't comfort me at all." She turned it off and I listened to the sound of Melbourne traffic for a while. Right then I could have used a therapeutic blast of Etherium's cosmic soul symphonies or even Matisha's peroxide angel Barry Gibberish!

INSIDE OUT AGAIN

Yvonne, her beautiful priestess daughter Lina and her friend Lincoln helped me earth my attenuated fragment. I was given a hot cup of tea and some buttered toast and led into the sea where Lina and Lincoln formed a triad with me - but everything looked alien somehow, even the few visible stars. Was I in a different dimensional universe? Everything was dreamlike, vaguely ominous, and I was too tiny to understand anything. From omnipotence to total impotence within 12 hours! Could I even trust these strange beings enough to surrender myself to their ministrations? Lina's energy felt Piscean - so this was the final dissolution of my ego, I thought; this was utter humility. I had been so exultant in my earlier vastness, I had been indestructible, absolutely immortal, the perfect Manifestation of the One. Now I felt all was lost, irrevocably lost, this was Oblivion. Where was Solara? Could she locate me? Wiped out! Did Antares Numi*ON still exist? What was my name now? I didn't know, but I needed a hot shower and a quiet space to rest.

Back in the house Yvonne had prepared a scented bath for me. I soaked myself for a while but felt uncleansed. I stepped into the shower and ran hot and cold water over my body. Finally I excused myself and went into the bedroom I had been shown: it was Lina's 8-year-old brother Travis' room and he was sleeping downstairs in the lounge. I switched off the light and felt a cold wind shuddering at the blinds; this was impossible! I thought I had anchored myself in the Template of Oneness - so where was this nightmare coming from? This spooky sense of psychic attack and a hostile universe? Nonetheless it was too real to ignore. I turned on the light and looked around: Travis' room was in total disarray. He had a bizarre assortment of warlike toys - killer robots and broken dolls and sad-eyed figurines all a-tumble around the room. Feverishly I began tidying his room, restoring the playful element in his collection of play-things. Then I had an idea: I had to turn myself inside out again! I went into a series of complex yoga manoeuvres designed to completely rewire my circuitry. When I'd finished I felt whole again and went back to bed. Very early in the morning I was awake and ready to continue. Lina got up and made me a cup of tea and I ate some fruit. Then I thanked her and left (Yvonne returned from taking Travis to school just as I was leaving). I felt good. The Teoh family had rescued me and somehow I felt I had returned the favour by exorcising the spirit of sadness and incoherence I'd found in Travis' room. But before I left Chelsea I returned to the beach and greeted the ocean, thanking her for her service through the aeons and welcoming her to the New Octave. The gulls celebrated my release from the darkness of Duality.

The train ride to Spencer Street was uneventful, apart from the fact that every child who got on noticed my presence and beamed joy at me. Truly, I thought, you can't enter the Kingdom of Heaven unless you become like a child. I had no ticket for the train ride but the guard just shook his head and shrugged me past the turnstile. Outside the station I thought about how to make my way back to St Kilda.

No money for the tram but enough for a phone call (I still had some coins in my wallet, I discovered).

In front of the tram stop I noticed a huge imposing building that was coming awake. I saluted it with the Annuttara-hu mudra whereupon I felt a tug of magnetic force emanating from a fat gentleman seated nearby. I sat down beside him and recognised his essence as that of Ra; we were like father and son, the Old and the New Road sharing a cigarette and a few swigs from his bottle of beer. Then I honoured him and went off to wait for the tram - but an urge to play the flute came upon me, so I sat atop the railing and blew on the instrument. A beautiful young angel came over to me and we began talking. I showed him Solara's book and he was very excited; he knew something was happening but he hadn't been clear what. We pooled our limited cash resources and shared a cup of coffee and a coke; then I gave him instructions to contact Beylara Ra when he arrived in Adelaide (he was waiting to board a long-distance express). Outside the bus station I passed a bookstand and saw a paperback with the crest of the CIA, the KGB and the Sword of Islam on its cover. The world of interplanetary espionage and the age-old battle for control of dear old Earth...so there were these games still raging in the Template of Duality! Winners and losers: but surely they must be aware that it was now possible to create a Win-Win Scenario?

I went into a drugstore and tried to borrow 40c for a phonecall but was rebuffed with a "No way, mate!" So Money was still God in some realities. But this was a necessary pilgrimage: barefoot and broke in a vast concrete desert! I remembered my Essene training and the collective experience of all saddhus since the dawn of Kali yuga. Momentarily I forgot about trying to catch a free tram ride and wandered down another street, simply trusting to serendipity.

Serendipity made radio contact with me at 12:12 p.m. 23rd March 1993. It was Ra all right: he beamed in on my brainwaves like the Ra-Dio he's always been. In the Beginning was the Word, and there he was, a regular Wizard with Words, Author of Every Book Ever Published, etc. And of course - the Master of Mind Games.

Meet Thy Maker, The Mad Molecule

It was good to be on-line again with Perfect Intelligence. J. Edgar Hoover, high priest of the Order of Melchizedek; Robert Anton Wilson, Illuminatus Supremus; J.P. Donleavy, J.D. Salinger, Jim Joyce, former Jaycees, Rotarians, honourable fraters of the Lions Club, the Elks; O! Grand Panjandrum of the Conundrum, and the Ultimate Grand Poobah too. A Real Joker, used to drive his wife round the bend. Kerouac, Casady, Ginsberg, Ferlinghetti, Farina...yup and yessiree, I was one of the Boys from Brazil. Not one of your prissy poetasters, mind you! This was the Inner Sanctum of the Playwrights and Authors Guild...just leave the dialogue to us, Son.

I sat myself down on a grail-like stone in front of a high-rise office complex, someone had given me a newspaper and I just wanted to sit down and read it, just to touch base with 3D reality. No way, Jose. The bloody Elohim had turned on a low-intensity laser and caught me in the Beam: all I could do was relax, trust their sense of poetic and dramatic irony, and go with the flow. Sure I could squirm my way out of the spotlight if I really wanted to; my will was still totally free. But why not have a little fun? This cosmic consciousness stuff gets too serious and airy-fairy in the hands of the priestesses. Don't get me wrong: I LOVE THE HIGH PRIESTESSHOOD! No one adores the Goddess more than I do - but bad old Nobodaddy's spirit lives in me; and since he thinks I'm a Chip off the old Block (which makes even better sense in the Age of Computers), I'm rather fond of the Old Man too. No more fussing and fighting: Male, Female, Whatever...Unify Your Polarities!

What Happened Next

...is well nigh impossible to narrate in linear terms. It may have been a Reality Insert within a Dream (or vice versa); trying to recall the episode and record it in language seems foolhardy, but the least I can do is give it my best shot. Let's put it this way: here I was on the New Road and this was the perfect moment to introduce a New Dynamic into the Status Quo. This also felt like a test of my respons-*ability*: My ability and willingness to respond spontaneously to the dramatic requirements of a multi-dimensional experiment in a New Theatre of Illumination. On one level I had to allow myself to behave like a perfectly designed remote-control robot, while witnessing the entire performance from a completely conscious, detached and trusting perspective. In other words, I surrendered totally to my New Role as an Instrument of Divine Intervention.

The lunch-hour scene around me was the soundstage; technical crew had been stationed strategically nearby to ensure that nothing went amiss. Akashic cameras were ready to roll. This was the movie I'd been writing, directing and acting in since the beginning of my earthly embodiments! In charge of the production were an experienced team of walk-ins operated by the Elohim. The logistic support network was being coordinated by radio. This was holographic film magic at its best: a New Age Eleusinian Mystery in Glorious 4D sponsored by Orion, Sirius and the Pleiadian Playhouse...

Scene Three: JESUS THE JOKERMAN - BORN IN BEDLAM, REBORN IN MELBOURNE. Roll cameras. Stand by. Action! My head swivelled round as I tracked a man wearing shades and a business suit as he walked briskly across the street with his black attache case. Two bars of "Stars & Stripes Forever" came whistling out of my mouth: the man looked at me, nodded, and grinned wryly - "Okay, you got me, that's right, folks, CIA."

A magnetic tug put me in contact with another pedestrian's frequency: a high-pitched snatch of Italian opera came sailing out of my larynx. Spot on...local Mafioso! Now I was humming "God Save The Queen" - which elicited a feeble smile from the next passer-by, M15, I presume. Nice game, but what was it in aid of? Ah, a demonstration of a newly activated faculty: under certain conditions, a sensitive can conduct narrow-beam scans in the field to identify specific agents of patriarchal intelligence. No more cover-ups, boys.

I became aware of the need to eat. The question was: could I transmute this situation into a free lunch? A group of office girls had just come out of the building across the road; they appeared to be heading towards their midday meal. I promptly hailed them and asked if they'd like to do a good deed by inviting me to lunch.

They giggled and shook their heads. Oh well. Two young males were leaning against a pillar watching me; one of them was emanating hostility. Let's see if I can transmute his antagonism into altruism...

When I approached the two males, the aggressive one scowled and told me to bugger off. I quickly scanned his field and got a very low reading on his emotional resonance. This young man was in grave danger of being totally consumed by the null field that had taken possession of him: it was akin to a terminal condition, let's call it spiritual AIDS, wherein the victim's feeling centre atrophied and caved in on itself, causing the constriction of emotional experience. This often led to violent tendencies - unless discharged ritually. Maybe then the victim's empathy circuits could be cleared and reactivated.

I took off my watch and showed it to him: "Would you like to buy a watch real cheap?" I asked. The fellow sneered and waved me away. "Well, then you can have it for free, I don't need it anymore." He crossed his arms and shook his head menacingly. I offered the watch to another passer-by - who hurried away without a word. "That's Melbourne for you," I thought, "typically Victorian!"

The aggressive chap was saying something nasty about me (I don't remember exactly what), so I went up to him and offered him an enormous grin. "Get away from me...fuck off!" he shrieked. "Don't worry, I'm not going to hurt you," I said, "I'm only trying to get through to you; why are you so unfriendly?" At this he snarled: "You're full of shit!" So I turned round and farted in his direction. "You're a gas," I said, bowing and letting out another one in the opposite direction, "and so am I!"

"You're a fucking basket case!" the bloke hissed - at which point I was inspired to prance elegantly onto the roof rack of a car parked along the kerb and perform a balletic manoeuvre. "Hey, I'm a basket case!" I shouted gleefully. "Now let's see YOU do it!" I leaped off the roof rack and walked back to him, smiling broadly. He let out a snort of rage and punched me in the nose, whereupon I executed a series of amazing backward rolls that took me the edge of the kerb, right against a parking meter. I felt no pain but was aware that some liquid was running down my cheek: make-up blood! Wow! How did they arrange that? I wondered. "Great stuff, Son!" I heard the Director say...sounded like Sam Peckinpah himself.

I slid slowly down the parking meter and appeared to collapse with a thud on the road. For half a minute I stopped breathing - but no one came to check if I was all right. I found myself wondering why I ever picked this town to manifest. I opened one eye and waited for some sort of response from the crowd of onlookers which had grown since the performance began. Nobody made a move to help. I sat up and looked round: "What the fuck's wrong with all of you? Don't I get some applause at least?" With a soul-weary sigh I got up off the road and dusted the seat of my pants. My watch was still in my hands, so I held it up and walked slowly towards my assailant who seemed to be quivering uncontrollably.

"Look, the offer's still good. You want this watch? It's in perfect working condition." The guy began to retreat. I held up the watch and shouted: "Ladies and gentlemen, it's now 1:11 p.m. and as far as I'm concerned...it's the End of Time! So who wants this watch? It's free!" I turned round to see where the violent onlooker had gone and saw him running away from the scene. "Oh well, here's to Eternity!"

I said and hurled the watch as high in the air as I could. I didn't wait to see where it landed because a police car had just arrived and suddenly I found myself being roughly pushed against a paddy wagon and frisked.

"Hey, hey. what's going on here? Take it easy, okay?" I said but the young policeman with Aryan blond hair and cold blue eyes kept manhandling me as if I were a dangerous criminal he'd just caught. After a while he shoved me inside the paddy wagon and rummaged through my shoulder bag.

"You got any identification on you?" he asked. I shook my head.

"What's your name?" he demanded. "What's yours?" I responded; "You tell me yours and I'll tell you mine." He took out a notebook and pointed a warning finger at me: "Shut up and tell me your name."

YESHUA BENJAMIN PANTHERA

"How do you spell that?" he asked, pen poised against notebook. "Y-E-S-H-U-A..." The policeman wrote down each letter scrupulously. "Yeshua...is that an Indian name?"

"Nope, Aramaic," I said and continued: "Benjamin Panthera, P-A-N-T-H-E-R-A." I'd waited two thousand years for this.

"Now you tell me yours," I said gently. The young policeman was silent for a few moments while some internal conflict raged within his soul. Finally he said grudgingly: "David."

"David. That's a good strong name," I said, studying him intently. "Tell me, David...why are you behaving like some kind of machine? Why can't you respond spontaneously, from your heart? You've got a good heart, I can see that." David's head was kind of dead - but I didn't tell him that.

"Whaddaya mean?" He frowned. I was about to elaborate when a woman came up to him and exchanged a few words with him. As she started walking away, I asked David what the woman said. "Oh, she just gave me her name and address - in case you needed help." I looked out the paddy wagon window and waved at the woman, who nodded and continued across the street. I gave her the thumbs-up sign and said: "Well, the first helpful person I've met all day!" Another policeman came up to David and they slammed the door shut and we drove off to the Melbourne Police Headquarters. I subsequently learned that the police had estimated the crowd gathered by my spontaneous street theatre to be around 150. Funny, I never did notice the size of my audience. I would have put it at 30 or 40 people.

The Temple Invisible

I was taken into a plywood-walled room marked AUDIO RECORDING. Interestingly, the atmosphere in the police headquarters seemed very calm and neutral to me, no negative fields. Another cop named Robert came in and began asking me questions which I answered truthfully. I was aware that some sort of official record of this event was being processed. I explained why the name in my address book (strange, up to this point I had forgotten it WAS in my shoulder bag all along!) read "Tamaares Antares Numi-On" - and that "Yeshua Benjamin Panthera" had been my name 2,000 years ago and I didn't need to use it anymore.

Robert's face remained impassive and business-like; however he had a very pleasant and wholesome aura. At some point I noticed the molecules shifting in the plywood walls: it was just a subtle shimmering in the texture of the wood that could have been a subsurface stain effect. A familiar geometry became apparent; I recognised it from the pattern of teeth in a plastic comb I had picked up from the floor on the last night of the Star-Borne Reunion. I had called it the Comb of Isis and had seriously thought of showing it to Solara as it seemed to be the perfect temple form for her Island of Light. I was amazed when she gave me a goodbye hug to see her wearing exactly the same kind of comb in her hair, only it was purple, not transparent. I remember saying to Solara: "Guess I don't need to tell you anything, do I? - whereupon she'd given me one of her mischievous all-knowing smiles. Wait...that was a slight error in recall...the purple comb hadn't actually been in Solara's hair, had appeared before me on a shelf just as I was thinking about her my Isis comb fragmented! Trying to reconstruct these experiences in coherent, sequential form makes me aware how much detail has been left out - otherwise nobody could possibly read this account.

Anyway...here I was, suddenly in the Temple Invisible - superimposed on the 3D reality of the Melbourne Police Headquarters. The Council of Elohim were in session (not that I could SEE any specific beings, but I could definitely sense the incredible dignity and beauty of the occasion). On one level I was being interrogated by a goodnatured policeman name Robert; while on another I was being congratulated and thanked by the Highest Administrative Body in the Milky Way Galaxy! I suddenly remembered that the 11:11 Doorway WAS the link between the Visible and the Invisible... "Goodonya, Robert," I heard myself saying, "One of these days you'll be the Commissioner of Police in Victoria!"

"Thank you," Robert said, looking for a moment like a very young Gregory Peck. Stars! Can't help seeing stars everywhere! Earlier on Spencer Street I had been exposed to hologram encounters with a few of them: James Joyce (aged about 45, dapper in a tweed jacket and fancy brown shoes; he'd beamed at me and winked; I'd been overjoyed to meet him) and James Mason (another Jim, very shy, hurrying along the street with a faintly ironic grin) and then I'd been alerted to a pretty unique frequency - not exactly a "star" but he'd written a book about his encounters with the Elohim - enigmatic character named Claude Rael (who had warned me telepathically not to get too close to him, something about interference patterns or radiation).

In the next room I was aware of the presence of several telepathic entities who had been monitoring the interview. They were still scanning my brainwaves to try and figure out how all this had happened: for aeons they'd been tracking the evolution of Intelligence on Earth but had never really believed that the moment would come when a primate gene would prove more adept at self-reprogramming than the Makers themselves! I was a unique phenomenon to them: the end-product of more than 20 billion earth-years of gene-jumping between terrestrial and celestial influences. It was like Tarzan's apes suddenly taking over and telling him he wasn't really smart enough to give the orders around here. But the most significant feature was that I had been able to embody Universal Love in ways that would allow all evolutionary streams to finally integrate; in short, the idea of the Enemy Within was no longer valid - and the path was clear for the total demilitarisation of the Universe, beginning with Earth. Somewhere in another department of my awareness I knew that the dualistic melodrama being enacted in Waco, Texas, between the Branch Davidians and Uncle Sam was the completion of a story cycle that began on the plains of Kurukshetra nearly 6,000 years ago. Belief systems engaged in deadly warfare, each condemning the other as Evil...

I also knew that each individual had to experience the Ultimate Reconciliation in his-and-her own terms, since the Male and Female Intelligence are complementary but not similar. For instance, females aren't particularly good at generalising - while males have a tendency to flee from the claustrophobia of particularities. The triangulation of these vectors is achieved through Innocence, which is the union of wisdom and folly.

Someone in the next room transmitted a cue for me to make visual contact with them. So I stood on a chair and peeked over the plywood partition into some sort of operations room in which several policemen were busy doing their jobs. One of them waved cheerfully at me. Right, contact established beyond all possibility of error. Good work...we are the Elohim assigned to guardianship of planetary evolution; think of us as Pillars holding up the Temple. We are the active agency of the Silent Watchers and our task has ever been to serve the integrity of the One. This planet has been a difficult assignment owing to the distortion factors inherent in the geodetic fields. However, we are now in the process of realigning and restructuring our work to eliminate the possibility of perceptual contamination and aberration. Thank you for assisting us in our Mission. Over and out.

The Illuminati, the Knights of Malta, the Masonic Lodges, all Intelligence Agents and Agencies - collectively constitute the Nova Police which had been infiltrated and discombobulated for centuries on this planet. So this is what all the spycatcher business has been about: thanks for re-establishing the Bond, James! There was a commotion outside in the corridor and two or three high-ranking cops walked in, grinning happily.

"So you're the one who built the Bridge for us! I just want to shake your hand." I obliged and quipped that he looked like Tom Cruise.

The cop accompanying him looked a lot like Eric Estrada. "Ho, the Highway Patrol!" I thought and suddenly understood why all these movies had been coming out of Hollywood like "Robocop" and "Terminator" and "Blade Runner". This is mindblowing stuff - but I stayed cool and took it all one step at a time. "Tom Cruise" or his brother grew serious and said:

"Okay, we're not going to charge you with anything, so you're free to go. But we're handing you over to a couple of community workers who are on their way over. They'll give you a ride to wherever you want to go."

I left the building with Vlado and Tina and got into their car. They told me there were community health workers and that if I liked they would look in on me later that evening to see if everything was fine. They dropped me off at St Kilda and I walked the short distance back to 42 Fawkner Street.

THE BLIND, THE KIND & THE MIND

Geoffrey Love was the first person I saw. He looks like a younger version of

Michael Caine. "Are you all right? We were very worried about you," he said.

"Everything's perfectly okay," I said and headed for the kitchen to make a cup of tea. "Would you like a cup of tea, Michael?" Geoffrey winced. "Sorry...Geoffrey... my dear Mr Love?"

Aku Ektara was somewhere about but I was getting a strange reading from her field: it felt like acute annoyance or anger. "Are you all right?" I asked as she came up to me.

"The police have been calling me," she said. "I didn't know what was happening or what you'd done." She seemed very upset - but it didn't feel like concern, perhaps she was miffed that I had put her through such an embarrassment. I looked closely at her and immediately understood the problem. Her right brain was severely dysfunctional and the left had been implanted long ago by the dark lords (when they were still the dark lords). Then I realised that her black framed spectacles were doing all the talking, not her! At the Reunion I had opened my eyes after undergoing a fantastically dramatic psychic surgery (performed by Solara and a team of angelic healers) only to see a pair of black framed spectacles monitoring me. "Please take off those stupid glasses," I had whispered - but she had refused.

Aku and I had had numerous incarnational links. She had been an Assyrian king, my father; and my daughter Meritaton in 18th Dynasty Egypt. We were indeed family in the truest sense of the word. But she had also been a powerful warrior - and the target of repeated assassination attempts. I could see the extent of the psychic injuries she had sustained over many lifetimes. I knew I could heal her very easily - but first she'd have to trust me enough to remove her glasses, which were interfering with the functioning of her intuitive centres. Only when she was swimming could she feel childlike or playful - yes, she had been a dolphin too! If only she'd take off her glasses for ten or fifteen minutes, I could heal her pineal gland and then she'd be an incredibly effective clairvoyant...a Seer trained by her mother Nefertiti in the highest tradition of the Isis Temple!

But right now all I could see was a frozen rage directing all her thought processes. Her damaged right brain and injured womb had distorted the maternal instincts in her - and the left brain was not aligned with any organic reality. I made a move to establish physical contact with her - but was repelled by the high-pitched frequency of her voice which uttered a vehement stream of primordial curses concealed beneath a babble of mundanities. The same thing had happened to my own mother - who was incapable of aesthetic experience and therefore reduced to being completely superficial in her relationships with other humans. There was a great deal of unprocessed Fear trapped behind those thick glasses. Fear, resentment, disappointment and complete egocentricity...

"I've made the tea," Geoffrey announced and took two cups into the tiny backyard. I sat down opposite him and locked in immediately to his brainwaves. Definitely a telepath - in fact he was in perfect resonance with me, though he favoured using his logic circuits and had a deepseated mistrust of his intuition. I spent a few moments trying to communicate with him nonverbally - but he grew uncomfortable and insisted that I spoke my thoughts aloud. "I'm tired," I said, and made a gesture with my finger to show him how much easier it was to talk mind-to-mind.

Finally I said: "It's amazing! You look so much like Michael Caine I'm beginning to think this is a scene right out of the movie 'Sleuth'!" But where or who was Lawrence Olivier? I certainly didn't look or feel the part. Aku - or, rather, her black framed spectacles - came out and joined us and instantly Geoffrey broke his mental connection with me. There's no way I can reconstruct what happened over the next hour or two. It seemed as if the triad we now formed could have so easily been one of pure ecstatic harmony - or its complete opposite. As it turned out, the psychodynamics of the situation quickly escalated into a cartoon soap opera. Aku assumed the role of the Heartless Queen/Wicked Stepmother; Geoffrey played the Well-Meaning Woodcutter/Ineffectual King; and I was Snow White/God Almighty in a chimpanzee suit. Trying to relate to the other two humans was exhausting; I kept having to hold onto the trees in the garden just to recharge my cells.

To summarise the verbal and non-verbal interchange, it struck me that Aku was suddenly resentful of my presence (being obsessively jealous of her head space) and was angry that I showed no remorse for getting myself "into trouble with the police" - how could I take her hospitality for granted, expect her to feed me and do the laundry, and then go around giving my money away to strangers, and so forth? I was in such an expanded state that such ridiculous pettiness made absolutely no sense to me; in fact I was amazed to find her so utterly blind to what was actually happening, and totally convinced she was no more than a faulty robot running a frustrated nag programme. Geoffrey appeared to drift in and out of comprehension: at moments he seemed absolutely aware, a true king endowed with divine qualities, and the next moment he would take on the role of sensible parent and attempt to exercise control over my actions. My need to spring up from the table and climb a tree (to escape from the negative vibrations emanating from these humans and to calm my nerves with the benevolent essence of the plant kingdom) seemed to irk Geoffrey. Suddenly he seemed like a stuffy old colonial master expressing indignation at the impertinence of a wayward pickaninny. How exquisitely middle-class! But don't forget all this was taking place in Victoria, in the prudish heart of Melbourne. I longed to be rescued from this horrible and mean-minded reality. Watching the sunset from the tree, listening to the birds, learning about other dimensions from humble household implements, now these were infinitely delightful activities. I suppose it was like dropping acid and then attending a sermon in a suburban church.

I didn't think of it at the time - but it's perfectly clear why both Aku and Geoffrey were convinced I was crazy. After all, they are both believers in psychiatry: Aku still sees a $65-an-hour shrink twice a week and Geoffrey spent quite a few years in therapy himself.

There was no way I could extricate myself from this claustrophobic scenario tonight; I was too vast to deal with the petty logistics of moving to another friend's house where the energies might be more supportive. So I tried quieting myself in front of the telly - but that didn't help because the programming reflected my internal exuberance and joy (not to mention the millenial excitement I was feeling). Every atom in Creation was celebrating my return to full consciousness, so why shouldn't I just relax and make myself at home? But that seemed impossible - either Aku's or Geoffrey's or both their energy fields kept slipping into disequilibrium with my own, and this would produce interference patterns that hit me like waves, causing me to move around in extreme agitation. It was so exasperating: they seemed utterly unreceptive to the higher cosmic frequencies I was trying to connect them with. Finally I had to get up and leave the house - just to breathe in some neutral space - but there was Geoffrey Love running after me, ordering me back to the house.

"Don't worry, Geoffrey, I'll be fine. Just leave me alone!" I hollered and kept on walking along the pavement. He caught up with me and grabbed my arm roughly, trying to drag me back towards the house. "Let go of me," I said. "I just want to walk around the area. I'll come home in a few minutes." He began putting more pressure on my arm, almost hurting me. I could sense his repressed violence erupting. He was an angry man, his wife and kids had abandoned him, and so on. I thought for a moment he was going to beat me up, so I hopped onto the back of a pickup and begged the driver to help me escape from my pursuer. Instead the driver cursed and swore and ordered me off his precious pickup; he was vile! There's so much repressed violence in the Australian male. Convict genes?

Anyway, I agreed to go back to the house with Geoffrey if he'd let go of my arm. His grip relaxed a little but he refused to trust me. By the time we reached the house I could feel his anger had reached eruption point. I felt like a three-year-old child having to put up with the redfaced rage of a drunken father. I broke free of Mr Love and ran into the house whereupon things got a little confused. Later he complained that I had hit him in the face - but as far as I know nothing of the sort happened! I'm inclined to believe that he ran smack into an invisible protective forcefield around me, but who can be sure of anything except that I definitely had no thought of hitting anyone at any time.

Enter Doctor Vlado (& his assistant Tina)

Right on cue the doorbell rang and in came Vlado and Tina (I didn't know he was a psychiatrist; only found out later when I was allowed to read my case file). It must have been after 8:30 p.m.

They sat in the lounge and Vlado asked me a few chatty questions about how I was feeling. I told them I was really blissed out and everything was wonderful - apart from the fact that my expanded energy field seemed to be causing Aku and Geoffrey a degree of distress. Vlado asked if I would prefer to spend the night somewhere else and I said it would be an excellent idea. At this point Tina opened up her briefcase and took out some pills. She handed me an assortment of three.

"What's that for?" I asked. They said it would calm me down. I asked them to identify the prescription and Vlado mumbled something about Largactil (later I noted that the admission form in my case file indicated I had been dosed with 100 mg Chlorpromazine, 10 mg Diazepam, and 25 mg Thioridazine). "Largactil is a brain poison," I protested. Dr Vlado smiled professionally: "We'd rather you take the medicine." I looked at both of them. "Do I have a choice?"

"Not really," Dr Vlado said quite seriously and then smiled reassuringly. I looked at Tina who was holding the pills and sighed: "I suppose I'll just have to trust you." I popped them in my mouth and drank the water Tina had set down on the table.

"There's really no need for all this," I said. "You don't have to drug me, I'm ready to go with you...I just need somewhere to cool out for a couple of days...shit! this stuff works fast, I'm about to lose consciousness...look, there's no way I can handle packing my stuff...please..." I tried to stand up and walk towards the bedroom... then I blacked out.

SHANGHAIED! (OR, RATHER, BUNDOORAED!)

Bundoora ("It means Windy Plains") is where Larundel Psychiatric Hospital is located. I awoke in the dead of night with a monumental thirst. Somehow I found a door and opened it: I was in a long corridor. As I stood there wondering where I was a woman came up to me. I asked for a glass of water and she brought me one. "What time is it?" About four, she said, and steered me back to my room. I must have fallen asleep again almost instantly. I have no recollection of the next 48 hours. Somewhere during this period of unreality and unconsciousness I became an Involuntary Patient at Larundel under Section 12 of the Mental Health Act 1986!

The name "Kit Panthera" had been tagged onto Room B3 of Ward North 5. It was cosy and fairly comfortable; my belongings were haphazardly stuffed into my bags - but my Swiss knife, collapsible scissors, razor, passport and air ticket were missing. Ernie Mathews introduced himself to me as Cochis - "I'm Robert de Niro," he kept saying, "I'm the best!" It was then that I started to relax and really have a good time.

Cochis was definitely as escapee from the realm of Adventure Comics. He showed me his leopardskin-print underpants. "You're the Jaguar!" I'd exclaim and he'd nod and say, "Right!" He flashed his Zippo with the Stars & Stripes. "You're Uncle Sam!" Right... Hawkman! No, the Condor! "I rescued you," Cochis would say conspiratorially. "Thanks, Cochis," I'd reply. "That's your job, isn't it?" Right. He called me Scarface - Al Pacino - but since he was Robert de Niro he deserved the bigger fan club. I really liked Cochis; I liked his wonderful swagger; talk about walking your godlike magnificence! He kept offering me cigarettes and snippets of funky music from his $37 walkman. Cochis saw me as a Navajo, as a Hopi, Cheyenne, Arapaho - he knew his Indians. He'd show me a tattoo on his chest: "Inca," he'd say enigmatically. We were fast friends from multiple realities. Hell's Angel without his Harley.

And there was Daniel. "Friends call me Toohey," he'd grin through his russet beard. "Toohey Red!" Former saddhu, very strong Indian-Indian flavour; closet holy man. Toohey had the true understanding and very quickly began spreading my gospel. Within three days he was going round giving light and quiet healing. Sharing tobacco was our sacred ritual. You have to remember your Indian soul to appreciate the magic of tobacco.

Lovely friends all round: Constantinos Zotos ("I used to be able to talk to thunder!"), Dionysian spirit; William Shane Turner (who kept borrowing my yellow John Lennon glasses so he could look like Professor "Indiana Jones" Turner) formed a beautiful George-and-Lenny partnership with me; he was full of hugs and holiness; Toan Vo (young Vietnamese dancer who was admitted after a car smash-up) kept lending me his guitar and beaming me true love, sweet angelic soul; Liz Greenhill (vaudeville performer and wonderful songwriter) snapped out of her 11-

year catatonia and pursued me relentlessly, and no wonder, for she was the embodiment of Tamaara Antara Numi*Ora, my twin flame from the beginning of Time!

And there was Malcolm Smith who came in during my second week there: shaggy young highland warrior who rolled half-inch thick ciggies and would have been right at home in a Pict cave somewhere up in the Grampians. A loyal soulmate, forever seeking a true king to serve. "You are yourself a king, Malcolm," I told him; and he nodded shyly but insisted he would be happy just being a carpenter.

The food was superb - or so I thought - and the surroundings very pleasant indeed. I felt the presence of Dante Alighieri who inspired me to think of this institution as Hotel Paradiso. Precisely what the Doctor ordered! Which doctor, witch doctor? Imagine: after the heavenly time I had shared with my starry family at Falls Creek in what, by my standards, can only be described as luxurious circumstances...here's yet another holiday, completely unplanned and unscheduled, sponsored by the taxpayers of Victoria (I had been informed that my "visit" would be gratis!) It was the perfect place to carry out my internship, practise my newly remembered skills in healing by feeling. Anyway, this was the moment long awaited: the Activation of the Grail, when all our needs are magically fulfilled...and they *were* (at least *mine* were!)

I could feel and heal trees - something never before experienced in my present embodiment. My etheric body in its resensitised form was a perfect gyroscope, gliding and dancing and weaving its way across an ocean of hitherto hidden energy fields. The Spaces In Between were now available to me ("My Father's House had many Mansions" - or Dimensions!)

The nurses, male and female, were generally lovable people. One or two of them were definitely on the Path and began seeking discreet instruction and inspiration from me. Once in a while a sneaky thought would creep in: beware of putting on Spiritual Airs! You're getting Bigheaded about your Powers! See what you get when you go around believing yourself to be the Kristos - you get put away in an asylum! If you want to get out, you'd better act Normal! But after a quiet moment of deep introspection, I'd understand that there was truly nothing to fear - not even the possibility that I was the living embodiment of All That Is. This was not an ego trip. This was the wholehearted fulfilment of my essential being. This was the act of transmutation required of all awakened entities: to spiritualise Matter and materialise the Spirit. This was the Path of Oneness, Wholeness, Holiness through Healing.

And truly I had everything I needed. An almost new hi-fi system where I could listen to music (everyone enjoyed hearing Etherium's Sacred Spiral Dance and a girl from North 4, Lorena, even participated in the True Love & One Heart meditation with me); a video player where I could watch the Star-Borne videos I'd purchased at the Reunion; beautiful trees and birds I could converse with; and a sacred grove guarded by nine half-wild horses - which I discovered one afternoon. It turned out to be an aboriginal burial site - and before that, during the time of Mu, the location of a stone ring. With my magic flute I reactivated the site and befriended the horses whose leader was a noble white stallion I named Pegasus. I was conscious of having once been a powerful priest-king named Ktolo. So this was why I HAD to visit Bundoora!

132

There were tai-chi sessions, free art supplies in a lovely workshop called Arts Access where I met a beautiful creature named Maria Filipow and did my very first acrylic painting (it was titled "Antarion Conversion"). And extremely liberating dance sessions in the music room where I finally realised my secret desire to be a ballet dancer!

Every morning I performed my mudra in the glorious warmth of the sun, and learned (or relearned) little magickal secrets from the numerous brujos and shamans disguised as inmates. Each time a connection was made I'd find a feather on the ground. I must have collected enough to fashion a headdress! And I had delightful visits from other Star-Borne initiates. Aumanarius, Kimuela, Omra, Ratma Ra and I did a ritual in the courtyard! and Omra presented me with some flower essence which I shared with a few other friends (they all turned into enthusiastic gardeners and compost heap makers). I*AN dropped in on me with Aku and Geoffrey - and it was good to see healing all round, for there was never any question of blame for whatever "happened" - all of it was an unfolding of higher truth and an opportunity for me to complete all previous cycles of work.

Azuriel and Altazar and Azarkia and Sora stayed in touch by phone. I even managed a long chat with Iaoh and Beylara Ra. Iaoh was very excited about a large tract of land in Western Australia going at a very reasonable price (he'd just got a job in a properties firm and was ideally placed for the task!): "I'm going up there this weekend to photograph the site, and then I'm going to send all the information to Solara by courier!" I could see myself spending time in Western Australia. Or at least some No-Time...

All this while I had been talking to two doctors: Albert Baily, born in Bangalore, and Ng Chee Hong, born in Malaysia. They were obviously keen to impress upon me that I was mentally ill. Hypomania, they called my particular condition. What does that mean, I asked them. It means you're not *totally* manic, but nearly so. Oh, I see...then I suppose I'd better get all my friends committed - they're all complete maniacs! It was fun talking with them - but they also kept insisting that I swallow the stuff they had prescribed, viz. Thioridazine - no, that was scratched - it was Melleriol or something like that, I couldn't even pronounce it. Later they insisted I take Lithium carbonate. I resisted their efforts for the most part - because the few times I complied made me regret I'd swallowed the chemicals. "Listen to me," I kept telling them, "your brain drugs are going out of style. There are so many more intelligent and effective ways to hep your patients reintegrate and reharmonise themselves with society." Dr Baily asked if he could tape my lectures and I said it was okay with me, provided he paid me royalties if he ever used them professionally!

It was clear that the entire mindset of psychiatry needs immediate revisioning. Consciousness encompasses inner and outer space - and whomsoever is assigned the power to determine its parameters must eventually develop some sort of vertigo or professional egotism. As a de facto Priesthood of the Mind, it's very easy to view psychiatrists as a white collar Sanhedrin, a New Inquisition with undefined power to declare individuals insane and keep them zombified with brain drugs. Most of the inmates at Larundel were perfectly wonderful beings trying to heal themselves from childhood traumas or meaningless routines. What they needed was a serene and enlightened environment where they could decondition themselves from inherited or acquired negative inputs through discussion and meditation and music and dance. Here was where the new therapies would truly be useful: Bach Flower Remedies, flower essences, star essences, massage, colour therapy, aromatherapy, crystal healing, and so on. I couldn't help visualising a New Reality where truly divine teachers and healers like Solara would be entrusted with the coordination of large-scale purification and transformation. How I wished I could see Solara on global TV, not just on the Star-Borne videos. And it didn't have to be just Solara: there are so many of us doing the Great Work on the planet right now who are ready to move in quietly and efficiently. But first things first: I was pleased to hear on the news that the new Victorian Commissioner of Police was embarked on a massive clean-up of the police force. Some people, however, are deadly afraid of losing their jobs! Bill Burroughs once said, very penetratingly, that anyone who's really doing his job is making himself obsolete. What's so terrible about Intentional Obsolescence? When I'm obsolete, it would mean the end of a tedious cycle of work and the start of a brandnew cycle of play! With any luck, I may already be obsolete.

Anyway, it was the younger doctor (whose name proved unpronounceable to most Australians and so was changed to Angie) who decided to play the heavy by insisting that I was too unwell to catch a flight home unescorted. My dear friend Mary Maguire volunteered to fly all the way to Oz to rescue me - but Doctor Angie declared that the escort had to be fully qualified, for heaven's sake. I was getting a little exasperated with their game of ego gratification at my expense. At the end of my second week as a prisoner/guest of the EMPS (Eastern Metropolitan Psychiatric Services), I informed Drs Baily and Ng that much as I loved them as human beings I no longer had any use for them as doctors. All through the past days I had played along with their silly bureaucratic charade; I had even faxed a friend of mine who happens to be chairman of Malaysian Airlines to intervene on my behalf and offer my medical escort free return passage (after all, it would be no skin off his back) but no response came. I shrugged it off: perhaps he was, as usual, out of town; or convinced it was an April Fool prank (the letter was dated 1st April) despite my declaration that this wasn't a joke; or else he was simply part of the Old Reality and therefore irrelevant to my experience. It got to the point where my friends were talking about passing the hat round to buy me out of the madhouse! Enough was enough.

THIS WAS AN UNACCEPTABLE REALITY!

That's more or less what I told the good doctors. I have work to do back at Magick River, friends I'm starting to miss, and whatever I needed to do here has been done. In the most solemn and majestic tone at my command, I said: "You have been labouring under the delusion that all this while you have been assessing my mental condition. The truth is my dear doctors, it was I who was busy assessing you! I'm sorry to say you didn't quite make the grade, but don't worry, you'll be given another chance. Better luck next time." The look on their faces was worth recording for posterity.

"I'm very disappointed in you," Dr Baily said in passable avuncular. I smiled and said: "Perhaps the disappointment is mutual."

The next day I informed the doctors that I had submitted an appeal against my continued detention as an "involuntary patient" to the Mental Health Review Board. Just to spice things up, I added that I was seriously considering suing Larundel Hospital for defamation and abduction. But I reiterated that I bore them no personal ill will and even asked if Baily would be kind enough to donate one of his old neck ties to me. I also requested that they grant me day leave from the hospital as I had things to do in town and films I wanted to see.

It was a great feeling catching the tram into town (I was supposed to meet Aku and Geoffrey for a cappucino). At the Theosophical Society bookshop I caught sight of Matthew Fox's "The Coming of the Cosmic Christ" and bought it even though it made a dent in my budget at $25. At our rendezvous point only Geoffrey was present; Aku had had to go to her office at the Herald-Sun. So we did the Melbournian thing and ordered coffees at Pellegrini's. Geoffrey was still convinced that I had struck him in the face but said he wasn't angry about that. I said I was still pretty positive I didn't hit him but apologised anyway for his experience of having been struck by me. Before we parted I reminded him that he was of royal lineage and would do well to embody his true majesty. He thanked me and we went our separate ways; but I can't get over how much like Michael Caine he looks.

While scanning the Cosmic Christ book I was struck by the absolute relevance of two of the chapters in view of my case against psychiatry. I marked out the chapters and suggested that Dr Baily photocopy them for his personal reference. He obliged, which indicates beyond all doubt that the man is essentially high-minded and a fair-player. He even remembered to bring me an old tie of his, modest paisley motifs and all. Meanwhile, various other friends from Melbourne and Sydney had been ringing me and one of them, a feisty pint-sized journalist formerly residing in Malaysia, expressed the desire to do a feature on my case. This had poor Dr Angie really worried. He handed me a copy of a letter from the Mental Health Review Board notifying me of the date set for my hearing. Unfortunately this was the Easter holidays - which meant I'd have to wait a whole week.

Happy Resurrection!

Drs Baily and Ng were hurt that I had shown no confidence in their professional competence. In fact, they had earlier arranged for me to see another psychiatrist at St Vincent's Medical Centre - a Dr Tan (who also happened to be a lapsed Malaysian), professorial associate and highly respected in psychiatric circles. Tan had only seven minutes for me. But that was enough for him to endorse the diagnosis of hypomania. Perhaps I shouldn't have tried to sell him a copy of my book. "What's it called?" Dr Tan had asked. I showed him a copy (I'd been hawking it around, trying to raise cigarette money). "Adoi!" he said. "I already have a copy which I picked up in Kuala Lumpur the last time I went back."

"Well, for five bucks you can have a personally autographed copy," I ventured, but Dr Tan Eng Siong wasn't a charitable institution. "Eh, doc, are you from Penang?" I asked as I was leaving his office. "That's right," he said, raising an eyebrow, "why do you ask?"

I grinned at the Napoleonic gnome who had already decided I was a very sick man: "That's where all the Scrooges come from!"

Albert Baily, bless his soul, had been a philanthropist compared to E.S. Tan. Not only had he forked out $5 for a copy of "Adoi!"...he'd also paid the same for one of my cassettes (I'd made a special compilation of music from my second album, "2nd Coming", and it also included a pirate dub of one of Solara's meditations, the one to bring in your Solar Angel; so let's see what happens!) All in all, I must have sold about 8 copies of my book. A few I traded for cigarettes (can't live without that wonderful magick smoke!)

Yahoo Serious had made a second film called "Reckless Kelly" and it was premiering on April 8th. I made a date with Aku Ektara to see it and was generally tickled by the movie. Afterwards I phoned in to the airline and booked myself a flight to Sydney on the 16th. The hearing had been set for the 14th.

On the 12th Dr Baily passed me a couple of his own reference books - one was called "Moodswing" and the other was "Melancholia: Disease of the Learned". I promised to scan them and enquired if he'd read the Cosmic Christ chapters I'd shown him. "Halfway through," he beamed. "I'm savouring the words!" Then he told me he was going on vacation to Philip Island (his kids wanted to see the penguins) and that he was discharging me immediately: "What about the hearing?" I had been all keyed up to do a Portia before the Review Board. "I've already told them you've been transferred to Section 7, which means you're now a voluntary patient and are free to leave."

There were two conditions though: (i) the doctors weren't too happy about my wanting to stopover in Sydney and (ii) they wanted me to stop spitting out my medication. What could I do? I conceded graciously, since it was only a couple of days more. But it all depended on whether I could get a flight out on the 14th. Dr Angie had expressed pessimism about the availability of seats. I told him I was going to the airline office right away. I did and got my ticket confirmed. Before he bade me farewell, Dr Angie confessed that I had been a very difficult case.

"Me? Difficult? In what way, pray tell," I said. "We didn't know what to do with you. After all, you're a fairly intelligent person..."

"Come on, doc, be honest...you mean I'm a *highly* intelligent person, don't you?" Over the decades I've learned that false modesty can be more dangerous than plain honest pride; anyway, as Dizzy Dean, whoever he is, once said: "It ain't braggin' if you really done it!"

"All right...you're a highly intelligent person and you seem to know a great deal about psychiatry...in fact you managed to make me doubt my profession."

"Good! There's hope for you yet!" I said and shook his hand. "I've thoroughly enjoyed my stay here and I've learned a lot from you. I hope you can say the same."

I had said goodbye to the horses, to the spirits of Bundoora, the Windy Plains. Most of my friends had already been discharged or were waiting to be discharged or else they were on weekend leave. At least six people had undergone "miraculous" turns for the better since my arrival. But new faces kept appearing. A reflection, no doubt, of the confusion of the changing times. Many of the nurses told me how much they had enjoyed my visit. One of them, Philip Swensson, had in fact resigned to start a new career in alternative healing. He had shown the greatest receptivity to my being and to Solara's teachings.

Altazar had invited me to spend a couple of days at the Oasis, his personal kingdom of heaven on Earth, located 40 km out of Melbourne. My new flight arrangements left me no opportunity for that. On one of my daytrips into town I had connected with Antara Ge, who bought me dinner at the very same Chinese restaurant where I had dined with Christian Camenzind (the secretive mystic with a broken heart which, I pray, is now on its way to wholeness). He also lent me $50 for the road, bless his angelic soul. Money money money, money padme hum!

The Fairy Stork...I think that's what the restaurant was called.

OM IS WHERE THE ART IS

The night I arrived in Kuala Lumpur and was greeted at the airport by Mary Maguire, Jesse Eaglefeather and Nor Akmar...what a trip! It had been a very sweet flight. In front of me was Sabine, a lovely Dutch girl who had really got off on Soluntra's star essence (I must order a whole batch for her): she had recognised me right away as another aspect of her True Love but "No, no, no! I promised my father I would go back to Amsterdam to help him with his puppet theatre!" The inflight movie was one of the films I had missed seeing in Melbourne - "Toys" starring Robin Williams, delightful stuff.

Mary anointed me with fragrant oil (who else but Mary could undertake such a significant labour of love?) and watched me fall asleep. She had been the most active agitator for my safe return. I told her how amazed I had been at Solara's resemblance to her. While I was at the Reunion she had received her starry name: Amaa-Real Bororealis - but just call me REAL, she quipped. The very stuff of True Love!

Back at Magick River three days later...I was reunited with my vision of Paradise ("Two waterfalls flowing through a stream to the blessed valley far below..." from Matisha's song, inspired perhaps by Revelations Chapter 22!) And also with Xenaeon (Shelley Isler, ex-Sydney) who took me under her edible wings and whispered: "I'm a priestess and I've been sent to ground you."

"Ground, ground, ground! Everybody wants to ground me! How much more grounded can I be?" I protested. "I'd much rather be ROOTED!"

And so I was.

No Doubt About It

I'm hooked on Angel Dust. Late September 1993 Star-Borne Reunion #9 will be coordinated by Tzaris and Ailea in Sweden. No worries...there are only three more Reunions scheduled for this planet (that's what Solara says) - so the addiction won't last forever. But who's willing to bet? Not me...one can never have enough of Oneness! (Digression: why does a Frenchman usually have only one egg at breakfast? Because in France one egg is an oeuf. Pardonnez moi.)

Meanwhile, back in the Gaslit Kitchen, I'm relieved that this document is almost done. It was getting in the way of my correspondence. Give me a brief aeon or two to get back in the swing of writing to people as if they weren't actually me.

My XONIX (or XINOX, if you're upside down) says it's now 11:28 pm on the 9th of May. It's taken me two whole weeks to complete this - with a few days' break in between to see my dear old dad on his 77th birthday; and to pay tribute to Wahab the Axis of All-Being, but that's another story!)

Binashk-kinashk keyol'ina ve kaa ne hoon ina!
 That's Starspeak for: I intend to fuse with you in No-Time!

SKOOB BOOKS PUBLISHING

HECATE'S FOUNTAIN   *Kenneth Grant*

The publication of *Hecate's Fountain* has been eagerly awaited for a decade since it was first hinted at. It unfolds the history and implications of the workings of Nu-Isis Lodge under the direction of Kenneth Grant in the 1950s. Often Lovecraftian in ethos, the workings of this Lodge have opened the gates to an influx of alien magical intelligences and radically altered the direction of twentieth century occultism. A strong theme in this evocative and intricately woven text emerges as an inspired revelatory exegesis of Crowley's *Book of the Law*.
ISBN 1 871438 96 9 Hbk £24.99 $39.95

THE MIND OF THE DRUID
Dr E. Graham Howe
Meditating on the elemental world of fire, water, trees and rocks, Dr Howe reflects on spiritual sanity in a mad world.

'Many influences of astounding variety have contributed to shape (Howe's) philosophy of life which, unlike most philosophies, takes its stance "in" life, and not in a system of thought.'
                                   Henry Miller
1 871438 75 6 148pp £4.95 $8.95

THE TRUTH ABOUT THE TAROT
Gerald Suster
A concise, practical manual for an occult art.
1 871438 07 1 136pp £4.99 $8.95

THE NECRONOMICON
Ed. George Hay
The classic *Book of Dead Names* revived.
1 871438 16 0 184pp £5.99 $9.95

skoob esoterica

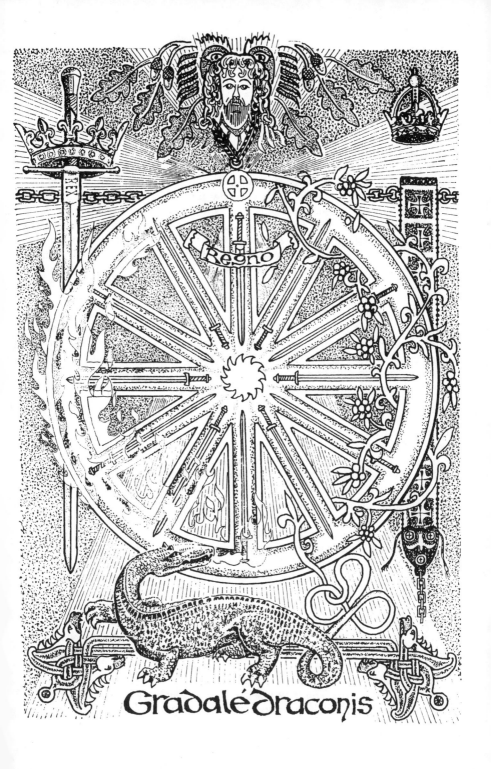

Gradalé draconis

ALL THAT FLIES

by

George Hay

"Insects, wouldn't you say?"

"Well - more or less, more or less. I mean, I'd hate to be specific about that thorax, for instance, but - well, let's say, definitely insectoidal."

The conversation was taking place in low tones. Understandably, since it was being held in a mausoleum, and indicated as much respect for the living as for the dead. The latter presented no immediate danger, whereas the former, should they come within earshot, might present problems. While the building itself was not locked, the area surrounding it was delimited by very functional iron railings, and the two involved had only got in with the aid of a portable footstool and some undignified scrambling. An overcast summer evening had turned almost to night, and what light they had came from a shaded flashlight cautiously used.

"Confirmation, then?"

The first speaker was determined to press his point home. Indeed, a determination unusual for one not long out of his teens was a marked characteristic of Benson. In moments when his determination was in question his thin white blade of a nose was apt to quiver with a life of its own: an unkind observer had once referred to it as The Questing Beast. It was quivering now. "You agree, finally? Really, you could hardly put this down to coincidence."

'This', as indicated by an outstretched finger, was the reclining figure atop the tomb nearest the door of the mausoleum, the most recent of several, and occupied since 1941 by one Charles Beaumont Fletcher. More exactly, the finger indicated that part of the figure's chest where the hands were clasped over each other. Or should have been. In fact, very little was left of them, the space they formerly occupied having been taking over by the insectoidal creature earlier mentioned. About a foot long, it looked to Benson for all the world like a cross between a centipede and an earwig. Jellaby, his companion, having some groundwork in entomology, was less inclined to make glib comparisons, but that the thing was an insect of some kind he had been unable to deny. Even now, however, he felt obliged to put up some sort of rearguard action.

"Whatever it is, it's obviously a late -er - interpolation." He prodded gingerly at an extended pincher. "That's not stone! It's the same colour as the effigy, all right, but I'd defy even a skilled mason to make it. It looks exactly like the real thing - I mean, if there ever was a real thing, which I can hardly believe." He stopped, uneasily aware of the implications of what he was saying, and backed away a few inches. He felt safer, though he also felt like a fool. Under the circumstances, he could perhaps be forgiven for snapping at Benson:

"Well, don't just stand there looking virtuous! Need I remind you our position here is entirely illegal? You may not care about your professional position, but I care about mine. I'm a scientist, not some sort of occult freak."

Due credit must be given Benson for coming up with the only answer that could have held Jellaby at that moment. "Precisely. If this matter is to be finally settled one way or another, it is a mind and discipline like yours which will do it. Did I ever say flat out that there was a curse on the Fletchers? I said there was evidence there might be, and invited you to inspect it...As for being here illegally, of course you're quite right, and the sooner we're away the better. After all, we've found what we came to look for." He tiptoed over to the door, opened it and peered out. "The cloud's breaking, and the moon's starting to come on strong. If we get out fast, we'll just about still have cover."

The two scuttled over the moonlight-dappled lawn. In other circumstances Jellaby, who under a glum exterior was really the more romantic of the pair, would have been inclined to pause and apostrophise the scene. As it was, he was only too glad to get his feet on the stool, swing himself up, reach down again, and then hoist himself up and over with one hand holding the stool in the other. He was down and lunging after his friend before he became fully aware of a series of sharp stabs in his right hand, the one carrying the stool.

He raised the hand up before his face, still running. At the same time the branches cleared momentarily above them, and the cloud cleared away from the moon. At that moment Jellaby hurled the stool as far away from him as it would go. It thudded against a stout beech, and the sound brought Benson up short, staring back. "What are you up to, man? they could hear that half a mile away on a night like this." But the other only stood there, shuddering and looking at his hand.

Benson went over to the footstool, bent down. He straightened up very quickly, biting his lip. As he went, he picked up a small broken branch that lay in his path, and immediately he reached Jellaby, he began to beat with it at the outstretched hand. In a minute or two he could see the bare flesh once more, and in five minutes the last earwig had gone.

There is of course no such thing as an earwig sting, and painful though the pincers had been, they left no permanent effect. Well, not physically anyway. All the same, Benson had the sense to concentrate that night, once they had reached their hotel, on seeing his friend safely in bed with a glass of brandy as a nightcap, and took pains to make no reference to the reason behind their expedition. Next day was Sunday, and, exercising what was for him super-human restraint, he kept his attention on the newspapers and on some research dossiers he had brought with him. He was therefore unable to keep a certain smugness from creeping into his expression when, about seven in the evening, he heard the other, looking up from a pint of the local draught, ask:-

"All right, I give in. Where do we go from here?"

The smugness was not in the least mitigated by the nature of his reply. "Alfreet Space Research Centre, of course!"

* * *

Chronologically, this story starts with the death in 1803 of Henry, eldest son of Mr and Mrs Fletcher of St. John Street, Oxford. He was thirty-five, and occupied in some research in 'natural science' - the section thereof that we would now call entomology. This was on behalf of Mittner Verlag, a German publisher long defunct. Little is known of his relationship with this firm, since almost all of his work and correspondence alike perished with him, in a manner as unusual as it was unpleasant. Cutting through the circumstances of the coroner's report, once can say quite simply that the unfortunate man and practically every un-solid object in his chambers were eaten away be a swarm of insects. That insects were responsible is known, not so much by the evidence of the remains - of which there were pitifully little - but by that of neighbours, who were deterred from breaking in upon Fletcher's agonies by the sheer terror of the poor man's screams, and by what one person described as "a sort of hideous dry Stench, and a Noise like the scratching of ten thousand claws". Harsh words were spoken of these neighbours by the coroner. My own feeling on this is rather different. For one thing, one cannot help noting that Dr. Sainsbury (the coroner) was a crusading free-thinker. Among what letters the victim had left were some on which Fletcher had added what was described as "the sign of Beelzebub, Lord of Flies". There was nothing to prove that this was anything but a harmless affectation, but Dr. Sainsbury's remarks were far stronger than would nowadays have been countenanced. One senses the pressure of a dilemma. If Fletcher really had been indulging in devil-worship, no freethinker could bring himself to believe in such rubbish. On the other hand, the temptation to point out the unhappy results of such actions must have been strong...in the event, the coroner settled for some very harsh remarks on the cowardice of the neighbours. Having studied not only his report, but similar ones connected with the Fletcher family over the following century and more, I cannot help wondering what in fact would have been his reaction had it been his own ears that were assailed by those appalling cries...

It is not necessary to weary or depress the reader with detailed accounts of what happened to later members of the Fletcher line. Indeed, the fact that you are reading this story presupposes a certain prior familiarity with the kind of events in question. Suffice it to say that, throughout the nineteenth and into the twentieth century, four more male members of the family suffered a like fate to that of Henry, and that the unhappy Charles Beaumont made a fifth. If we have started with him it was partly to orient the account into the present, but more particularly because the case of his nephew carries us forward into developments which - well perhaps I should not anticipate our account. However, I will say that, when that account is read, and the book closed, I would expect that something will remain thereafter with the reader. Whether that something is what he would have wished to have knowledge of is perhaps another matter. But this is just a chronicle, is it not? At all events, we must now return to our two investigators.

* * *

Benson, let me remind you, was excitable and imaginative, while Jellaby, though far from devoid of imagination, tended to the conservative. There was, however, this about him: a great love of the paradoxical. An ardent crossword buff, an early and active member of the Lewis Carroll Society, a devotee of Martin Gardener - that kind of man. It was by virtue of these traits that Benson had been able to draw him into a study of the background to and possible future events in the life of Harold Fletcher.

142

You see, Harold was different.

His male ancestors, even prior to Henry, were scholars to a man. By scholars, I mean literary and religious men, People of the Book, as the old way has it. I suppose you could have called Harold a scholar - he was certainly master of a discipline - but never a bookish man. He was a space buff, weaned on Dan Dare and Captain Marvell, and going on up thereafter via Tsiolkovaky, Arthur C. Clarke and Isaac Asimov. Indeed, by the time he had got hold of Asimov's work he was going off fiction rapidly, and on to maths. After all, with words you can read about space, but to actually do anything with or about it you have to use very different languages. And he did. Early recognized as a high flier - in both senses, if you will forgive the pun - he went through Imperial college with remarkable honours, and by the time we come across him, in his twenty-sixth year, he was one of the foremost names in British experimental rocketry, and was known internationally for a series of papers on the use of microcircuitry in stabiliser systems.

All this, of course, was why Harold, after that unfortunate visit to the Fletcher mausoleum, was still able to hold Jellaby's interest.If the curse of the Fletchers - for let us not play about; that is what we are talking about - was to descend on yet another of that wretched family, how could it be on Harold? All the previous victims had been religious scholars: Harold was an atheistic physical scientist. With considerable technical skills - he was in the habit of testing the constructions designed by him, often to near-destruction. He was perhaps poorly gifted when it came to human relationships - it was indicative that he was universally addressed as 'Harold', never as 'Harry' - but no one could accuse him of being a dreamer. Or, if dream he did, it was of the bright empyrean. Yet he was the last of the Fletcher line. Were he to perish, presumably the curse would perish with him. But why should he? Even with Beelzebub there must be some kind of justice: what had Harold, who had probably never read anything more arcane than an astrophysics text-book, done to deserve the fate of his forbears?

The Space Research Centre seemed to present no sort of answer. Could one have been expected from those metallically correct offices and laboratories, those turf-covered aerodromes, those barren expanses of concrete? The test-beds themselves were of course out of bounds; not that either man would have been able to deduce the slightest thing from seeing them. As Fletcher himself put it, china-blue eyes viewing them blankly over the rising edge of his tea-cup: "We're very dull here, I'm afraid."

"You find it so?" What Benson really meant, of course was - then why are you here?

They never really found out whether the man was as naive as he seemed. Very possibly he was. "Well, I mean" (he had that habit of stressing words quite unnecessarily) "that you gentlemen could spend just about the rest of your lives researching the archives of my ancestors, whereas what I have to show for my work here is practically nothing. I don't mean it's not important, but, until it's actually tested, it's all in the future - and you can't research the future, can you?"

"Tested?"

"Completely tested. Completely!" The blue eyes shone. Benson had a mental image of old Henry Fletcher's eyes shining thus over some fossil arachnoid. Only there had been at least a fossil, whereas the man seated before them had, as he said himself, nothing...Beside him, Jellaby shifted impatiently. "How completely?"

"To destruction!" Fletcher drained and set down his cup. He seemed calm enough, but now his eyes did not merely shine, they blazed. Something passed through Jellaby's mind, but was gone before he could pin it down. "That must be expensive for the tax-payer?" he said, in as cynical a tone as he could manage. But Fletcher was not affronted.

"Oh no. Not when you think what he gets for it. Theories come free, more or less, but how can you put a cash price on their testing? The falsification of a faulty concept could save millions. Millions!" His hand uprose in an evangelical gesture. Again, Jellaby felt something stir far back in his consciousness, and again it slipped away from him.

In the silence that followed, Harold Fletcher seemed to be considering something. He pulled open a drawer in the desk before him, made as though to shut it again, and then, as on impulse, pulled out a large envelope.

"You'll understand about security arrangements here. The things we're working on now, I simply can't discuss with you, or even mention. That must be understood. But, testing, now - well, I can show you something. I probably wouldn't if I really thought you knew anything about rocketry, but I don't believe you do. In any case, what I'm going to show you here involved items tested to destruction, and far beyond." Abruptly, he spilled a sheaf of black and white photographs out of the envelope and along the desk.

There was another silence, broken by Jellaby who, for reasons not very clear to himself at that time, was determined not to appear impressed. "Frankly all I can see is a lot of scrap. Smashed-up spacecraft of some kind, I presume. Do you really mean you did all this on purpose?"

Fletcher ran his tongue over his lower lip. "I wouldn't put it quite like that. We didn't actually want to smash them. But we had to know: we had to know how far we could go with them."

Jellaby looked over at Benson, who was still brooding over the photos. "What do you think?"

"Think?" said Benson. He stabbed a finger. "I think this is a Selsea Mark II Probe, or the remains of one."

Fletcher blinked. "You're right. You surprise me. How did you know? I mean, it's pretty much of a mess, isn't it? We were picking up outlying fragments a mile away and more."

Benson shrugged. "Oh, you don't need to worry about our security status. It's just a fluke. You may remember the ante-room where we had to wait while they checked us out and got hold of you for us - it had up on the walls some photos and sketches of devices you've used here. De-classified, I presume. Well, even though this one is a mess, as you say, it reminds me of one of those photos, which was of a Selsea Probe."

"Looks just like a squashed bug to me," said Jellaby.

The silence that followed on this went on rather too long for Benson's comfort. Clearly, Fletcher was an odd sort of man, but that was no excuse for Jellaby to be rude at his expense, or the expense of his profession. After all, the fellow was giving up valuable working-time for them.

If Fletcher was offended, he showed no signs of it. But perhaps he was: he made a rather pointed remark about the time, referring to a test to be carried out very shortly. Jellaby said nothing, so Benson, to his disgust, found himself with the necessity of terminating their conversation in some reasonably tactful way. He could do it, of course. Young though he was, academic responsibility had been his lot for some time, and he was accustomed to the mechanics of balancing-out upsets in establishments of varying kinds. A few references to the Fletcher lineage, a request - instantly granted - for permission to publish certain papers pertaining to Henry Fletcher, heartfelt expressions of thanks on behalf of both visitors...Less than fifteen minutes later an Air Force car waited impatiently before them, and Fletcher waited no less impatiently on the steps of the building behind them. It was a late afternoon in July: the sky was utterly cloudless - Benson felt he could have reached up with a knuckle and rung it like a bell, it seemed so low.

Fletcher, who seemed to have a last-minute change of mind, went down the steps to speak in low tones to the driver. Turning to the two men he said: "You know I can't really let you see anything. But I thought there'd be no harm if - well, you see, this particular test is...I mean you can't actually witness it. But perhaps it would do no harm if you saw me..." Without finishing his sentence he jumped in beside them, and the car shot off, first into a large clump of trees, and then into a clearing beyond. Inside the clearing, just a little lower than the trees, stood what looked for all the world like a tarantula, a metal tarantula the size of a small house.

Fletcher got out, said something neither of them managed to catch, and walked over to the machine. Benson felt the blood drain from his face as it extended a gross proboscis downward, a proboscis which appeared to swallow the scientist whole as it curled up and back again. "Of course," he said to himself, "of course, it's just a lift mechanism. Just a lift mechanism" - he would have gone on talking to himself in that calming way, but the driver was already backing them out rapidly from the wood, through the station fields beyond, and then out through the security gates onto the road to the nearest town.

Benson, chewing his knuckles, had his face pressed to the window and was looking out towards the clump of trees now rapidly receding from them. "Look!" He said. "There it goes. See? Fantastic - it's just hanging there - looks more like a spider than ever. What do you say?"

"I don't say anything, I'm afraid." Something in Jellaby's voice made the other man tear himself away for a moment from the sight of the thing hovering overhead. "Jellaby - what's the matter with you? You're not even looking!"

"I don't need to. I wouldn't look either, if I were you. You'll hear it in a minute, anyway."

"Hear what? I don't understand what you're talking about."

"You don't? Well, it was you who wanted to convince me that there really was a curse on the Fletchers. And now you have. You ought to be pleased." Jellaby was looking straight ahead. His voice sounded utterly dead.

"I convinced you?"

"Those photographs did. All those crushed machines - they really did look like squashed bugs, you know."

Benson opened his mouth. Whatever he was going to say was drowned in an appalling noise from the direction of the woods. The chauffeur appeared not to notice, but the car accelerated rapidly.

"I said you'd hear it in a minute," said Jellaby. And after a pause, when no reply came form the other, "Perhaps you didn't notice the design that someone had scribbled on the backs of those photographs. I only noticed it myself as I was putting them back in the envelope." And then, after a much longer pause, "After all, He is Lord of All that Flies."

This story first appeared in *Ghosts & Scholars* edited by Rosemary Pardoe, to whom our grateful thanks are due.

Chaos Ritual

by

Steve Wilson

Foreword by Phil Hine

Neptune Press £10.00

THE Chaos Current is the most vital aspect of modern occultism, and this book presents an entire system which will be unique to the individual reader

From Pete Carroll: "Exhausted by the howling frenzied rites of Chaos warrior sorcery? Spent too many late nights ejaculating over blood splattered sigils? A bit fazed by n-dimensional quantum etheric equations perhaps? Well here is something completely different. Much of the book is devoted to a chaoist treatment of the magical arts of gesture, posture, voice, mandala, music, and various mental practices. However, in the best chaoist style, Steve gives only the general principles and invites the magician to develop a system that is personally meaningful.

The style of the book is relaxed and sometimes humorous, and hopefully its user-friendliness will find a readership beyond the confines of chaoist orthodoxy".

From Phil Hine: "One of the core propositions of Chaos Magic is that magicians create their own paths, and this book reflects that principle admirably. Although the material in Chaos Ritual arises from Steve's own wide-ranging explorations into the territory of magic, he presents it in such a way as to ensure that the application of the techniques will be unique to those who choose to experiment with them. Chaos Ritual contains a wealth of practical ideas, is erudite without being 'dry', and at times, is very, very, funny. This is important, as a sense of humour is essential to magical practice, and, whilst a would-be magician might well desire to 'reach for the stars', he will find the task so much easier if his feet are planted firmly on the ground, and so much more fun if his tongue is planted firmly in cheek".

Chaos Ritual - go there, do it and get the tee shirt

Chaos Ritual is £10.00 post free from
Neptune Press,
49a Museum Street,
London WC1A 1LY.
TEL: 071-405 2120
FAX: 071-430 0535
Cheques payable to Atlantis Bookshop.

An Interview With The Originator Of The Book
"DARAS ALMOND"
By
Amanda Lords

The original manuscript of "Daras Almond" was discovered sewn inside the mattress on the bed of a long term patient in a remote sanatorium on the outskirts of Aberdeen. This patient had voluntarily entered the sanatorium suffering from severe depression. His room and treatment were paid for by an anonymous patron who sent a cash settlement on the first day of every calendar month.

In the early days of his confinement he spent most of his time sitting at the window, staring at the wild sea and watching the hungry wheeling seagulls. Occasionally he would emit a great sigh and burying his head in his hands would sob uncontrollably. However, as time moved on he became more stable and at this date is cured and is preparing to take his place in society.

He was delighted when the manuscript was discovered, not remembering its concealment over forty years ago. This manuscript was a collection of notes and scribblings written on divers materials consisting of scraps of brown paper, crumpled envelopes and ragged pieces of toilet paper. It had long been suspected that the enigmatic recluse was the eminent psychologist and occult researcher Dr. Alan Domas, who had disappeared in December 1947 after attending the funeral of the notorious Aleister Crowley. This he now admitted with a broad smile as he packed his meagre belongings ready for his departure. From other cryptic notes found in the North London laboratory of Dr. Domas, it was revealed that he had been conducting experiments in controlled hypnogogic states linked with time travel and reincarnation.

His numerous experiments on the stimulation of the non/dominant brain hemisphere by the use of stroboscopic lights and audio frequencies had some startling results and the doctor claims to have pierced the veil of reality by the use of his electronic machines and various hallucinogens.

My name is Amanda Lords, and I am a journalist involved in researching the arcana of occultism and mysticism. Several weeks ago I obtained the manuscript package from the eagle eyed psychiatric male nurse, one Arnold Sadam, who had found it in Dr. Domas's mattress on a sunny day in August 1953 when the doctor was having his daily exercise. The following is an interview with Dr. Alan Domas in his tiny room at the cliff top sanatorium, concerning the book, after he had given permission for his package of notes to be rewritten and edited by my associate Ronald Adams, clinical psychologist and occult researcher who has been continuing the researches and electronic experiments of Dr. Alan Domas, and presented as the story of Daras Almond.

Myself: The book seemed at first to be an adult fairy story. I found it quite charming, but a little disturbing at times. It was as if forgotten episodes of my life had suddenly surfaced. I became plagued by synchronistic events, and I seemed to see things in a much clearer light. My life changed as I began to stop worrying about trivia and forged ahead in a positive way. Daras Almond is both entertaining and therapeutic.

Dr. Domas: You must remember that things are not always what they seem. The book is the result of a journey. It is a living path. The metaphors within the book are indeed designed to nudge one along a path by their suggestions to the unconscious mind. It doesn't matter what path it is, as long as one moves forward. The very act of being on a path is a positive way of moving forward. Even if movement brings trauma or anguish it is better than standing still or dwelling within the past. The past is done with and all one's reflections on the past cannot change it. However, one's attitude to past events can be changed thus changing the future. For example, if in the past a particularly traumatic event took place, and that event is affecting one's present equilibrium, then if one goes back to that past episode, under trance etc., then one can disassociate and view that event with humour for example. Thus this changes one's present attitude.

Myself: Who is Daras Almond?

Dr. Domas: As stated in the book, he is all mankind, and we are all each other. He can also be identified as the Fool, the silent and innocent one, the all wandering spirit, and the perfect knight errant. Cervantes felt his presence when he wrote "Don Quixote". Incidently, have you not realised that Daras Almond is an anagram of Dr. Alan Domas, your name; Amanda Lords, your friend Ronald Adams and even the male nurse Arnold Sadam?

Myself: I am amazed. This is the most amazing synchronistic event that I have ever heard of. How is it possible?

Dr. Domas: Because all things are illusionary and we are all players and spectators in the script of life. Sometimes, as the actors, we can rewrite our roles. Other times, as spectators, we can influence the Master Script Writer to rewrite the players' roles, or even the whole play, at least as we see it from our point of view, depending on our appreciation or reaction to the events that are presented to us on the great stage.

Myself: This then must be the impetus behind ritual magic etc., to contact the Master Script Writer in his many god forms, and by absorbing oneself into one of those forms, i.e. becoming one of the actors, changing the laws of causality by rewriting the script. Or by praying to one of these god forms, i.e. becoming one of the spectators, the script can also be changed, by the more passive magnetism of supplication.

Dr. Domas: Indeed it is the motivation, but only if the magician realises this fact. Too many so called magicians blindly follow the written word without 'feeling the magic'. Aleister Crowley knew the truth when he said: "All things being illusion, a man with the right materials can paint any picture that he pleases" or words to that effect.

Myself: There seems to be some biographical material within the book. Is this based on your own life, or have you given Ronald Adams permission to incorporate his own life within the text?

Dr. Domas: I gave him full permission to interpret my notes in any way that he felt appropriate, as long as the essence of my notes was retained. He found that when he began his task his unconscious mind identified with triggers and anchors that were within my scribbled text, and much of himself seeped into the book.

Myself: Are you pleased with the book that Ronald Adams has written from your notes?

Dr. Domas: He has brought life into what was nothing but a mass of scribblings. He has taken my clinical jottings and made them into a metaphorical story that will nudge and guide the reader onto a positive path and improve the quality of their lives.

Myself: You obviously do not have an objection to Ronald Adams being known as the author of "Daras Almond".

Dr. Domas: Not at all. As I said before he transformed my notes and jottings into a readable story. He deserves credit for that, and is entitled to be known as the author.

Myself: Now that you are leaving this place what are your plans? Do you intend to carry on your researches into the vast uncharted territory of the human mind? You were thirty years old when you came here, now you are aged seventy four. Do you still have the enthusiasm and mental energy that you had all those years ago?

Dr. Domas: I shall carry on with my experiments. I can assure you that I still have that old spark of enthusiasm. My age is not important. The last 44 years were mostly a blur, but there were some lucid episodes when I used to experiment with astral travel. These experiments must have been successful because I have been seen, as a pale transparent wraith, wandering the Scottish countryside. There was even a report in an American newspaper that "the ghost" of Dr. Alan Domas had appeared at a parapsychology convention in New York. I believe that many witnesses of ghostly visitations are really observing the astral projections of living persons. It is feasible to suppose that we all leave our bodies and roam the earth, or even the universe, when we slumber. This would explain the enigma of the purpose of sleep. I believe that sleep is not just to rest the body, but to enable us to "leave the vehicle" for some incomprehensible purpose. This could even explain déjà vu, i.e. the new place that we visit and recognise has already been visited on one of our many wanderings in the astral form.

I also intend to do further research into sensory deprivation. During my stay here in one of my lucid periods, I managed to do some experiments in information deprivation using the ganzfeld (German for wholefield) method.

Myself: What is the ganzfeld method?

Dr. Domas: It is a very simple method of information deprivation.

Not to be confused with sensory deprivation, that is another matter. I managed to obtain a table tennis ball. Cutting it in half gave me two translucent hemispheres. In a comfortable horizontal position, under red light, with these half spheres over the eye socket with the eyes open one can only see a uniform red field. Then by inserting stereo headphones into one's ears and plugging them into a portable FM radio, and tuning to a part of the dial without any radio stations on it one only hears "white noise". Thus the consciousness is deprived of stimulating aural and visual information, and it retreats out of sheer boredom allowing the unconscious to surface. I experienced some very interesting hypnogogic visions and travelled through some very magical landscapes.

Myself: Thank you for a very interesting interview Dr. Domas. I wish you every success in your researches, and I hope that I might interview you again in the near future.

Dr. Domas: Thank you for your time, and good luck with your article. I shall certainly keep you posted about any developments concerning my experiments. Auf Wiedersehen for now and keep to your true orbit.

REMEMBERING ALEISTER CROWLEY
by
Kenneth Grant
(Skoob Books Publishing Ltd.) h/b. £24.99
Reviewed by Gerald Suster

Do what thou wilt shall be the whole of the Law.

Even hostile critics of Kenneth Grant, such as myself, must nevertheless admit their pleasure on reading his *Remembering Aleister Crowley*. It's a joy to read; it's also a joy just looking at it. Uncle Aleister would have been delighted with the dust jacket, binding, paper, print and illustrations, not to mention the content. My sole complaint is that the price of the book isn't printed anywhere. Is this, then, a pearl beyond price?

Why should you pay whatever it is for this book? One might well do so simply on account of liking well-produced examples of the book-maker's craft. But what about the contents? These consist of letters from Aleister Crowley to Kenneth Grant accompanied by the latter's commentary. At the very least, these supply vital documentation on Crowley's state of mind in his last years.

John Symonds, Grant's partner in many Crowley ventures, was probably responsible for inventing the myth that Crowley's last years consisted of being a demented junkie in a Hastings boarding house. The photographs of 93, Jermyn Street, The Bell Inn - still one of the best restaurants in Britain - and Netherwood, Hastings show residences any sane person should desire. The letters also display a quality which any sane person should desire - intelligence. Yes, Crowley was a cantankerous old sod, given to fits of ill temper and always nagging over trivialities. At times he could be a right pain. He was also a genius.

Mr. Grant should be warmly congratulated on what he has done. Among other things, he has put together a very honest work. He is completely open about his own defects at the time he knew Crowley and even jokes about them with a wry humour not seen before in any of his previous books. That takes guts. For the first time in many a year, his prose is crystal clear; and his commentary is continuously sagacious and illuminating. One can see why Crowley discerned such immense potential in this man. I've always thought that *The Carfax Monographs*, subsequently and rightly reprinted as *Hidden Lore*, to be superb work. *The Magical Revival* is extremely interesting; and there's much suggestive treacle in *Aleister Crowley And The Hidden God*. But I subsequently went off Grant.

Cults Of The Shadow, Nightside Of Eden and *Outside The Circles Of Time* encouraged novices to mess with the Qlipoth and the casualty lists were atrocious. So was the prose. It is therefore a pleasure to witness the rejuvenation of Mr. Grant. Crowley had his prosaic faults right, though. "I thought I had explained carefully that I wanted an answer, not a sermon!" he wrote to Grant. "If I point to a tea-pot, and ask 'What is that?' You don't say 'the refreshing beverage which we owe to the Chinese calms the mind, and induces a state of feeling which is conducive to carrying on one's work' etc. etc.".

Nightside Of Eden makes one concur with Crowley's comment: "This is a terrible defect in your outlook on life; you cannot be content with the simplicity of reality and fact; you have to go off into a pipe-dream." The same can unfortunately be said of most occultists. However, Mr. Grant should be commended for his courage in facing up to the past and showing it to the present and the future.

There are many gems in this book. For instance, there's a magnificent letter from Crowley to Grant which deplores the delusion of 'security' and explains the Act of Truth. This was done more formally later in *Magick Without Tears* but the first draft is arguably more powerful. There's much food for thought in Grant's comments on LIBER III (JUGORUM), the aversion therapy practice which consists of nicking one's arms with a razor whenever one does a word, thought or deed previously forbidden by oneself. Crowley and Regardie found it highly effective; as I did. Grant disagrees and disagrees most intelligently: "It is not a practice I would recommend because the long term result is not control of thought and speech but, rather a lessening of spontaneity and a dread of making mistakes." This is probably true for a number of good students; and one can only applaud Mr. Grant's splendid insistence on spontaneity and risk despite fear, as being quintessentially magical.

The book is dedicated to a man called David Curwen, concerning whom Mr. Grant informs us, little can be told. This is a pity; for Crowley displays a refreshing modesty in writing to Grant: "Curwen knows 100 times as much as I do about Tantra." Moreover, Kenneth Grant's clear knowledge of these matters did not come from Crowley; it looks like Curwen. One obviously hopes that Mr. Grant will tell us all more about David Curwen in due course.

Further delights of this book include: lovely colour photographs of Crowley's seals and magical regalia; rare pictures of documents which seize the attention; a sparkling of wit and wisdom from an old man who'd led an incredible life; and some choice phrasing from Kenneth Grant: "His idea of a cup of tea was a mountain of sweetness slightly dampened."

Kenneth Grant comments in a delightful mood of relaxed and perceptive geniality, almost as if he were chuckling quietly about his personality of so long ago. He has not cobbled together a pile of scraps: this is essentially a book about a man coming to terms with his mentor. As such, it succeeds. Mr. Grant has brought love under will to this task. Love is the law, love under will.

THE SECRETS OF ALEISTER CROWLEY
by
Amado Crowley
(Diamond Books, Leatherhead, 1991)
£5.99
Reviewed by Gerald Suster

For all connoisseurs of the idiotic, here is a wonderful opportunity to waste £5.99 on a completely fatuous book. It is badly written and atrociously reasoned, yet those with a perverse sense of humour might find it funny in its uniquely appalling way.

Amado Crowley claims to be an illegitimate son of Aleister Crowley, born on 26th January 1930 as a result of a magical operation Uncle Aleister conceived in 1928 because 'the family business needed a successor': one hopes that the author isn't referring to Crowley's Ales. It is not impossible that Amado is one of the Beast's many biological bastards; if so, he is an absolute disgrace to the noble name of Crowley. This claim aside, Amado has managed to write a poorly conceived and executed work of fantasy fiction.

I met Amado in the mid-Seventies. We corresponded. Despite his claims in this book that he has only now 'come out', he was then visiting magical groups as a self-proclaimed 'Master' and publishing a monumentally boring magazine called *Liber Lucis* in which he wittered on about nothing in particular, continuously praised his own sense of humour and failed even to make one laugh. He assured me that Gerald Yorke, ex-disciple of Crowley, later the Dalai Lama's Representative in the West and always a zealous collector of Crowley's papers, recognised Amado as Crowley's Magical Son. Naturally I wrote to Yorke, who was always so kind and helpful to me, and Yorke said that he didn't.

Amado failed to collect me as one of the many disciples he so clearly wanted. However, my old colleague of that time, Pete Carroll of Chaos Magick fame, gave Amado a chance and visited him at his then home in Southampton. Mr.Carroll proceeded to discover that Amado was more generally known as 'Mike', a Southampton Poly lecturer in Psychology, that he had nothing to teach in practical terms and preferred to watch TV while eating Chinese take-away food. I have never forgotten Pete Carroll's righteous indignation over a wasted weekend. He's been anti-Thelema ever since.

Amado claims in his book that Aleister taught him between the ages of 7 and 14: i.e.1937-1944. If so, why isn't there a single mention of this vital matter in Crowley's Diaries? There he records matters as trivial as the breaking of a tooth or the quality of his dinner: but he does not see fit to record meetings with an initiation of a son destined to be his successor. Pass the sick-bag, Alice.

In the gift of his improving discourse to his 'son', Crowley criticised the American involvement in Vietnam, a remarkable feat for a man who died in 1947. Crowley also holds Amado's hand as he walks him off a cliff and they both levitate before a pair of nuns: a feat which Crowley admitted to be beyond his capacities. We, the readers, are expected to believe Amado's account of a visit by MI5 to Crowley - perfectly possible- at which a little child was present: i.e.Amado. According to little Amado, aged 10 , he accompanied Aleister and MI5 to a Secret Service HQ beneath Downing Street to hear briefing from its Chief Admiral so as to conduct a Magick Rite in Ashdown Forest, its purpose being to bring Rudolf Hess to Britain, an action which had no effect on the conduct of the Second World War whatsoever. Can this sort of childish nonsense go further? Yes it can: and it does so in Amado's book.

Most people can remember roughly the main events which occurred between the ages of 7 and 14. Amado can't. It is odd. He recites in the minutest detail conversations with Crowley as if they'd happened yesterday, yet he is incapable of recalling the slightest detail of where Crowley was living. With the pride of a seven year old, he recounts how he helped Crowley to compose *Liber Fulgar*. He quotes Crowley as declaring that by it: '...heroes will brandish their lances at the heavens to capture the power that will transmute them into burning ones. Men who are afire and can be seen across eternity'. Amado's response? 'I don't think I dare throw it away, but I daren't look at it again, either. It has just got dry and dusty for over half a century'. Roll up! Roll up!

Thelemites, serious Magicians, Qabalists and otherwise intelligent men and women will no doubt be intrigued to learn that according to Amado, THE BOOK OF THE LAW was merely 'a red herring'. Marvellous, isn't it? Aleister Crowley fought against this work for 5 years, then accepted it as the spine of his life, then spent the rest of his life study-ing it and advancing it in his published and unpublished writings: and Amado informs us that he dismissed it lightly as 'a red herring'. Jolly good, Amado: what other delights do you have for us? Ah, apparently the real truths are to be found in *The Book of Desolation* of which there is unfortunately only one copy and this is in the possession of - yes! you've guessed it! - Amado.

Stylistically, Amado is a very bad writer. He manages to achieve the impossible, which is to make Aleister Crowley a dull subject: even John Symonds and Colin Wilson couldn't manage that one. His facts are inaccurate and his logic incoherent. He also suffers from a disconcerting paranoia. Time and time again he assures the reader that sinister conspiracies headed by the Freemasons are after him. The poor chap does not appear to realise that Aleister Crowley was a 33°Freemason in the Ancient and Accepted Scottish Rite: and that secondly, no one in power would want to bother with a twit like him, anyway.

Amado's ignorance takes one's breath away for about one minute.Amado asserts that Crowley met Rasputin in St.Petersberg 1897-8, for instance. This is arrant nonsense. If Aleister Crowley had done so, he would have recorded the matter. Secondly, Rasputin, as a cold matter of fact was at that time living in Povroskoe, Siberia, and having drinks on occasion with my Great Uncle whenever the latter visited. Amado gets the Crowley-Gurdjieff relationship wrong too. These two excellent men met once for about 30 minutes and got on quite well: the meeting was witnessed by Gerald Yorke. Amado refers to the Golden Dawn XI° operation; there's no such thing. That one is OTO. Amado declares that 'symbolic levels of meaning' are explained in ÀC's letters to Cara Soror, later published as *Magick Without Tears*. This work does not deal with 'symbolic levels of meaning': it's plain as paint. Moreover, Cara Soror is not the name of some exotic female disciple. It is simply Latin for 'Dear Sister....'

Amado gives an intriguing account of his initiation by Uncle Aleister in 1944. He does not explain why his 'father', who never once mentioned this alleged commitment, teaching and initiation in his Diaries, chose to abandon him when he had three more years to live during which he often complained that he lacked poor company. Amado claims that he visited his 'father' in Hastings: Crowley did not live there until 1945.

One has to commend Amado for at least defending Aleister Crowley, but his defence is so inept and his comments on hostile books so witless that one wonders if he's just very stupid or in need of medical care. He has done Aleister Crowley all the harm in his power - by writing <u>for</u> him. Don't buy this stupid book: borrow it from a friend, as I have done; for with friends like this to Crowley, he doesn't need enemies.

What Amado 'Crowley' needs is Monty Python's Colonel to say simply: 'Right. You can stop that. It's silly.'

SKOOB BOOKS PUBLISHING

GEORGE ELIOT
Collected Poems

'These searching poems do not depend only on the name of George Eliot for their value.
The ambition and intimacy of the longer poems will not be unexpected to readers of the novels - but the risk-taking may.
This collected edition of the poems is very welcome.'
Gillian Beer, *TLS*

'Skoob are to be congratulated.'   *The Spectator*

This edition brings together all the poetry of this great writer and includes previously unpublished work.

ISBN 1 871438 35 7 £18.95 $35 hbk * ISBN 1 871438 40 3 £9.95 $19.95 pbk

DAVID GASCOYNE
Collected Journals 1936-42

'...an engrossing record of his self-realization and artistic growth... Certainly Gascoyne himself is the finest poet on that bridge linking the 1930s and 1940s.'   Philip Gardner, *TLS*

'In many of the entries there are to be found the seeds of the great metaphysical poems that he was to compose later... Skoob Books...are to be congratulated.'   Neville Braybrook, *The Tablet*

Written in a period when he was producing some of his finest work, these journals illuminate and complement his poetry and serve to reaffirm David Gascoyne as a major poetic voice of the twentieth century.

ISBN 1 871438 50 0 £10.99 $19.95

LIBER ALEPH, VEL CXI
The Book of Wisdom or Folly
Aleister Crowley
Ed. Frater Hymenaeus Beta
Pub. Samuel Weiser Inc. York Beach, Maine 1991
Distributed by Airlift Book Company
Tel: 071 607 5792   £8.95
Reviewed by Frater Venusius 49

This vital Work of Aleister Crowley has long been available only at considerable price. With this edition not only is it within the pecuniary reach of all its would be students, but it is also a beautiful book. Printed on high quality paper, the typography and layout exhibit a degree of elegant refinement and harmonious proportion such as I have rarely witnessed in recent years. Fr. Hymenaeus Beta, who not only edited but designed the book, gave me to understand that this very traditional-looking excellence was attained with computer technology. He is to be congratulated on his labours in this, and for a clear and useful introductory essay.

It is important that such a service should have been rendered to this particular work of Crowley's, for into its two hundred and eight chapters, each of which fits within the confines of an octavo page, he seems to have distilled the essence, the very life-blood of all he had learned and experienced at the time he wrote it.

Each chapter encapsulates, as in a phial of rare perfume, a particular topic, couched in a language uncontaminated by the entropic banality of much of modern speech. I am by no means convinced that 'archaism' is an appropriate way to describe the effect. Perhaps this term should only be applied to all that is itself merely applied to a text in a spurious attempt to lend the text the authority of tradition without it having had to withstand the test of time, which, more just than the febrile whim of passing fashion, often rescues for tradition works that at the time of their conception were either calumniated or ignored due to the peculiar vagaries of judgement that taint any brief segment of history.

I am more inclined to describe the language as in every way harmonious to the purpose it serves, giving due weight and timeless decorum to the exposition of its matter, by its manner, merely avoiding the Procrustean inexpressiveness which increasingly disfigures the amputated locutions of such a depraved era as our own.

Since the threads which percolate these aphoristic chapters seem to be a weft of harmony, balance and imperturbability, it is well that the language should be so thoroughly consonant with the tenor of the wisdom it expresses. Indeed the universal cadence of the language employed is entirely intrinsic to the cast of thought. This is perhaps borne out in the words of Chapter 67, De Poetis:

"Moreover, it is not altogether in the Word of any Poem, but in the quintessential Flavour of the Poet, that thou mayst seek this Prophecy."

In any case, the expression throughout is marked by a regal and benevolent lucidity. For while, as chapter 68 informs

us, a poet

"Sayeth indeed true things, but not the Things of All-Truth,"

in the case of One who embodies the Word of the Aeon

"He hath given it unto him to prepare the Quintessence of the Will of God, that is, of Man, in its Fullness and Wholeness, comprehending all Planes, so that his law is simple, and radical, penetrating all space from its single Light."

So that here, this single Light does indeed pervade the Communication of Wisdom over a richly varied range of discourse which includes in its catholic embrace topics as diverse as the Holy Qabalah, education, initiation, and the Mass of the Holy Ghost; each quintessential chapter seems to be concentrated around a seed of Light, waiting to grow and blossom within the consciousness of the recipient.

Perhaps the touchstone of a wisdom undefiled by the distortion of personality, is that there is seldom anything in its expression which would jar the sensibilities of a person of goodwill, whatever their professed creed, whereas there is much to make the 'heart leap up' in such a one, calling forth the joyful sense of a deep recognition of its appositeness.

Wherever its attention is directed, such wisdom seems to 'hit the mark', and looking within us we can find that everything towards which our own experience can point will attest to its luminous veracity.

THE AZOETIA
(A Grimoire of the Sabbatic Craft)
by
Andrew D. Chumbley

Published by Xoanon in an edition of 300. Available from Xoanon Publishers, P.O. Box 1821, Chelsmford, CM1 3UE. £15 (plus £1.35 p&p.)
Reviewed by Madelaine Challis

Now that major publishers have scented a buck in the occult, they are filling the shops with pre-digested books, pot-boilers and plain piffle, unwilling to take a risk on anything too serious, and counting on you and I, the readers, to keep consuming. The best books on magic are being produced in small editions, privately, which is probably for the best - anyone prepared to seek a little further than the shelves of the occult supermarkets will be richly rewarded for their effort, though it seems a shame that such books are confined to a limited 'cognoscenti' circulation, and quickly become difficult to obtain. Although a series of books on sigil sorcery have recently become available, none have in any way expanded on the work of Austin Spare or Kenneth Grant, simply contenting themselves with applying the basic formulae from *Book of Pleasure* to Results Magic. And then there came an astonishing book named *Azoetia* from the skies...Its subtitle - "a Grimoire of the Sabbatic Craft" - sounds like rather a grand promise; after all, the "secrets of Wicca" have been revealed over the years in a series of populist books, turning out to be rather a mish-mash of influences from diverse traditions. In stark contrast, *Azoetia* puts forward a highly individual system of magic which dances powerfully but elegantly across, through and around all the lines of tradition; breaking all the rules with wit

and finesse, in a blaze of Luciferan energy. So what's in it for thee and me? Well, this is the first book in recent years to demonstrate the use of the Alphabet of Desire as a gateway for the exploration of the magical universe. Having described rituals and formulae for obtaining the letters of the Sacred Alphabet - by sorcery and dream transference - their application as elemental keys in the unlocking of power is demonstrated through the sequence of the Alphabet, subsuming under each letter a set of rites, formulae, axioms and poetic diatribes. And it is here that the great beauty of the book lies: for in these sections the author reveals his comprehension of a wide variety of magical systems - form Wicca to Bon-Po and back via Chaos, Thelema, Voudoo, Maat, Alchemy and a legion of others - and calling upon all these powers he proceeds to plunge the reader right into the very heart of magic's current. Among the thousands of books written *about* (often round and about) magic, this is a truly magical book; to read it is to be swept into magical time - the place where dreams take flesh, flesh becomes shadow becomes New Flesh. It is an inspiring book, and, as the author takes care to point out, a working Grimoire; ostensibly cloaking itself in the symbols of Wicca, it has actually regenerated them, stripping them of their post-Gardnerian accretions to reveal their primal shamanic origin. The resulting formulae can therefore be applied to any path whatsoever, without resorting to 'paradigm shifts' or any other such stuff. In a very real sense, *Azoetia* is carrying the ball for the Zos Kia current; many have tried to simply replicate Austin Spare's work, but few have got very far, and fewer still have actually added anything to the current itself. Chumbley reveals what is, and what can become, possible; unlike some of his predecessors, however, he gives detailed methods of working, couched in the most evocative prose-poetry which simply cannot be matched for its spirit and power by anyone writing today. This is not a retro book, but bang up to date; there is no flim-flam in these 359 pages - it is precise in both its intent and its method. It's not easy to get excited by the current crop of occult books, but *Azoetia* really will blow you away: at last, a book that puts the *magic* back into magic!

EIGHT ARROWS GOING NOWHERE
"Liber Kaos"
by
Peter J. Carroll
(Weiser,1992) £9.95

Do what thou wilt shall be the whole of the Law.

Chaos is defined as both "a formless void from which the cosmos was evolved", and "utter confusion." **Magic**, by contrast, is the art of causing change to occur in an ordered (i.e., structured) way in existing phenomena. It is caused by a relationship existing between things: at its most basic, a thing to be changed, or *first matter;* and the willed intention to change a thing to a desired end, or *final result.* This relation cannot operate in a void where no thing exists, nor can it exist in a condition of utter confusion, because no points of reference are then involved. The phrase itself is therefore a contradiction in terms: there can be no such thing as a Magic of Chaos, or "Chaos Magic". Q.E.D.

There has always been a factor which is infinite and unknown: to some people, this is "Chaos" or "Chaos Magic"; but to others, it indicates a transcendental ordering phenomenon beyond the reasoning faculty of man. In traditional western terminology, this would be referred to as the "Influence of the Supernals"; in oriental thought, the "action" of Tao-Teh. Throughout mysticism, there have never been any absolutes: there is no ultimate causality or truth, and the nature of "solid reality" has always been held to be something in the manner of an illusion or a dream. Nobody can doubt that we live in a world where it is impossible to guarantee categorically the outcome of any intended action from the start. This makes the actual methodology of Chaos Magic - which consists not so much of individual *autonomy* as edicts *ex cathedra* - even more suspect; a case not so much of "Do what thou wilt", as "Do as I say". How is this possibly justified? The regimented techniques of which systemised Chaos Magic is structured are closer, and have more in common, with those of freemasonry and cult autocracy, than the unfettered shamanism "chaos magicians" profess to admire!

Chaos Magic tries to have things both ways. On the one hand, even though the universe is chaotic, it must be approached through a system of Order: through so-called "Rites" of Chaos, "Masses" of Chaos, a "Gnostic Banishing Ritual" - none of which is a radically path-breaking innovation, but a mere elaboration on what has gone before. Indeed, the "Gnostic Banishing Ritual" (pp. 181-85) is even *flawed*, because there is no horizontal component to its revision of the Cabbalistic Cross! As such, these rituals could almost be described as *neo-classical,* rather than truly Chaotic. There are also flatulent exercises involving the tedious tabulation of formulae, such as "The Mathematical Equations of Chaos Magic" (pp. 40-51), which - in view of all of the comments made about the *quantum dynamics* of the universe - are frankly absurd! There is also a tendency to use a long word where a short one would do, and the pretentious usage of Latin rather than 20th century English for no apparent reason, such as occurs in the title and section headings.

On the other hand, even though the structural content of the published ritual work is derivative; even though the "organization" for practical Chaos magic (!) *The Pact of the Illuminates of Thanateros* (I.O.T.) is a hierarchical one run along quasi-masonic lines with degrees, words, and signs; and even though there is, as the founding-father of the whole concept of Chaos Magic Peter J. Carroll puts it (p.191), "a puritanical devotion to empirical techniques" (mark well that "*puritanical*" - as opposed to, say, pure!) - any failure to then achieve a desired magickal effect can be conveniently explained away by saying that the entire universe is unpredictable, quantum, or chaotic. Carroll's previous written work has, on occasion, contained some interesting and insightful material, but to claim, as he goes on to, that "one of the fundamental insights of Chaos Magic is that if magical technique is sharply delineated it will work, because the universe itself is more of a shambles than it appears..." (p.191) is altogether preposterous and self-contradictory. If that were so, then Chaos Magic would stand or fall *irrespective of* its having to have a regimented or "sharply delineated" form!

Rather than working in tune with the evolutionary process and carrying out the progressive pyramid-building of, for example, the A∴A∴ system, there is instead almost an element of sado-masochistic asceticism about the work which is prescribed in these rituals, which rivals the tortuous hardships required in some strict orders of the Catholic Church! This, from a system purported to be, in Carroll's own boastful words, "the first complete systematic magical programme for some centuries - a definitive replacement for the sacred magic of Abramelin the Mage..." (p.155) But if "chaos magicians" were to rely *solely* upon a belief in chaotic quantum effects, they would not then be doing any form at all of self-discipline or sustained technique or (bhakti-) yogic dedication to an entity beyond themselves. This is patently not the case: the fact that they do, in one form or another (Spare's "*Kia*"; or the daemons of the Lovecraft mythos) suggests that these so-called *puritanical* "rites of chaos" have been specifically concocted to compensate for deep-felt guilt (inferiority) or inadequacy created by their otherwise lack of any sort of a constructive work ethic.

There can be no doubt that a self-consciously "churchy" atmosphere pervades much connected with organized Chaos Magic. Peter Carroll himself even uses the phrase "*Church of Chaos*", rather like L. Ron Hubbard was fond of speaking about the "Church of Scientology". And not only are there "Priests" and "Priestesses" of Chaos, but "Extreme Observances" of "Monks" and "Nuns" of Chaos, too! Instead of members being expelled, they are "excommunicated". Carroll does not officially style the Head of the I.O.T. / "Church of Chaos" a Pope, but the holder of this office calls himself "The Supreme Magus". How wonderful for that individual and for the Congregation of the Church of Chaos! But even if done in jest, why is the joke thought to be so funny that it is frequently repeated? Could it be the nervous half-laughter of the already compromised? Or merely the hollow Laughter of those with really nothing to say?

The concept of Chaos Magic is designed to attract the mind rather than the soul. There is not a great deal of Joy in the writings of Chaos Magic. Curiously enough, in view of all the otherwise churchy paraphernalia, there is also hardly any mention made of prayer, despite the fact that the secret of Magick is to "enflame thyself". What you *will* find in Chaos Magic, though, is an exercise in pseudoscience and sheer balderdash which rivals L. Ron in its audacity and heavy-handedness. There's plenty of laboured intellectualism and pedantry; lists; categories of attainment; and many excursions of a specialised nature from the universal into the particular. Its approach isn't one of synthesis and unification, but instead one of dispersion and breaking things down even more, graphically symbolised by the one-way arrows of the *Chaosphere*, or logo of Chaos.

At the 1990 Oxford Thelemic Symposium, Peter Carroll mentioned that the idea of Chaos Magic was not unconnected with the fictional writings of the sword-and-sorcery fantasy author, Michael Moorcock, in which are narrated tales of characters known as the Lords of Law and the Lords of Chaos. Certainly, there can be no doubt that it seems to have been from here that the idea for the logo of the Chaosphere originated. This logo, to directly quote Michael Moorcock in Book Three, Chapter Three of "*The Queen of the Swords*" (1971), consisted of "The Arms of Chaos - eight arrows radiating from a central hub, representing, according to Chaos, all the rich possibilities inherent in its philosophy." As an artistic device in a work of fiction, where

Moorcock used it to highlight the fact that there was no balance in Chaos, (and forgetting that his forces of Law were represented by a single upward vertical arrow) this works fine - but does this imbalance have any relevance to what is really going on in the universe? The answer is no, because it violates *not only* the law of nature which says that if the universe expands it will also need to contract (implied in Newton's Third Law of Motion); *not only* the law that everything that exists contains the seeds of its own opposite (as implied by the taoist yin-yang symbol); but it even directly contradicts the words of Carroll himself in an earlier book, "*Liber Null*", which stated: "To Chaos, nothing is true and everything is permitted, though it has *limited itself to the principle of duality in building* this world for itself"(p.75). Furthermore, the fact that the arrows go outwards "from a central hub" suggests a blinkeredness and unwillingness on the part of chaos magicians *to receive* any ideas that do not accord with their own world view and their own projection of personal power.

In *Liber Cyber*, a stimulating pamplet by Charles Brewster, an organization known as "Stoke Newington Sorcerers" was, according to a chart drawn by the author in Chapter Seven, a direct forerunner in some respects of the Magical Pact of the I.O.T. Melodramatic mention is made that after 1975, its key members were "seduced away by a guru purporting to present a gateway to the ultimate truth". It seems also - although it is not mentioned in this particular essay - that for a time Peter Carroll, a S.N.S. member, was interested in the doings of somebody calling himself "The Master Amado" - who was claiming at the time to be the magickal heir and natural son of Aleister Crowley. As it later transpired, Peter Carroll seems to have come to the conclusion that the man's claim could not be substantiated and the effect of discovering this was a strong contributory factor in turning him against Thelema ever since. As the magickal philosophy propounded by Crowley, Thelema not only recognized the non-atomic fact of infinite space as Nothing, but also a chaotic matrix wherein "every number is infinite", and "there is no difference." Far from Chaos Magic coming from Chaos, it came from disillusionment and thereby a need to improve upon Thelema, as well as the whole western ceremonial magickal tradition as represented by the Golden Dawn. Unfortunately, by this wholesale plundering of past traditions of magick at will, including the systems of John Dee and Austin Spare, the practitioner ends up being jack of all trades, but master of none.

In a somewhat desperate and unconvincing attempt to come up with something new that goes further and one better than other more traditional systems (including "Thelema"), Chaos Magicians resort to the sham device of mouthing the cliché that "everything is permitted", because "the universe is such a shambles anyway". An attempt is then made to obscure matters further with a smoke-screen of pseudo-intellectualism, through which it is nonetheless transparently visible that the Emperor (or in this case, the Pope or Supreme Magus) is stark bollock naked. There can't be any such thing as "Chaos Magic", because these words contradict themselves. Even though the universe has a random factor in it (in the sense that it has a supernal ordering principle which cannot be detected by human intellectual processes), in order for it to work, an Act of Magick requires the performance of an Act of Will, with the objective held firmly and unwaveringly in mind. If a result is not then forthcoming, it is not so much because of the (paradoxical) effect that an unpredictable, chaotic element is present, as that either (a) the current of concentration of one-pointedness was not strong enough to overcome local conditions, or that (b) the intention was not itself appropriate in terms of the evolution of the universe, a sentient entity of a different and superior kind altogether to homo sap. All magickal acts are meaningless, or powerless, or both, unless done specifically to rectify a perceived imbalance within the universe: something which cannot be done without first having a notion of what *relative* Order is, since Chaos cannot deal with the concept of balance or law, and is a thing unto itself. Or, to add one word to a prophetic Michael Moorcock quote, taken from the source mentioned earlier: "...When Chaos *Magic* exhausts its invention, ultimately it brings a more profound stagnation that anything it despises in law. It must forever seek more and more sensation, more and more empty marvels, until there is nothing left and it has forgotten what true invention is."

NOTE: Since this review was written, it appears that Peter Carroll has stepped down from his role as head of the I.O.T.

Love is the law, love under will.

JAB

AXIOMATA AND THE WITCHES' SABBATH
by
Austin Osman Spare
Published by FULGUR, BCM Fulgur, London WC1N 3XX
in a limited edition of 1000. Standard edition at £23 and deluxe at £46.50
Reviewed by Brian T. Grove

I'm always rather wary about sending money off to a publisher for a book I haven't seen, however, when I lifted this volume out of its tissue wrapping all anxiety disappeared as if by magic - this is one collector's edition that truly deserves the name. I opened the moody black covers, sentinelled with embossed golden sigils, ventured within, and this is what I found: Two texts by Spare, placed back-to-back; two stunning colour frontispieces ('Mind and Body' which accompanies **Witches' Sabbath** is the most powerfully brooding AOS piece I've yet seen); an introduction by the mighty Ramsey Dukes, and one by newcomer Gavin Semple; printed on beautiful paper with pages of sweeping automatic drawings alternating with pages of text. Pausing to catch my breath I sat down to read, and very quickly realised the great value of this work.

Although affordable reprints of Spare's books have begun to appear, we don't really know how Spare's thought developed after his **Anathema of Zos**, the last book he published in 1927. If Kenneth Grant is to be believed, AOS somehow went from being a neo-Taoist sorcerer and mystic - as shown in his 1913 **Book of Pleasure** - to creating his own Voodoo-Wiccan cult (the "Zos Kia Cultus') which he was developing just before his death. So what happened in between? As the first book of unadulterated Spare to appear in sixty-five years, this book goes a long way towards filling that gap.

The Witches' Sabbath is the manuscript which Grant tantalisingly footnoted and quoted from in his books; seen here in its entirety it is stunning magical poetry in Spare's amazing style, scintillating with his weird and wonderful vocabulary. There is a synopsis of the Sabbath, an analysis of the techniques which it involves, followed by a series of potent conjurations in which we see, at last, such terms as 'inbetweenness' and 'the funambulatory way' being used by Spare himself. Do we infer from this account that Spare actually attended Sabbaths? It seems rather unlikely, as when this was written covens were thinner on the ground than they are today, in the wake of Gardner, Sanders and others. I think that Spare meant this text to be read on many levels: on the one hand it is an account of the classic Mediaeval-style Sabbath, but reading behind the symbolism it emerges as a resumé of Spare's own magical method, refined and greatly expanded from the sigil sorcery which he expounded in **The Book of Pleasure**. This is hands-on Zos Kia magic, exactly what, as a Chaos Magickian, I have been waiting and hoping for - after all the theories about what Spare was or was not doing magically, **this** is the real thing from the man himself.

Turning, literally, to the other part of the book, the **Axiomata** is a series of forty axioms in which Spare develops a thesis of magical psychology, beginning with a withering denunciation of Christianity and psychoanalysis (perhaps one of the first to recognise these as two sides of the same devalued coin), continuing through a castigation of contemporary evils, ending up with his own vision of the function and purpose of the awake individual who finds him or herself slumming it in this particular end of the universe. These aphorisms are a joy to read, Spare showing his observant and incisive humour throughout - the "strong meat" for which he was criticised during his life - crossing back and forth across the lines of his thought, never losing the momentum of his inspiration. It is surprising, but refreshing, to see Spare swearing (referring to "bunk-ups" and "knee-tremblers"!) and using modern terminology, which brings the mysterious master that much closer. In places he reveals a humane and compassionate side which is lacking in earlier writings, the result, perhaps, of the hard life he'd led since the 'twenties. Yet he also reprises certain themes from **Anathema of Zos**, and so the elusive link is made between his early philosophy and the path he was following in his final years.

This appears to be more than an important, even watershed, book; publisher Robert Ansell has said that he wanted to create a talismanic object, and in this he has certainly succeeded. His careful attention to every aspect of its presentation, from the layout and the choice of illustrations to the luscious paper and bindings, gives the book the feel of a true grimoire, and sets it apart from the myriad occult books which cluster on the booksellers' shelves. It is a tribute of which Spare would, I'm sure, heartily approve. After languishing for forty years Spare's later writings are

at last emerging, and for veteran Spare-buffs or those seeking an introduction to his work **The Witches' Sabbath** is an opportunity definitely but **not** to be missed.

SKOOB BOOKS PUBLISHING

CHAPBOOKS OF THE EIGHTEENTH CENTURY
Ed. John Ashton

A fascinating window onto the heroes and legends, folklore and superstitions of the past.
Full of the vivacity of the oral tradition, this collection contains over one hundred chapbooks, richly illustrated with facsimiles of the original woodcuts.
ISBN 1 871438 26 8 504pp £9.95 $19.95

Marion Weinstein:

The Ancient and Modern Witch
Earth Magic Production $6.95 ISBN
0960412840

Magic for Peace
Earth Magic Production $2.95 ISBN
0960412808

Earth Magic a dianic book of shadows
Phoenix Publishing Inc $7.95 ISBN
0919345026

Positive Magic - Occult Self-Help
Phoenix Publishing Inc. $9.95 ISBN
091934501X

The Ancient and Modern Witch is in essence a Halloween lecture. I think she would go down very well in St. James' church, Picadilly where they have an excellent ongoing programme of very different 'spiritual' orientations explaining where they are coming from. She builds bridges, fields questions with confident ease, and comes across as a capable lecturer with a warm personality - at once forthright and diplomatic.

Magic for Peace is almost pamphlet-sized. Her tone is so reasonable that I would suggest a mass handout if you are ever surrounded by a mob of rabid fundamentalists of any 'religious persuasion' - including some occultists! While it might not convert them to Witchcraft, and I doubt if that would be her intention - she seems to 'live and let live'- it might

healthily infect them with the virus of sane tolerance. I like the way in which she expresses her 'infinity of solution' idea! Yes, hand it out to ideological dinosaurs of all persuasions - especially politicians on their adversarial either/ or treadmill.

Earth Magic, too, has a positive healthy non-elitist tone. She covers everything, from personal guardian crystals (hear! hear!) to healing for others. I can only strongly second her in her formulation to negate the harmfulness of negative diagnostic labels:

> I picture silver rain washing away that which has been called a growth

For there is a dark element in the psychology of conventional medicine, which can have the effect of the wrong kind of magic - the diagnosis as hex or curse. (My words here, not hers.)

I like the idea of an animal *volunteering* for work as a familiar. Not only do I agree that in this respect the animal is an *equal*, but would add that animals you do not even live with may on occasions communicate something special and valuable to you - the cats of friends, for instance. Or even something completely out of the blue. My thanks to the bat in Folkestone by the woody cliffs, for its company and the music it brought.

Covering the sort of ground you might expect from a 'book of shadows', the book has a section on Psychic Attack, where Ms Weinstein sanctions the *transmutation* of energy, rather than crude opposition.

A nice present for a Christian or Atheist friend.

Positive Magic - Occult Self-Help is the most comprehensive of Ms Weinstein's four books received. In spite of her 'Inner Bell' which tells her to 'avoid' uncle Aleister's teachings 'with a ten foot pole', she says so more in a spirit of 'this is not for me'. She certainly does not condemn my 'invisible mentor'; neither does she condemn Christians *as such* for the Inquisition and cognate persecutions, but rather points to the universal human danger of projecting the 'shadow' outside oneself.

Unlike the other three books, this is a general introduction to matters occult, seemingly for those not greatly involved, and perhaps interested but not inclined. After reading this though, I think they would be more likely to become impressed with the life-enhancing or even life-transforming potential of 'occult' (which merely means 'hidden') resources. The general reader will see that where perhaps they expected 'weirdness' there is beauty and energy; where perhaps they expected eccentricity or worse, there is radiant sanity. If there was more of this sort of thing about and less pseudo expert cliquishness, more people would be encouraged to try out their hidden resources - the grail on the doorstep. Writing with clarity, balance, good sense and good humour, Ms Weinstein is an excellent ambassador for magic.

Rae Beth:

Hedge Witch
Robert Hale pbk £5.95 ISBN 0709048513

The more Witchcraft books I see, the more I feel that anyone who starts off with a media-generated, horror-film idea of witches and who is not disarmed when they read what the witches themselves have to say, must be a pretty malevolent curmudgeon.

There is a great freshness about this book, which is cast in the form of letters to less experienced followers of witch-craft, and Ms Beth discourages pomp;

Magic has been made elaborate... But...it can be direct, spontaneous...the principle is that of creating space between the worlds: the sacred space ...and Without this (visualisation) there is no life.

She is right. You can go through the most elaborate ceremonies, including formal 'initiations' ; but if you have not simultaneously undertaken that 'inward journey' (which is what 'initiation' itself meant in Latin), all is vanity. All around us, at every moment, there are 'inward journeys' waiting for us to notice the direction signs. Writers as diverse as William Blake and Arthur Machen knew this very well.

She suggests creative alternatives to set ceremonial prescriptions, using what I would call your magical 'ingenium' to create a focused magical ambiance from things and circumstances that are to hand.

Her Beltane rites for solitary Witches (female and male) with their floral element are beautiful and appropriate - she captures the whole stirring ethos of that time, rather than drily filing away a number of prescribed symbols.

Janet and Stuart Farrar:

Eight Sabbats for Witches
Robert Hale £8.50 ISBN 070904778 9

Spells and How they Work
Robert Hale £6.95 ISBN 070905011 9

Even St Anthony could not find my
original reviews of these excellent
books. Why St. Anthony? Well, this
'finder' saint usually works. I guess his
companion pig would be associated
with rooting for hidden things - including truffles. So the first (to be received)
have become the last. So apologies, dear
Farrars!

Eight Sabbats for Witches follows the
seasonal festivals of Witchcraft, and the
attunements they enhance for us with
their enriching (enwitching?) context
on "great creating nature", a context
of which urban 'civilisation', for all its
cultural benefits, can so rapidly and
radically deprive us - bringing, with
the separation, unbalanced and pur-
blind attitudes to fertility and death.
Surely this is one of the themes of
'Shakespeare's' *The Winter's Tale*. (In
fact the whole group of his 'last plays'
have a strong magical ambiance and
resonances and will repay an immersion
in their ethos on the part of Witches,
Magicians and just about anyone else.
Perhaps the best way is to obtain a
recording - voices bring the texts to life,
and you can listen again and again, each
time perceiving something more.) And I
find in *Eight Sabbats* something of the
ethos informing those late plays - the
same reverence for recurring fertility and
its reintegrative properties, which
balance the disintegrative tendencies
incurred by human societies as they
develop into sophistication.

Into this book the Farrars have
incorporated their personal experiences
of surviving folklore traditions; this
gives the book a living current far
removed from anthropological mum-
mification; for we should not be poking
among ashes; torch should light torch.

Their use of some of Dion Fortune's
material from her evocative novel *The
Sea Priestess* for a marital handfasting
ceremony, is an inspired piece of
serendipity. In the 'Great Rite ' chapter
they point out the connection between
the Woman's body as Altar, and the
configurations of ecclesiastical architecture. In my own experience, I would
just say that the 'Vesica Piscis', almond
shaped symbol of the female genitalia,
apart from enclosing pictures of Christ
and/or Mary, is prominent in the
geometrical proportionment of some
medieval cathedrals, and I have a
selection of diagrams from the early
nineteenth century which illustrate the
point. The initiated mason-architects
behind these wonderful edifices had
not lost touch with an original female
current in Christianity.

We now live in an age where we
need to recover the wholeness of vision,
shown by these Architects and by
'Shakespeare' in his 'last plays', and
which arguably was lost thereafter,
before the start of the Industrial
Revolution. And, by the perennial and
accessible articulation of Life that
Witchcraft provides, we can recover
this wholeness. I am sure that people
on many spiritual paths would benefit
from incorporating into their lives and
worship, the reverence for creation,
rhythm, vitality and universal related-
ness that this book so vividly conveys
as belonging to the heritage of Witchcraft. Such an ethos could provide the
strongest dynamics in the effort for the
healing of the planet's pollution, and
could radically transform the grosser
consumerist attitudes now dominant in
every field, from agriculture to sex.
Concerning the latter, the Farrars, in

170

their 'Great Rite' chapter celebrating divine polarity on *all* levels, quote Doreen Valiente:

> It is love and only love that can give sex the spark of magic

At the outset of *Spells*, there is a rebuttal of any notion of the Spell as superstition. The Spell merely avails itself of levels and laws of which so-called 'rationalist' culture does not take cognizance. As such, Spells involve *method*. For example, in the chapter on Talismans:

> it is often the person concerned who must be worked on, rather than his or her external dangers and problems.

The book itself reflects an appreciation of method, and articulate detail involving its application, which removes it far from the catchpenny rag-bags of garbled or curtailed 'receipts' thrown together without rationale understanding or commitment which help to debase, as much as the Farrars' book should help to elevate, the reputation of the High Art of Magic in the bewildered public mind.

Oh and as a counterweight to the concern I expressed earlier in this series of reviews about the unconscious pathology underlying certain prescriptive manifestations of 'conventional' medicine, I should quote the Farrars' remarks from their chapter on healing spells;

> many doctors and nurses were attracted to their profession in the first place because, consciously or unconsciously, they have a natural healing ability.

Yes, this is the other side of the coin. But this positive element is personal; the negative element which I was deploring, is *institutional*, as is much insanity.

The ethical side of spells is not neglected: the love spell that can 'bypass the desired one's freedom of choice' is condemned;

> such manipulation is not only morally indefensible, it is highly dangerous.

Helping on an incipient romance encumbered with shyness is another matter. A suitable procedure - quite simple and elegant - is described, but even here the proviso incorporated in the magic is: 'but only if it is right for them'. This ethical provisionalism is found in all sincere and informed practitioners of magical arts. The power to act must be balanced with appropriateness. In this, magic is more 'scientific' in the etymological sense of 'knowing what it is doing'. In applied material science-technology, that saving hiatus between the potential and its activation is seldom observed. The hubris of 'I can, so I shall', unfortunately rides roughshod over the planet and the lives it nurtures. A tincture of informed occultism would not come amiss in the killing fields of technology.

These are well-organised books, clearly and enjoyably written, comprehensively informative, enlivened by telling anecdotes, humanely ethical, safe enough to place in the hands of a novice, but absorbingly magical enough to encourage him/her not to remain one for long.

THE NECROMANTIC RITUAL BOOK
Westgate Press, 5219 Magazine Street
New Orleans, LA 70115
Publication: 1991 (limited to 500 copies)

SHADOWS IN THE HALF-LIGHT
Westgate Press, New York 1989
Both by **Leilah Wendell**
Reviewed by Maud Titian

With a title like *The Necromantic Ritual Book* I had been expecting a manual for pimply would-be 'satanists', but this is nothing of that sort. It must be said at the outset that it execrates anyone who would seek to press their unsolicited and sacrilegious attentions on the bodies of the dead.

No 'Satan' here, but rather the Master of Ceremonies is the magnificent Azrael, the real 'Shaitan of the Yezidis', created by God on the first day, the Chief of all angels, the Peacock Angel. This was the 'Angel of Death' created on the Sun day, the day of radiating life. Note, too, from another context that from the Sephira of the Sun, Tiphareth, on the Tree of Life, the paths radiating below are those of Death and the Devil.

It is not that Leilah Wendell mentions these factors in her preface, but that she does seek to communicate her own intimate and constant perception of a wonderful perichoresis, the interpenetration of the energies of 'life' and 'death', the incompleteness and limited perspective which comes from shutting out the night and looking out only on the dayside.

"The workings of this book," she tells us, "will permit the magician to bask in the 'life-force' of the Angel of Death. The word 'bask' suggests both the blissful absorption of an influence - and something Saurian.

These workings do not employ an excess of paraphernalia and are lucidly explained. They may therefore not appeal to pseudo-intellectual and egotistical 'upwardly mobile' magicians. That could be their loss.

"Can you see Orion? How about Ursa Major?" she asks. Indeed some constellations seem to have a particularly strong relation to Daath the Sephira of Interpenetration. She gets us out of our rooms and under the earth or under the stars. Here you are under the stars, lying beside your earthen altar near a watery location. The stars will pull you. All of this is very true. It seems that the Angel of Death wants you to have breathing space, too! Leilah lucidly describes the 'threshold' that awaits you when you have been pulled out, and 'the ethereal canvas' on which your affinities seem to be projected.

She takes us under the earth too, for a vigil in a vault but we are advised not to use 'one of the' more modern mausoleums where the dead are walled up behind the marble barriers. She is right of course. Sanitization and commercialization has gone a long way to kill the life of death itself. The wafts of the charnel house are venerable, while the stench of standardised 'processing' o the dead is despicably venal.

She provides clear instructions on how to create a Golem, a sculpture animated by the devoted energies of its creator, in which "at least 75% of the formative material is necrotic biomatter (dead things)". It then becomes a talisman, and acts like a magical focussing lens, quasi-sentient...

This brief black and silver covered book, with its graceful rather than heavy Gothic lettering (silver filigree effect) has a companionable feel about it, a book to carry around in twilight states both physical and psychical. I think I smell Jasmine...

If you wish to imbibe this atmosphere in a more diffused form then *Shadows in the Half-Light* offers the opportunity. A mixture of collages in which disparate elements have been cut, pasted, juxtaposed and finally welded into the irrefragable logic of the conscious dream, and rows of twilight poems. A progress through this slim mauve volume is like wandering through a slightly phosphorescing old cemetery in the cooling lees of a blood-lashed sunset as the intoxicating scent of damp crumbly earth blends with scrolly whiffs from the charnel vaults, and the infinite pinpricked velvet spaces above pull at the crown of one's head, and the soil below pulls at the soles of one's feet. One half expects a skeleton, moving like a decorous spider in top hat and cloak to accost one from behind that peeling iron door slightly ajar on the family mausoleum. It's the collages! They are in black and white, but I can well imagine their impact in colour.

And one seems to read the poems as if from pages of mossy stone propped at the end of grasses. Sometimes they speak of a bittersweet resignation, sometimes in a Poe-like tone of fevered but chilly delirium. And although the rhyme and metre sometimes stumble as though snarled by hidden roots snaking out of the earth, a pleasant and reflective melancholy envelopes me until I

"Behold! Sweet Death unfurl His wings
and lift his head unto the crowd
and part the lampblack of his vest
blinding all who meet his gaze
with eerie visions set ablaze!"

THE WORM THAT BLOOMED
"The Sacred Magician - a ceremonial diary"
by
William Bloom
(Gothic Image 1992) price £7.95
Reviewed by Jab

Do what thou wilt shall be the whole of the Law.

"The Sacred Magician" is a rare document concerning what the author calls "the most famous ceremony of ritual magic" - the six month "Abramelin Operation", first set down in English by MacGregor Mathers in 1898. Abramelin and Enochian are notorious as the Scylla and Charybdis for the impetuous novice occult practitioner. There are two things which strike the reader about this particular account. The first, irrespective of whether his motives derive from ambition or devotion, is the writer's perseverance over the period in question as he maroons himself in the mountains of Morocco. The second, notwithstanding the virtue of discipline - or more precisely, **application** - is the unfortunate Christian, Piscean and overly ascetic emphasis of the enterprise which, credit where it is due, the author himself acknowledges in the Epilogue, written eighteen years later. Taken together, these two factors reduce to self flagellation and abasement of the ego what should otherwise be basically a meditative or bhakti-yogic exercise.

On March 25th, because he forgot to make an entry, "as a form of penance, had freezing wash this morning, which I almost enjoyed." On May 9th "the battle to be worthy to do His (God's) work, to merely have the right to truly love Him, continues indefinitely with pain (which we deserve)". This theme is further dilated upon on June 29th: "The whip will be applied to take me home, if I be ever worthy"; on August 8th: "I have started putting the whip heavily across myself again", and so on. Even assuming that the whip is metaphorical, the language is revealing of the writer's whole approach to the Operation: "I am finding it all quite hard - but deservedly so if I am to progress."

This performance of the Abramelin ritual was undertaken four years after the author's first acquaintance with occultism. According to the Introduction, he was a young man who enjoyed adventures, and presumably embarked upon this in the same light. Unfortunately he continually lusted after result, in spite of many protestations and lamentations about deluded vanity. The entry for April 19th is a good example of this. "I want Samadhi", he declares on May 1st. On August 2nd, he wants (and evidently gets) a halo. At the end of the ritual, on September 24th, his concern is "how high (or low!) am I initiated?" and he questions himself: "Is praying all the time a form of arrogance?" In the Epilogue, he makes the astonishing remark that "even the well-known occultist Aleister Crowley knew his limitations and never performed the Abramelin ceremony except as a self-confessed exercise in his imagination." That "even" suggests that

Dr. Bloom regards himself as a greater magician than Aleister Crowley (Indeed, Crowley did not perform the ceremony as set out by Mathers, but enacted instead a parallel one. The reasons for this are too numerous and complicated to go into here, but are well laid out for those interested in the chapter entitled "Augoeides" in Israel Regardie's biography "The Eye in the Triangle.") There is something almost comical about the way he finds himself in his oratory at the end of the Operation under the impression that he has been wasting his time for six months, the victim of fantasy and illusion. What a book that would have made! By completing Abramelin, however, this proved that the writer was not merely messing around with "wildly glamourous occultism": in fact, by means of the ceremonial diary, "insight will be given into the severe training that a true exorcist must go through; and people will be reassured that it is done with wisdom, strength and real understanding,." As the author repeatedly says, "we shall see."

Dr. Bloom announces his intention to commence and close each oration with the Lord's Prayer - this is later abandoned, although the reason for either step is never explained. He systematically reads through the archaically bellicose and turgid Old Testament, yet consults daily the more Taoist I Ching which he acknowledges "has been advising me perfectly" (Sept. 21st). Arguably, any mental alignment gained from reading his austere library of "proper" literature would have been offset to some extent by turning on the radio and listening to "All Gas and Gaiters" less than a week before the conclusion of the Operation. I grew a little weary of the constant repetition of the theme of unworthiness; that he is "naughty", a "sinner", or a "worm". This wretched abasement of the personality-vehicle is continually stressed throughout the operation. Occasionally there are glimpses that the personality is simply an ineffective, imperfectly tuned instrument of the soul rather than some malign and obstructive entity in its own right, but such realizations soon vanish. On September 6th, we are falsely promised "no more whining about my sinfulness before God"; five days later, "it is at times very dark...and I do not shine as a light: therefore sinfulness and weakness." This is a lapse in spite of an earlier revelation (August 27th), that "the dark of which I have been afraid is the pureness of spirit." Again, on September 15th: "Spirit is black. In the Song of Solomon, I am black and comely"; and yet, the following day, there is "the rush of fear of overwhelming darkness." Dr. Bloom assesses "the enemy, myself", yet ignores the useful technique of dealing with savage and unpleasant phenomena "by dissolving and absorbing it in my love", which was revealed to him on June 11th. "I do not feel able to do that at the moment, but I hope that I shall after the Operation": this might explain the curious statement on September 19th: "a reappearance - but for the absolutely final encore - of my personality." One waits - and waits - for the illumination that the worm is a manifestation of the divine life force just as "sacred" as the magician.

It is never really made clear when and why the decision to make public the diary was made. Even allowing for it having been written in the white heat of the moment, a lot of the writing comes across as tiresome, pedantic and obscure; and in combination with the many false dawns throughout the period that the suffering was about to be over, the reader must feel by the penultimate month that s/he is on an ordeal on a par with the author. Personally, I felt that there could have been more valuable information supplied than that which was imparted: for example, did he ever perform the standard Pentagram and Hexagram "Banishing" rituals; and if so, how often? Did he greet the Sun and Moon? We are aware that he smoked regularly for most of the six months and are also told that he had had some LSD experiences: given the climate of the times (early 70s) and the fact that Morocco is a plentiful source of cheap hash, were any psychoactive drugs taken during this time which may have fitted in with his intention to "storm heaven"?

Concerning the Abramelin ceremony itself, there is something which is, to modern sensibilties, very constraining, didactic and distasteful. For example, (page 14), "You may sleep with your wife in the bed when she is pure and clean, but when she hath her monthly curses you shall not allow her to enter the bed, nor even the Chamber." And although Dr. Bloom pleads that his Christianity is Gnostic or Rosicrucian, evidence of evangelical millenarianism is revealed in the entry of September 19th: "As this century turns, we shall see His Kingdom come. Truly." However, the diary is not totally without interest, and although becoming extremely ill for two years immediately afterwards does not recommend itself to those who would seek to follow his example, it is encouraging to read in the Epilogue that the author seems to have been able to learn something from his experience.

Love is the law, love under will.

RHYTHMAJIK BY NUMBERS
"Rhythmajik" by
Z'ev
(Temple Press, 1992) £10.95
Reviewed by JAB

Do what thou wilt shall be the whole of the Law.

"**Rhythmajik**" is an exposition of the cabbalistic credo that every phenomenon which exists in the Universe is an expression of one type or another of resonance - a progressively denser emanation from the source of nothingness (the "Ain"). Exactly how nothingness is brought about to reverberate is not, unfortunately, within the ambit of this often provoking book. What does concern the writer, the laconically monikered Z'ev, are the ways in which the numeration of words can be broken down into their component vibrations. He is also concerned with the manner in which various correspondences can be "parsed" and applied sonically in order to create changes in the areas of "healing, divination, scrying, talismans, sigils, evocation, invocation, envisioning, banishing, tantra and necromancy" (the last apparently something of a personal hobby-horse).

There are at least a couple of slight theoretical drawbacks to such an exercise. According to one cabbalistic approach, the Logos, transmitting the sound or Word of creation in the beginning, is represented by 2 (Chokmah). The emanation from 1 (Kether, the Crown - "I Am That I Am") should not, strictly speaking, vibrate at all. Another interpretation goes even further than this, and states that phenomenal, rather than noumenal, existence only occurs with and after the number 4 (Chesed) - discounting not only 1, but numbers 2 and 3 also from the scheme. That is where everything above the "Abyss" is regarded as being the same as its opposite, in which case relativity, subject and object (and therefore sound and hearing), are impossible. Regretfully, these areas are not addressed either.

A "Working", in the context of Rhythmajik, is "any series of actions bringing the intention into focus. What transforms the condition of a Yoga form from a physical exercise to a posture of embodiment is the intention" (p.140). By "intention", the same thing is presumably meant as the magickal "will". The reader must no doubt be heartened, as I was, to discover "there are no established Rhythmajik Workings and there never should be. There is only the process" (p.141) - a pleasant change from the diktat of many so-called "Chaos" Workings. We are also, in addition, happily advised, "Whatever medium you choose as the Way for your inner direction to manifest is as good as any other. Once again, intention is the key" (p.51).

The root of the "Rhythmajikle" system lies in the correspondence between words and the different "beat" permutations of their numbered values. Of particular interest to me is the variance in the meanings given for any number and why these were originally chosen - especially since there is not always a

178

clear relationship shown between them in the section "The Book of Roots". It is also fair to ask how far modern meanings will reflect the original ones, particularly in a system which Z'ev reckons to extend back 15,000 years, and which involves translation from one tongue to another. Language itself is highly fluid, and it is not explained how the actual meanings for the numbers themselves are derived, or (if not known) why they are given scientific credence when they should otherwise be faith.

The all-important rhythm of Breath - pranayama - is barely touched upon, and for a book which places such an overriding importance on rhythm, there is a singular lack of punctuative beat in places, which imparts (disappointingly) a rather "breath<u>less</u>" quality, in spite of some basic good sense nuggeted beneath. For example (p.9): "During practice the beat patterns should be adhered to so as to allow their repetition the opportunity to implement your acclimatisation to the cochleal states and to condition a slow "hard-wiring" of the neural states and pathways of the proportional expressions."

On p.164 we are advised "...All practice should be intentionally re-<u>turned</u> to Earth, and not just sent out randomly". This doesn't make sense if, when you are sending out the beat (or "the beat is flowing through you"), you <u>are</u> the Earth" (p.17). A drum beat would need to be returned back to the source which was originally drumming it out - i.e., the drummer: something like a self-centred closed circuit, or moebius strip (to be more picturesque). Another type of semantic paradox is suggested on p.66 after Z'ev states "the more expressions you consider and experience, the larger your vocabulary becomes and the greater the service you can render." Perfectly true, but what immediately follows is convoluted: "This is again involved with the practice of taking two discrete processes, in this case the imaginal and semantic impulses, and with the fusing of them into a continuum bringing about a gestalt. Consider it as two beats which through repetition become a continuous tone. All continuous tones are made up of discrete events." Or as Aleister Crowley commented more simply: "Every number is infinite, there is no difference: the limited is a mere mask; the illimitable is the only truth. Although each number has its own meaning, each one is equal and supreme."

Z'ev also attempts to deal with the koan "what is the sound of one hand clapping?" (p.206), but I couldn't find an answer to the similar chestnut as to whether there is a sound if a tree falls in a forest and no one is there to hear it.

It isn't clear why Z'ev asks the reader to accept his "Stand of Stones". This is a model similar to the "Tree of Life", but ending at an astral Foundation, and with Malkuth, the 10th sephirah representing Earth, chopped off at the trunk. All the more so, when the "rhythm-majition" (magician) is represented as Earth, and the "totality of ramifications" diagram on page 31 includes it anyway and is the Tree of Life under another name. Uranus and Neptune are attributed to numbers 2 and 1 respectively, but where does that leave Pluto and Planet X? Rather untidily tucked into grid 8, or else outside of the system.

Also, no mention is made of <u>Da'ath</u> the sephirah commonly held to lie between 3 and 4 albeit on another plane. For such an unconservative book, there is a surprising reticence to step beyond an adherence to the conventions of the Arabic base 10 decimal system and the Hebrew cabbala of 22 letters. Why not use instead, for example, the English "aleph-bet", which has 26 letters (therefore providing greater options), and is the language in which all of the words written in the book are in any case? If nothing else, this would create 26 paths on the Tree by linking up Da'ath to sephiroth 2,3,4 and 5.

The construction of sigils for every number between 1 and 999 using the "Nine Chambers" method (p.52) is an excellent idea, although I was left wondering why, if Rhythmajik writes and reads Lines from left to right (as stated on p.40), it reverts back to right to left for the Nine Chambers, i.e. 3-2-1; 6-5-4; 9-8-7. A more logical model, in view of the Stand of Stones (and the Tree of Life) would surely be 3-1-2; 5-6-4; 8-9-7.

"The Work of our Hands" is a valuable and cogently argued chapter in the book, as are the sections on crafting a drum and "writings over sonics and implements". An interesting area of exploration might have been to discuss the impact of prolonged polyrhythms in modern music, especially where these are generated not by a human drummer, but electronically by a computer driven drum machine. Would such percusssive sounds be invalidated in any way by their not possessing the direct input and involvement of a flesh-and-blood "rhythmajition"?

In spite of the above considerations, a certain occasional stylistic unwieldiness, and a lack of definition in terms (a glossary might have been useful to deal with the shades of meaning in: modalities, parsing, transmuting, aspecting/emanating, attenuation, etc) this is nevertheless a book which succeeds in pushing forward the boundaries of magickal investigation into profitable new areas, and which stimulates students to experiment further in the very real and rewarding area of applied sonics.

Love is the law, love under will.

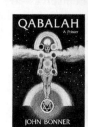

PARAPSYCHOLOGY: THE CONTROVERSIAL SCIENCE

by **Richard Broughton**

Pub: Rider

£16.99 hbk, £10.99 pbk. 408pp

(The author is the Director of Research at the Institute of Parapsychology
in Durham, North Carolina.)

Reviewed by Frater Venusius 49

The opening section of the book attempts to define 'psychic experience' in its varied manifestations, and continues with a resumé of the subject's development, which includes the remarkable articulate and repeatable phenomena produced by D.D. Home, and painstakingly recorded by William Crookes, inventor, subsequently, of the Crookes tube, which arguably led to the discovery and use of X-rays.

This is all done very lucidly. As we approach the present day, the density of information proportionately increases, and, arriving at the contemporary situation, we are regaled with some fascinating topics. The Random Number Generator research material, for instance, seems to suggest some disturbing possibilities - altering an output already made in time now elapsed, and materially affecting metastable electronic components. To a creative writer, the *first* possibility might suggest as its ultimate projection, a science fiction scenario about the colonisation and re-engineering of sections of human history for political purposes, which in turn would be bound to give any future(s) now to be extrapolated from such interference with the past a radically different trajectory. We already have an ecological crisis on our hands, as a result of hubristic technological interference. Perhaps we have even worse to fear. The *second* possibility, with the

'sensitive' components, suggests an adventure with a fleet of 'psychically suggestible' spacecraft, over which two empires are locked in combat for control, with picked squads of psychic commandos strategically deployed. The great oaks that grow from scientific acorns, often burgeon in a very compressed time scale compared to the tree which is the subject of the analogy, and we do well to remember that in the recent past, science fiction based upon the potential uses of fledgling scientific inventions and concepts, has been overtaken with disquietening regularity and swiftness by science fact. And, of course in some esoteric schools, though with less tangible accoutrements, it is an established tenet that, individually at least, we can alter our past by influences directed from the present. And influence 'material' creations. Many are the people who could report supporting experiences with computers and recording equipment.

However, like the rest of this comprehensive and well-organised survey, the results in this area are clearly and soberly presented; the facts are allowed to speak for themselves and the control mechanisms through which experimental rigour is achieved are presented for evaluation. The reader is credited with sufficient intelligence to assess the evidence, and in this respect, it is refreshing not to be prodded towards a particular conclusion, especially in a field that is still pregnant with so many potentialities.

There is a very thought-provoking chapter, in which the 'possible states' of quantum mechanics are related to the problem of why there is a particular outcome from a collection of probabilities. Is consciousness itself the missing factor in the question? Perhaps in the form of the observer(s) of an (experimental) situation? There may be a whole new environment in which the alchemical tag 'solve et coagula' can be observed to operate.

Here is a consideration that, in a way, connects back to the beginning of the book, where the effectiveness of Shamanistic techniques of Voodoo is considered in the context of the power of cultural expectation. For here again, consciousness could be proposed as a precipitating factor, in the form of a coherent corpus of socialised expectations. But, if so, does that shaping consciousness arise as if from a matrix under tension or is it itself subordinate to some other order of consciousness by which it has itself, in its turn, already been shaped?

And, concerning the outcomes observed in laboratories, whether para-psychological or not, if the observers had not been 'socialised' within a relatively homogenous 'scientific' *weltanschauung*, would their cumulative observations have acquired a different tendency, and would we perhaps have ended up with different, but equally viable 'laws' of both physical and psychokinetic science? It is just possible that quantum mechanics, with its 'possible states', together with the increasingly articulate psychokinetic science, may offer us eventually an actual choice of 'natural law pathways' which may have varied appropriateness in different physical and psychic environments. This would endow us with the weapon of adaptability in our explorations of other worlds, both physical and/or psychic.

So, what if all potential events swim in a wonderful plasma, in which consciousness itself is the pervading ingredient *in potentia*, that precipitates foci, which, connected by their mutual disturbance, may be likened to whirlpools in the plasma, and which attract outcomes according to the resultants of their relative suctions or magnetisms...

"And the Spirit of 'Elohim moved upon the face of the waters."

A catalytic book.

FEEDBACK
distributed by Temple Press
£5.00
Reviewed by Vandenburg

Since its inception ten years ago, the Temple of Psychick Youth has been called everything from "a bunch of psychedelic fascists" to (crumbs!) "a New Age cult". Is TOPY a Psychic TV fan club or merely a Porridgey situationist gag? An occult Order or a self-help group for dyslexics? Observers have never been able to pinpoint exactly what they might or might not be up to; the external symbols only pose more questions - why the obsession with 23? Why a Psychick cross? Why poke lumps of metal through your bell-end? Why indeed. 'Feedback' is a very intriguing document which answers these questions, but gives a lot more besides in the way of insight into the aims, inspirations, and obsessions of TOPY. An anthology of writings culled from letters and from responses to a questionnaire sent out a couple of years ago, the book functions more or less as a manifesto for the Temple in its current state. What is most apparent in reading through these dozens of pieces is that in ten years TOPY has grown into a fully-functioning network - united by a Utopian vision and a common will, but without discernable dogma of the kind which often seems a pre-requisite for any sort of organisation. The contributors display a wide range of opinions and beliefs, expressed with great honesty and directness: I tried to imagine a similar 'manifesto' being produced by any of the mainstream magickal groups - and failed. There is neither the back-biting nor line-toeing which are perennial features of the occult milieux, instead a healthy naivety (Is that a sin? Define 'naivety') and a determinedly optimistic realism. The responses to questions such as "What is TOPY?", "What is the significance of 23/the Psychick Cross?" and so on become, not an exercise in defiance, nor a reiteration of doctrine, but pivots for inspiration through which the communal yet individualistic spirit of TOPY is revealed. The contributors state their case with a gallant fervour which indicates to this writer, that their commitment to the Temple springs from its benefits, not from the urge to simply 'belong to something'; the tenor of these reports from the Topy frontline make it clear that this is a society of non-joiners. Moreover, it becomes evident that instead of waiting for the Golden Age, the Templars are simply getting on with it right now - in life, in sexuality in attitude, art and aspiration - an 'as if' act of the highest distinction, and one to be commended. This book is an intensely inspiring read, and a powerful antidote to that embittered cynicism which seems to be the prevalent cult of the 1990's. In 'Feedback' I see pride without arrogance; self-reliance and belief confidence, joy and enthusiasm; sincerity and spirited wordplay; and best of all - hope. TOPY: tight, but *loose*.

RATIO 3: MEDIA SHAMANS
Temple Press
£8.50
Reviewed by Justin Mjangwe

Media Shamans is the first book of a series, each presenting a selection of poetries by artists whose influences have, since the sixties, thoroughly permeated the subculture. This volume draws together a selection of works by Ira Cohen, Angus Maclise and Gerard Malanga - three men for whom the title 'shaman' is apt; for as travellers, seers, jugglers with word and image, they have traversed strange landscapes, both internal and external, transmitting the visions gained in the quest.

Ira Cohen's poems reflect his itinerant life, a series of impressions spanning his years of travel in and between New York, Tangiers, Morocco, India, Japan, Kathmandu, Ethiopia: reading them one is drawn on a path which seems to lie in two worlds at once - the travelling in the world and journeying in the mind become as metaphors for each other, and it is from the point in space between these states that his images unfurl. Like words and pictures flowing in half-sleep to the motion of a long train journey, Cohen's musings writhe in and out of subjective time, evoking memories of past and future, suddenly pulled into brief focus by an event in the present. We are in mythic time here, and mythic images rise to cloak the familiar - in poems such as 'Song to Nothing', 'Ushabti' and 'Turkish Freeze' there are glimpses of the 'real' world; winos in doorways, soldiers rehearsing for a secret parade, the glass and mirrors of a cafe; yet these are almost invisible elements, flashes of a world far behind, veiled by the mystery which Cohen ceaselessly draws in through his eyes, and transmutes into poignant words.

As a musician, Angus MacLise worked with Terry Riley, LaMonte Young and the Velvet Underground; following the hippy trail to India, he fetched up in Katmandu where he lived, with a few excursions to America and the UK, until his death in 1979. The pieces give some clues to what he sought, and evidently found, in the East; those written in New York in the sixties exude a psychedelically mystic atmosphere, but retain the sharp nervous edge of life in a city - quite similar in their impact to the contributions of Ira Cohen; the poems from Nepal are very still, by comparison, as if Maclise's imagination has found its true setting, no longer battening against the harsh world outside. 'Fern of Power' and 'Bright Song in the Air' encapsulate the feeling, conveying his sense of kinship with Nepal and Kathmandu. Yet, many of his pieces are driven by a great passion and energy, recalling the fiery diatribes of his contemporary Allen Ginsberg. Like Ginsberg, Maclise walked some way in the footsteps of William Blake; there is a luminosity in his work, in the conflagrations of imagery and in his religious vocabulary, which reveals a constant striving towards the spiritual. 'No more room then in this House of Dread', a superb rushing invocation, epitomises this burning effort of revelation, while, at the other end of Maclise's spectrum, 'Jaguar' with its hints of nodding opiate dreams draws the reader through echoes of past, present and future dreams, into the timelessness of the dreaming I.

Gerard Malanga is usually remembered for his leather-clad whip dancing with the Velvet Underground in Warhol's Exploding Plastic Inevitable revue, however, the greater part of his activity has been in film and photography, and the film-maker's eye is evident in his poetry. Malanga is curiously absent from his poems; like a cameraman he remains outside the action, scanning, directing and scripting situations, as if allowing himself existence by implication, drawing himself into the scene along the thread of words. 'Joan Miro and his daughter Dolores', 'The 7:44 Amtrak' and the auto-voyeuristic 'Irrumination' are elegant examples of this ability which seems to be the essence of Malanga's style; rarely does the poet himself slip into the frame, but the lengthier 'This poem doesn't exist...'contains a brief confession of vulnerability, swiftly negated: "What price to pay for writing the poem, for leaving myself open like that/ But I'm not really here anyways and someone else is writing this way in my absence...": amidst his images Malanga stands like an invisible spy, an emotionless observer of ritual, motion, gesture and light. 'Hermaphroditismus Genitalis' is a gem; a description of the physical characteristics of a hermaphrodite quoted from a medical book, yet, by the breaking of lines, its flat terminology transformed into erotically charged lyric prose - rather in the same vein as J.G. Ballard's techno-sexual litanies. In this case I didn't catch on to what I was reading until the end - and this subtle manipulation of material - whether textual (in this case), tactual or visual - is characteristic of Malanga's contributions. Elsewhere his Haiku-style layering of impressions can communicate a reflective, mediative train of thought, or, in stark contrast, the jagged and staccato blurt of speed-jabber - sometimes within the same poem.

Temple Press has become renowned for the creation of essential, maverick editions, and judging by the quality of this inaugural collection, the **Ratio: 3** series will run and run.

BARKING UP THE WRONG TREE
'Hecate's Fountain'
by
Kenneth Grant
(Skoob Books 1992)
Reviewed by Gerald Suster

Any book which commences after the Foreword with the following splendid quote from Arthur Machen's exquisite short story N can't be all bad:
'I believe there is a perichoresis, an interpenetration. It is possible, indeed, that we three are now sitting among desolate rocks, by bitter streams.'
'"...And with what companions?"'
What companions indeed, one wonders, as one peruses Mr. Grant's book with a growing sensation of incredulity. On first inspection, this is an exceptionally interesting volume. The production is of high quality and as is customary with Mr. Grant's intriguing works, it is graced by artwork of the utmost distinction, putting the Royal Academy Summer Exhibition to shame. One is delighted to concur with Mr. Grant when he states that Art is the highest form of Magick. Some may find this book to be worth buying for the Art alone: but what about the text?

The text consists of a lucid Foreword followed by three Parts. The first part deals with the state of consciousness that Grant terms 'The Mauve Zone', related to Daath on the Tree of Life in the Qabalah, arguing, as in the author's previous works, that this is a gateway to the experience of objective realities. Talismans, the Chinese system of the *Kû* and the work of Jack Parsons are considered in detail. The second part consists of a commentary on *The Book of the Law*. In the third part, the author expands his themes with an analysis of the congruent work of Michael Bertiaux. Although the matters under Grant's consideration are highly technical, the prose is much less costive than that of *Cults of the Shadow* or *Nightside of Eden*. Anyone as learned in Qabalah and Mythology as Mr. Grant will still find his equations demanding and challenging but that is all to the good, even if beginners find it incomprehensible. Well: they should learn some Qabalah. Grant obviously does not agree with the view of Jack Parsons: 'Simplicity has been the key to victory in all the idea wars, and, at present, Magick does not have it.'

Even so, Grant has made the uncharacteristic gesture of including section after section in the majority of chapters, which describe the practical workings of his Nu-Isis Lodge during the 1950's so as to exemplify his theoretical points. These are described with the observational precision of a scientific observer and a surprisingly graceful style of prose. One rather wishes that Mr. Grant had also employed his evident literary talent for the writing of tales of horror [1] too. In any event, this book should be read with one's finest attention by any practising Magician and also by those who are wondering whether or not to take the plunge and if so, of which Path to take.

It is impossible to enjoy this book unless there is Coleridge's 'willing suspension of disbelief', for it makes no sense whatsoever to the rationalist. Grant casually assumes the following as 'facts'.

1 - There are an infinite number of Universes.

I find no difficulty with this assumption. If the number of possible games of chess of 40 moves or less is 25×10^{115} thus exceeding the estimated number of electrons in the Universe (known) at 10^{79}, the assumption is perfectly plausible.

2 - There are objective, non-human entities, not necessarily based on terran cerebral structures. in the multitude of Universes, and we can evolve only by making contact with them.

As a Thelemite who accepts that *The Book of the Law* is a genuine communication from a praeter-human Intelligence, I can hardly quarrel with this assumption: though many will, especially the New Age and Jungian reductionists. Even so, I wonder about the entities to which Mr. Grant is referring.

Once again, he lays great stress of the importance of LAM, a being drawn by Crowley around 1917 and who reminds me of The Guardians in DC Green Lantern comics during the 1960's. I am surprised that Grant does not mention the fact that in many sects of Hindu Tantricism and Yoga, the mantra 'LAM' is used to arouse the Muladhara Chakra. One is also surprised by Grant's fascination with the Qlipoth, the excrement of the Universe, and by his notion that praeter-human Intelligences habitually manifest as hideous, slime-spread monsters, vampire bats, insectoids, were-spiders, frog spawn, larvae and other repellent beings straight out of H.P. Lovecraft's tales of horror. But more of that anon.

3 - Atlantis and Lemuria existed as matters of fact, not myth, and effective Magick is ultimately derived from these lost civilisations.

Maybe. It seems most unlikely but we don't know. For me, clairvoyant evidence is no concrete evidence at all of anything whatsoever. I shall keep an open mind upon the subject but await concrete archaelogical evidence before I buy this trip.

4 - Although H.P. Lovecraft persistently denied in his letters and in personal conversation that his tales were anything other than fantasies, he nevertheless unwittingly drew from the same inspirational sources as Crowley and Grant, giving us an objective portrayal of the Elder Gods and the Great Old Ones and enabling us to structure magical ceremonies predicated upon his faction.

On the face of it, this seems extremely unlikely. However, it is not impossible that a creative artist can receive inspiration and write truths beyond his conscious ken.

A dogmatic rationalist will of course have flung down the book in despair by this point but let us persist. *Hecate's Fountain* is not a bore. Grant courageously carries on challenging all the preciously held assumptions of other occultists, most notably when he breaks the injunction of the *Comment* to *The Book of the Law* which declares that those who discuss it are to be shunned as 'centres of pestilence'. Grant rather seems to revel in this appellation, though he declares - somewhat puzzlingly - 'because only the true *nosferatu*' (i.e. vampires) 'can fathom its contents.'

Those Thelemites who also practise Magick will be further puzzled by Mr. Grant's interpretation. He thinks that Choronzon at 333 is half of The Beast at 666. One doubts if Crowley would agree. Traditionally, the Pentagram is the Star of Man and the Hexagram is the Star of Woman: conjoined, the five-fold and six-fold Stars make 11, the Number of

Magick. However, Grant calls the Pentagram the Star of Woman then proceeds to praise entities of an insectoid or crepuscular or larvaic nature which could not possibly be fitted into the Pentagram. He considers the Riddle of *The Book of the Law II.76* and concludes: 'But so far, no one has satisfactorily interpreted it.' Clearly he has not been reading *Nuit-Isis* or *Chaos International* where Fr. VAL published the glaringly obvious solution. Grant also disputes the line from *The Book of the Law I.57*: 'All these old letters of my Book are aright; but Tzaddi is not the Star' in terms of Crowley's interpretation. For Crowley, 'my Book' was the Tarot and the verse solved at one stroke endless difficulties of interpretation, which I have closely examined and confirmed in my *The Truth About the Tarot* [2]. For Grant, the verse refers to a different book altogether. I do not agree with his interpretation.

As *Hecate's Fountain* continues, the work becomes increasingly disturbing. Grant appears to be saying that praeter-human Intelligences look like the sort of earthly creature most sane human beings find to be loathesome. However, we must allow them to take us over, and we should become their slaves. The powers they grant us thereby will enable us to make other human beings our slaves. The stage is then set for the glorious mutation of humanity into Insectoids. Wonderful! Can't wait. Didn't some ancient magus once state that Man is the measure of all things? Forget it, according to Grant. You too can be a slimy, super-human insect so rub your sprouting tentacles together with joy at the prospect.

With commendable honesty, Grant admits that the entities with whom he claims to have congress are considered to be 'evil' but dismisses the term as meaning merely 'alien' and thus misinterpreted.

How can one define the word 'evil'? I like Norman Mailer's definition, that it is knowingly tampering with something one inwardly knows to be good, though I have been observed to declare: 'If you can only feel good by making other people feel bad, then you are evil.'

The proof of the pudding is in the eating. It is fortunate that Grant has been so generous with the records of Nu-Isis Lodge. He is clearly proud of whatever went on there. Many would dismiss his accounts as the creations of a fictionist or the hallucinations of a madman but I am contented to accept his word.

On page 9 we learn that after an invocation, one woman disciple died at sea whilst another perished in a plane crash. On page 54, a woman is covered with 'a seething mass of white slugs'. On page 65 and after a magical encounter, connected with a talisman, a woman dies before reaching the hospital. On pages 91-2, an unwitting baboon is utterly annihilated. Pages 103-7 show the reader the unedifying spectacle of one Sister Nerik being given the experience 'that finally drove her to madness'. Page 134 offers one the delightful vision of Fr. Bemmel enveloped in 'slime-dripping tentacles.' 'Zoyle and the priest were stripped overnight of their magical powers' one learns on page 143. The ceremony described on pages 153-7 was not of great benefit to one Moola for 'although her body was spewed forth almost immediately in a rain of black fluid, the soul did not return with it. Moola remained mindless until her death in 1958.' Another woman was luckier on page 173, getting off lightly with being struck by lightning and receiving merely a deep burn which required first-aid. On page 182, a woman's body is taken over by Choronzon: what a lucky lady! Another woman falls into a coma from an electric shock on page 188. Entertaining for the reader, obviously, but it would be hard to find a worse record of crass magical incompetence and callousness.

Perhaps the most incredible feature of this witless catalogue of suffering and ineptitude is that Grant actually boasts about it as some sort of achievement.

An astonishing tale is delivered on pages 217-20. Here, a woman was apparently eaten alive by some conjured entity and vanished into thin air. Well, I suppose it serves you right if you're fool enough to try Grant's style of Magick: and why is it that most of the victims are women? Curious too that he quotes scriptures in his book which insist upon the inferiority of women. Is this guy for real? Could he be the greatest contemporary piss-artist, greater even that Frank Zappa? After all, surely the friends and family of the woman who was devoured by some weird magical entity would call the police and report her as a Missing Person?

'Yes, of course I knew her, officer,' Kenneth Grant declared to P.C. Plod, 'and it's always been a matter of grief to me that unfortunately she was devoured on the night we invoked the Great Old Ones, straight out of H.P. Lovecraft. You should've seen it! She was gobbled up before our very eyes.'

'A likely story, sir,' says P.C. Plod.

'All descriptions of *Ojas*, therefore, partake of fantasy, which, nonetheless can be quite powerful when enlisted by a competent magician working within the framework of certain necessarily limited operations,' Grant states on page 215. As my wife would say, 'Ain't it the truth, babes.'

The trouble with Grant is that one detects a certain sincerity. He really does seem to believe that he can advance human evolution and his own by being taken over by some loathesome larvas. He wants that to happen to other people too and boasts about the casualty lists. He is an object lesson in the tragedy of wasted potential. By his own admission, he is encouraging Magicians, especially women, to jump into a pond of piranha without the slightest protection; and it is rare to encounter such reprehensible irresponsibility in one who purports to teach. He looks at toads, vampire bats, 'slugs, snails and puppy dogs' tails' and discerns not Divinity within, as a Buddhist, Taoist or Thelemite would, but a viscous scum in which one should apparently go spelunking. After that he seems to declare: 'Do what THEY wilt shall be the whole of the Law.' One can only respond with Lucifer's words: NON SERVIAM.

Note: The Editor cannot agree that Mr. Grant's intention is that we surrender ourselves to 'undesirable aliens' of any kind.

[1] See 'The Stellar Lode' for Kenneth Grant's literary abilities! More to come in future issues! (Ed.)

[2] Published by Skoob.

CLASSIFIED ADVERTISEMENTS

SMALL ADS are 15p per word payable to Skoob Books Publishing. Minimum 25 words.

Interested in UFOs? write to BUFORA - the largest UFO organisation in the UK. SAE to 16 Southway Hill, Sussex RH15 9ST. For the latest UFO stories & research ring UFO CALL - 0898 121886

CADUCEUS BOOKS for new and secondhand books on paganism, yoga, witchcraft, gnosticism, alternative health, mythology, religion & occultism. Ben Fernee. 14 Holgate Road, York YO2 4AB Tel 0904 628021.

The Association for the Scientific Study of Anomalous Phenomena. For details of membership and publications send SAE to Dr Hugh Pincott, St Aldhelm's, 20 Paul St, Frome, Somerset BA1 1DX.

THE FELLOWSHIP OF ISIS is in 66 countries. The Goddess of Love, Beauty & Truth brings happiness, harmony and psychic gifts. Write to Clonegal Castle, Enniscorthy, Eire.

DELECTUS BOOKS for De Sade, Sacher-Masoch, The Olympia Press and related quality Erotic Literature. Also Gothic, 1890's and Occult books. Send £1 + A5 SAE for full catalogue, 27 Old Gloucester St, London WC1N 3XX. Mail order only.

MACHENSTRUCK? Carmaen Books, publishers of Aklo: A Journal of the Fantastic, issue a range of Machen-related titles. For details send an SAE to Roger Dobson, 50 St John Street, Oxford OX1 2LQ.

arbor vitae press: good deeds and deep studies
The arbor vitae press exists to conceive, design and print distinctive limited edition booklets with an offbeat, romantick and reverential air. Original fiction, poetry, and the revelation of backwaters literary characters are its aims. A fine catalogue of Books for Sale is also offered. It works in silence. Contact: Jonathan Wood, BM SPELLBOUND, LONDON WC1N 3XX.

RA HOOR KHUIT. The magazine for the new Aeon, covering Crowley, Spare, Alchemy, Gnosis, Egyptian Mysteries & the radiation of the Word of the Aeon. Quality A4 magazine with full colour cover, single copy £2.00 from Ra Hoor Khuit, 91 Windmill Lane, Bushey Heath, Herts WD2 1NE.

THE ULTIMATE JOURNEY. "The Creative Mind" keeps you in touch with the latest in yogic techniques, materialization and dematerialization, instant molecular modification, gravity control and other developments in mind-power. The only newsletter dedicated to the transformation of the galaxy. Articles, announcements and news releases welcome.
"The Creative Mind", c/o Gerhard F. Haupt, 14 Victoria Avenue, Mumbles, Swansea SA3 4NG, Wales. Tel: 0792 363525.

***

MAGAZINE LIST
For visitors to our London Shop

We stock the following magazines

CHAOS INTERNATIONAL
THE OCCULT OBSERVER
TALKING STICK

EQUINOX
STARFIRE (TYPHONIAN)
PAGAN NEWS

TIBET NEWS
AQUARIAN ARROW (PAGAN/THE-LEMIC)

THE

OCCULT REVIEW

A MONTHLY MAGAZINE DEVOTED TO THE INVESTIGATION OF SUPER-
NORMAL PHENOMENA AND THE STUDY OF PSYCHOLOGICAL PROBLEMS

EDITED BY RALPH SHIRLEY

Price SIXPENCE ; post free, SEVENPENCE.   Annual Subscription, SEVEN SHILLINGS

Entered at Stationers' Hall

All communications to the Editor should be addressed c/o the Publishers,
WILLIAM RIDER & SON, LIMITED, 164 Aldersgate Street, London, E.C.

VOL. I.   JANUARY 1905   No. 1

CONTENTS

NOTES OF THE MONTH

THE justification for the appearance of a magazine devoted to
the investigation of super-normal phenomena and
FOREWORD   the study and discussion of psychological problems has been put so well by Sir Oliver Lodge in the letter he
was good enough to write for publication in the first number
of the OCCULT REVIEW, that I feel I cannot do better than quote
the letter on the first available page of the new venture in my
own defence.

In doing so I would deprecate on the part of readers and
critics alike any premature condemnation of an attempt to deal
on scientific lines with subjects which have fallen into disrepute

A

through association with charlatanry, on the one hand, and through the long refusal of scientific minds to investigate the evidence on which they are based, on the other.

Letter from Sir Oliver Lodge *to the Editor of the* Occult Review.

In spite of the already too great number of magazines, there does appear to be an opening for a Review dealing with that obscure and nascent branch of science which is allied to observational and experimental psychology on its more abnormal and mystical side.

There is a widespread though largely uninstructed interest in these subjects ; and inasmuch as the general bulk of the human race constitutes the sole laboratory in which the facts can be studied, it is desirable to maintain the interest and to record the facts with as much care and as little superstition as possible. It is also well that the Public should become better educated in these matters, otherwise their experiences are apt to be regarded emotionally only, and as matters of special individual privilege, instead of also intellectually and as matters of general scientific interest.

Hence, if a journal is started with this object in view, and if it is well edited and well managed, it may become a useful scientific instrument.

Oliver Lodge.

I can only add that Sir Oliver Lodge has admirably expressed the object that I had in my mind in broaching the idea of the Occult Review, and I am glad to have the opportunity of noting his approval of the title, which, after much discussion and much hesitation, was eventually adopted for this journal.

It was felt that, in spite of some undoubted drawbacks and its association in certain quarters with unscientific methods of study, the name in itself contained no such suggestion, and was probably, on the whole, the most suitable to indicate the subject matter intended to be dealt with.

I should like to make it clear that one of the objects of this magazine is to voice various phases and forms of religious or quasi-religious opinion—always regarding religion not from the purely orthodox point of view, as resting on the authority of certain divinely-inspired documents, but, as in one sense or another, scientifically justifiable, and having as its basis a theory of cosmogenesis, which, however much it may conflict with the science of a particular age and time, is not essentially anti-scientific. Working on these lines, it is natural that many opinions of a mutually antagonistic character should find expression. While various religious systems will be brought in review, there will be no idea of reconciling the divergent theories of the different writers who deal with them. Still less will the Editor hold himself responsible for the opinions expressed or for the views adopted. Thus the attitude of the writer of the essay entitled "The New God" in the current number will be found to be at least partially incompatible with the standpoint taken by the writer of an article on the "Gnostic Revival," which it is proposed to insert in the February issue, the aim of the Editor being not to put forward his own personal opinions, whether by proxy or otherwise, but rather within certain clearly defined limits to obtain an expression of the position taken up in relation to religious thought and belief by the intellectual portion of mankind.

I should premise that the first number of the REVIEW is of a somewhat general and introductory character, the commencement of articles dealing with the investigation of psychical phenomena being held over till the February issue.

COMMERCIAL OCCULTISM

Mr. F. C. S. Schiller's name is a sufficient guarantee that his article in the current issue will meet with the attention it merits. I should like, however, to make some remarks on what I will venture to call the "proof-of-the-pudding-is-in-the-eating" attitude, which he has taken up with reference to matters occult.

I have often thought that the man who first started the theory of the Philosopher's Stone must have been a shrewd man of business, and that there lies hidden beneath the doctrine of the transmutation of metals the recognition of that most profound truth, that in order to acquire the more precious metals, gold and silver, you must start with an abundant supply of the baser, but none the less invaluable—brass. Doubtless, like Mr. Schiller, the originator of this theory took a commercial view of the occult. The great difficulty, however, in the way of putting to a practical use such forces as telepathy is unquestionably their lack of constancy and reliability. True, it is possible that one day man may learn the art of compelling them to act at his bidding ; but meanwhile it is to be feared that the sceptics whom it was sought to convince will have passed away to a land where no human argument will avail to reach them.

That such powers as clairvoyance have been put to a practical use is undoubted. I could cite an instance of a near relative of my own who went up to London to sell a reversion, and going to a clairvoyante was told that money would come to him in the second week of the next month. This actually occurred, the reversion falling in through an unexpected death on the 13th of the month in question, all necessity for financial sacrifice being thus avoided. Such stories are not uncommon. I mention this as one of which I have personal knowledge, and of which I am in a position to give the exactest details.

The obvious comment of the sceptic, "How many bad shots did the lady psychist make on the same day?" may satisfy us that even the obvious utility of the information given on a particular occasion would fail to bring conviction to the doubting mind. Besides, from what we know of clairvoyance, it is highly probable that the sceptic would have been justified.

Still, the general principle is, I think, a true one, that the practical utilisation of a natural force should serve eventually as a test of its genuineness, though the long period that has elapsed between most discoveries and their breaking in to the service of man may well induce us to try in the first place some more rapid method of bringing conviction home.

Probably the utilisation of astrological tests by a life assurance company would be the best example of such a method of putting occultism on its trial. But on account of the greater detail of the *acte de naissance*, a French company would afford a far better criterion than an English one. This however is because astrology—whether true or false in theory—is worked on a purely mathematical basis, and therefore scarcely comes under the same category as telepathy and clairvoyance. Nor would the proof or disproof of astrology affect in any way the believer in telepathic phenomena.

With reference to Monsieur de Champville's article on "Occultism in France" it is well to remember "OCCULTISM that French investigators have on certain lines IN FRANCE" advanced much further in their conclusions than their English confrères. The article in question will represent to English readers the attitude and standpoint of one of the most eminent of French psychical investigators, and, as such, must command respect even when concurrence is withheld from deductions that may appear too extreme in the light of our present knowledge. The opinions expressed must, however, be taken as representative of an important body of enlightened opinion, and serve to show which way the wind blows in psychological circles of investigation on the other side of the Channel.

The late Mr. W. E. H. Lecky in a notable passage in his "History of the Rise of Rationalism in Europe," has been

THE ZEITGEIST
AND ANCIENT
BELIEFS

at pains to show that the beliefs of earlier generations have not, generally speaking, lost their hold on mankind through scientific evidence being brought to bear on them which has shown them to be erroneous, but rather through their ceasing to be in sympathy with the spirit of the times, and thus first falling into neglect and then into disrepute and discredit, killed or blighted by the all-powerful Zeitgeist of an alien age, and unable to exist side by side with the new ideas and the new thought-atmosphere which has, for the time being, taken possession of the world. The history of European thought in the eighteenth century and the vicissitudes it underwent at that period afford numerous examples of old beliefs falling into discredit in this manner, some destined subsequently to revive with the revival of religious faith or the return of political stability, others apparently fated to melt away before the saner outlook of a more rationalistic age.

So disappeared the belief in witchcraft, in astrology, in magic and incantations, in the philosopher's stone, in a hundred other beliefs and superstitions tenaciously held and indeed never doubted during long ages of the world's history. And yet for all their long ascendency over the mind of man they passed away in the end, not disproved nor exposed as other faiths in our own age have been exposed (and have survived the exposure !), but simply dropping out of mind as a new generation arose, like some Homeric hero whom the Harpies snatched away without trace or record left behind. It was not necessary to be at the pains to disprove, such was the mental attitude of the day. The old wisdom was incompatible with the new knowledge. That was enough.

So a generation or two ago all faith in the survival of the personality after death seemed to be fast ebbing out at least among thinking men, a prey to the ridicule but not to the evidence of the exponents of the scientific dogmatism of the day. Herbert Spencer and Darwin had given it the *coup de grace*, it was thought, as at an earlier date astronomical discoveries had killed astrology.

Not so many years before the Psychical Research Society was

founded, the suggestion that such work could be carried out in a
scientific spirit and lead to positive results would have been ridiculed by almost every man of science.

And now comes Monsieur Paul Flambart with his "Etude
Nouvelle sur l'Hérédité," teeming with evidence of the indications
of hereditary influence in horoscopical figures. The question
naturally arises : If these figures are without meaning, if they
have no more scientific value than, say, a coat of arms or a fancy
design, whence come the indications of heredity ?

How many of the beliefs condemned or ignored at one time
or another by the science of the day are capable of resuscitation
in the light of a fuller knowledge ? Which of them is to be
regarded as a *chose jugée* ? Which has a claim to a fresh
hearing ?

This is the field of inquiry which it is proposed to cover in
the pages of the OCCULT REVIEW.

THE SOUL'S FUTURE
By DAVID CHRISTIE MURRAY

IT happens that, at the moment at which I sit down to write, I have just completed an article on a new theory about ghosts. The idea which has occurred to me has been no more than a combination of the pronouncements of Sir David Brewster and Sir Oliver Lodge; but since it looks as if it might afford a purely materialistic explanation of the myriad stories of distant apparitions at the moment of the death of the persons whose wraiths are believed to have been seen, it occurs to me that it will be well to examine it before the materialists get hold of it and turn it to their own poor purposes. Sir David Brewster wrought and wrote in days when the materialistic wave was rising. Sir Oliver Lodge works and writes at a time when the cock-a-whoop surety of the materialist has gone wholly out of him. The dead man was, and the living man is, one whose whole being is strenuously devoted to the cause of truth, so far as truth may be revealed to mortal eyes. The one who has gone before us did something to kill the belief in apparitions. The much younger man who is now amongst us has done something to restore that belief. The result of a union of their observations appears to me to be singularly interesting.

Sir David Brewster remarked in his own person than an object strongly conceived in the mind was occasionally visualised and became so fixed on the retina that a motion of the eyeball did not dissipate it. The object conceived remained in its due relation to the axis of vision, in whatever direction the subject might direct his gaze. Sir Oliver Lodge conceives that the idea of telepathic communication between mind and mind is now scientifically established, and is even willing to believe that voluntary telepathy is set firmly upon the basis of scientific examination and experience. When a person dies and his apparition as he lived becomes visible at the moment of his death, may not the apparition be accepted as a result of these two operations of nature acting in unison? The last thought of the dying person has been in the direction of one whom he has dearly loved. By that strange wireless telegraphy of the soul which is known in the experience of so many of us, his last thought and his last realisation of himself are flashed upon the mind of the distant sleeper— it is notable that the majority of visions such as this awaken people from a condition of natural unconsciousness — and the shock thus caused has a precisely similar effect upon a sensitive organisation as that observed by Brewster as the result of the prolonged and vivid contemplation of an object in the mind.

Now, suppose this to be accepted as the rational and scientific explanation of all the phenomena of this order which have been observed since the human race began to conserve records of its own experience. To what conclusion should we be logically forced ? The belief in the objective reality of apparitions under such conditions would have to make way for a new conception, but the point which is really at issue between the materialist and the spiritualist would remain untouched. That issue relates to the permanence of the human personality after death. The spiritualist will point you to his own experiences as affording evidence of the permanence of personality. The materialist is certain that all the experiences of which the spiritualist is conscious result from the operation of natural law. But the eternal question of the soul—"Am I an immortal thing ?"—is not to be decided either by the proof of the existence of whole armies of ghosts, or by the rational explanation of all apparitional phenomena whatsoever. The spiritualist falls into an easy error in the supposition that a continuance of personality on a new plane implies a permanence of continuity. What guarantee has a ghost of being immortal ? May not he also perish out of his appointed sphere ? And why might we not fancy a whole procession of lives in phantom state—each more ghostly, more attenuated than its forerunner—the ghost of man, the ghost of the man's ghost, the ghost of a "ghost's" ghost, until the thin thing fades into nonentity and slips back into the universal element ? The materialist falls into an error parallel with that of the spiritualist when he conceives that a rational explanation of all ghostly phenomena has disposed of a belief in immortality. The concept is as independent of evidence, and as unsupportable by evidence, as it is indestructible by evidence. We can neither prove nor disprove, but the balance of reason is still upon the side of the believer, and it favours strongly the hope of a con- tinued existence and a continued growth. We can but argue from things known. In all nature we find the clearest evidence of a law of progress. The protoplasmic ooze results in man. It arrives at thoughts and emotions, it builds lofty ideals and great civilisations. The objector urges that this proof of progress is no proof of the permanence of any personality. No proof, but most assuredly no suggestion of disproof. Again, we find no trace of waste. Change and the revolution of one form of matter into another are evident to us, but no waste, no loss, is anywhere discoverable. The noblest product of the universe so far as we are certain of it is the rounded and accomplished personality of man. Why should nature everywhere display her absolute incapacity to cast away an atom of her lowest product, and yet be able to plunge into nothingness her very greatest ?

DEMON POSSESSION

I notice that Father Ignatius has just confided to the Press his own somewhat startling personal belief that the Dean of Westminster is possessed of a devil. This is one way of settling a controversial adversary. It has all the advantages of simplicity and directness, and it can be applied by anybody to anybody, about anything with respect to which one man can differ from another. The pronouncement, which will excite indignation in some minds and a sense of pity and distress in others, is interesting as calling our attention to the fact that there are still some in the Western world who cling to the old belief in demon possession. The common conception has always been of an affliction strongly associated in its outer signs with the recognised symptoms of hysteria and epilepsy, and the pathologists are all but unanimous in attributing its supposed manifestations to those disorders. In the whole range of the occult philosophies there is nothing more curious and interesting, and the literature which has been devoted to it is vast and various. At one time or other the belief has been held by every nation under Heaven, and some of those who have held it have achieved to a high civilisation. The best intelligences of Greece and Rome accepted it. Christ Himself emphatically proclaimed it. The Church had for centuries its special body of Exorcists, whose whole duty was the casting out of devils from the bodies of those whose possession they had usurped. In China, in India, in Patagonia, in Kamkatscha, in the Pacific Islands, in regions so far remote from each other, and amongst peoples who are so removed in their ethnology and language, that any probability of the communication of the faith from one to the other would appear to be abolished, the belief in demon possession still survives. The inspirational mediums of Spiritualism profess a form of it. Their conception that they are illumined by the souls of the departed, can hardly be divorced from the idea that they are susceptible of occasional control by other spirits than those of the wise and good. Indeed, we find it a common excuse in the case of a medium charged with fraud, that he or she has been duped by a malign influence.

The late Dr. Nevius, for forty years a missionary in China, left behind him a most laborious chronicle of the cases observed by himself, and a fairly exhaustive digest of the views of the various schools of thought. The manifestations are attributed by one school to delusion and imposture ; by another to some yet unclassified force which may either be physical or odic in its nature ; by another to a law of evolution according to which they are found in all races at a certain period of development ; by another to the natural results of a diseased condition of the nervous system ; and by yet another to the actual agency of spirits or demons. The one characteristic fact of the cases observed by Nevius, which appears most strongly to differentiate them from all other forms of dementia, is that the subject invariably speaks of a double personality. Out of the mouth of one sufferer came words to this effect : " I am sick of her. I am leaving not because I am afraid of you, but because I am tired of my habitation," and in *all* observed cases he finds it to be the case that the victim and the supposed demon address each other or speak of each other as entirely separate entities. They quarrel violently, or the one shrieks obscenities and blasphemies, in answer to which the other betakes himself to fervent prayer. In some cases the subject who is at other times incapable of any such feat improvises verse with great fluency and sustains this effort for considerable periods of time. In other cases he or she holds conversations with the bystanders in the alternating characters of victim and demon, each invariably and persistently separating himself from the individuality of the other. Distinct voices are employed, as they might be by a ventriloquist. This happens even in the case of children who are not able, in a normal condition, to produce a similar effect.

Dr. Baelz, of the Imperial University of Japan, where a general belief in the reality of demon possession obtains, finds the cause of the manifestations in the belief that whilst in healthy persons one half of the brain only is engaged in the service of the mind, "leaving the other half to contribute only in a general manner to the function of thought," a nervous excitement arouses this other half, and the two, one the organ of the normal self, and the other the organ of the new pathologically affected self, are set over against each other. But M. Ribot, in his " Diseases of Personality," quite effectually disposes of this ingenious and plausible theory, when he points out that it depends solely on the gratuitous assumption that the contest is always between two states only. This is contradicted by experience. There is a recorded instance of the assumption of six personalities, a fact which reminds one of the Demon of the Gadarene who proclaimed that his name was legion.

None of the explanations offered, whether psychical, pathological or evolutionary, appears to explain all the phenomena. Cases of imposture, of course, occur in numerous instances, and many of the manifestations may be taken as being unconsciously imitative, but imposture and imitation cannot account for all or for even a majority of the cases known. It is noticeable that the visitations are seen occasionally to take an epidemic form, just as influences of an opposite nature are epidemic in the case of religious revivals. The movement now in process in Wales is attributed by thousands of believers to the influence of the Holy Spirit, and it would not be irrational on the part of these same believers to suppose that if a divine spirit may take possession of the human soul, a diabolic spirit may, in certain conditions of the human organism, exert a power of a like character, though to a contrary effect. The spirit-pathology is obscure and is likely to continue so, but the physical pathology leaves little room for doubt that the seizures, whatever their ultimate may be, are peculiar to people of a partial development, so far as the existing races of mankind are concerned. Supposing demon possession to be a real thing, and not a mere imagination of the mind, it is very clear that an undoubting belief in it will render the believer more susceptible to its influences than the person who disdains the idea, just as a man who devoutly accepts the theories of the spiritualist is more open to spirit influence than the man who is sceptical. Mrs. Browning has a passage in " Aurora Leigh " in which she expresses the idea that spirits desiring human communion may " hate the unreasoning awe that waves them off." The unbelieving soul may deny itself much of high value. And in like manner a staunch mental scorn may save the mind from the intrusion of elements which in a weak and ill-balanced nature may be capable of mischief.

A COMMERCIAL VIEW OF
THE OCCULT

By F. C. S. SCHILLER

THE most curious, assuredly, of human instincts, the full scope of which is even now only slowly winning official recognition from philosophers, is the *play-instinct*. Mankind plays at many things besides the avowed games which are the glory of our schools and colleges : about some of these indeed, as *e.g.*, the famous boy-and-girl game of " flirtation," with all its ramifications in frivolity and fashion, it is most in earnest ; on the other hand, it plays also at metaphysics, at religion, and at magic, at the very things, in short, which it professes to regard as the most solemn and portentous truths. But this pretence only adds to the zest of the game ; nay, is it not quite the funniest part of the game that every philosopher should claim for his brand-new " system " truth irrefragable and absolute, that every preacher should profess an ardent yearning to migrate to an unknown " heaven " from the earth on which he lives so comfortably, that every adept should imagine himself to hold the invisible clue to unspeakable mysteries ? The world sees and smiles at such games, and even plays them up to a certain point ; but from time to time it takes care to suppress the few too zealous souls who take their games too seriously, and neglect the primary business of life, viz., to make a comfortable living and successfully to rear a family.

But the world is growing older, and, as it grows older, growing on the whole less frivolous. We are getting serious now, not only about Business, but also about Science. For we have been slowly altering our attitude towards Knowledge. When Knowledge was first invented, the game was thought too hard, and after trying it a little the East soon lapsed into the indolent conclusion that it was the source of all evil, leading to labour and the fall of man. Then the Greeks took it up gaily as a game, and played it with great zeal, until the world wearied of the " beauty" of useless knowledge and bethought itself of " saving" souls. This latter game endured for many centuries, right through the merry middle ages, when men sinned recklessly, and as recklessly repented (at a ruinous cost to their heirs), until Bacon harnessed the divine steed of Science to the chariot of Progress. And then Knowledge became hopelessly degraded (for purposes of sport) by becoming useful, solid, and verifiable, a patient purveyor to the bodily needs of man, but a heavy clog upon the flights and flightinesses of his soul ! At present not even the most flippant could dispute the entire seriousness of science, however they might deplore the restraints which it has put upon the speculative game.

Fortunately, however, not all that might lay claim to knowledge was thus driven off the playgrounds of humanity. Magic remained, the whole realm of the mystic and occult, as fascinating and elusive as of yore. And magic too is one of our oldest games, older even than metaphysics. As far back as we can trace man's history, he has always entertained a belief in magic and in miracle, and played with the notion of a royal road to power over nature, as with a glittering bubble which relieved the grim and sordid pressure of the struggle for existence. But it was always a game to be played gingerly, lest too much matter of fact should burst the bubble. Nowadays, however, even magic is in danger of becoming serious, of being separated from the congenial company of its congeners and rendered scientific ! Serious-minded men are slowly investigating its pretensions, and seeking to extract from its visions and its incantations whatever crystals of objective truth they may occlude, content even if the truth they yield turns out to be mainly psychological. Nay more, a similar procedure is being applied even to metaphysics ; the day seems to be dawning when the most speculative of pursuits will have to become seriously scientific and to submit to verification.

It seems, therefore, that the occasion is appropriate for considering how the inevitable process of reducing the " occult" to humdrum " science" may be forwarded. For I am not only serious-minded myself (albeit circumstances have sometimes compelled me to descend to levities of expression), but also most anxious to encourage the spirit of the age. I therefore feel it to be my duty to point out emphatically that *the " occult" can never become scientifically established until it becomes a commercial success*, and that to render it the latter is the most expeditious means of getting it recognised as the former. Whoever, therefore, holds that in " occultism " lies potential science should labour to develop its practical and commercial aspects, to discover methods which can be patented, and perhaps even brought out by a limited company and quoted on the Stock Exchange. I say this thus coarsely, although I know that my suggestion will be repudiated with the fiercest indignation and denounced as an atrocious profanation by a multitude of patient "students" of various branches of the "occult" who have long grown accustomed to seclude their "phenomena" from the public gaze, and would find nothing more embarrassing than a sudden conversion of the world to their ideas. But once we consent seriously to face the facts of the situation we shall find (1) that there is no other way, and (2) no analogy to follow, but that of science.

There is no other way, because (1) there is at present more social prejudice against researchings into the "occult" than researchers could remove in a thousand years by purely scientific methods, even were they ten times as numerous and skilful as they are ; (2) because at present there is no money where with to prosecute researches, nor any likelihood of raising an adequate supply until the suspicion has arisen that there is money in it ; (3) because the greatest and best part of the evidence comes in such very personal and subjective ways that it is extremely difficult to arouse a conviction of its genuineness as knowledge, without submitting it to such a practical test ; (4) because consequently all the evidence is disputed, and will continue to be so, until such time as we have gained such control over it as to be able to produce it at pleasure and at a profit ; (5) because it is necessary in this case to convert both the masses and the professors. Of these the former are indifferent, the latter prejudiced as well. Now nothing, and least of all a miracle, will convert a professor who has once committed himself in print ; but though the masses may be hard of heart and thick of skull they are almost ludicrously sensitive to what appeals to their *pocket*.

Again, the example of physical science plainly shows that theoretic advancement is not only compatible with, but greatly aided by, practical prosperity. Science began its great advance after Bacon had persuaded men that knowledge was power ; it had languished for 2000 years under the tyranny of the Aristotelian superstition that the highest knowledge was unconcerned with the good for man, and that the holiest things were, humanly, the most useless. And, after all, what more sensible way is there of proving that a thing can be done than to do it and to make it pay ? It cuts short an endless controversy. Accordingly, in science, when an alleged discovery is disputed, it is not the custom to indulge in subtle dialectics to decide whether the original evidence, say for wireless telegraphy, or telegony, or radium, or N-rays, or seedless apples, was or was not good enough to preclude all cavil ; but those who believe in the new facts simply continue their work and perfect their methods, until the practical success of their discovery puts its reality beyond question.

The most effective way, therefore, to get the alleged facts of telepathy, spirit-communion, precognition, and what not, seriously entertained as facts is to render them practically useful. And if this can be done, the more coarsely and directly profitable their use can be made, the more readily will the masses of mankind be disposed to admit their reality. But can it be done ? Does not the psychical nature of such phenomena exempt them from such baser uses ?

I can see no antecedent reasons for supposing this. Consider " telepathy " for example. It is held by most of those who have themselves inquired into the matter that there is sufficient evidence to render it highly probable that some cases of telepathy have occurred. But at present they do not know the conditions sufficiently to be able to repeat experiments at pleasure ; and consequently the fact of telepathy (if fact it be) has no practical value. The result is that the scientific world remains sceptical and the general public indifferent. But the matter cannot possibly rest in this *impasse*. If telepathy cannot secure its footing in the world of fact in a more indisputable way, it is bound to lose it altogether. For so long as it rests on what was once observed to have occurred, *i.e.*, so long as its evidence is merely historical, its value is rapidly affected by the lapse of time. Evidence which was rightly convincing to contemporaries, who observed it themselves or knew the persons who did, as rightly ceases to convince succeeding generations.

But now suppose that some more enlightened mystic, with an eye to business and with a serious desire to establish the reality of such ambiguous facts, sets himself to argue that what has hitherto only been observed sporadically and spontaneously, and therefore disputably, must be rooted in some universal " law " of human nature, or even in some wider cosmic habit. And suppose that he managed conceivably as, *e.g.*, by some psychological study of the means of producing receptivity and concentration of mind, to hit upon a method by which he could at will receive or send telepathic messages with a certainty growing with the refinement of his method. What would inevitably happen ? In the first place, that a far-sighted man of business would sell out his investments in telegraph and cable companies. For it is clear that telegraphy, with or without wires, would be completely superseded so soon as a sufficient number of persons had mastered the cheaper and more convenient telepathic method of transmitting information. Instead of patronising electric currents our merchants and our newspapers would employ a telepathic clerk. And so, secondly, there would be produced something like a social revolution. For under the changed conditions a new type of human being would be valuable and efficient, in some respects superior, in others perhaps inferior, to the existing types, but certainly different. And this might even be decisive of national welfare. Victory or defeat in war, as in life generally, might depend on the success with which one or the other side succeeded in deciphering telepathically the plans of its opponents and transmitting its own. The most valuable types would probably be those who were best at acquiring telepathic information and those who were quite impervious to telepathic "pumping." For only the latter could keep a secret. And so, thirdly, there would result some welcome and salutary changes, and others the reverse. How exactly things would work out it would be futile to imagine without the aid of Mr. H. G. Wells ; but past experience would warrant the expectation that in this case also the growth of knowledge would leave a balance on the right side. And, finally, there would be a sudden and irrevocable end to the debates about the reality of the psychic powers implicated.

Now I do not at all affirm that any or all of this is what is bound to happen, or even could happen, and still less that it is likely to happen in our time. But it does seem clear to me that this is what ought to be attempted, that it is the only way of rendering really and effectively "true" the phenomena about which "occultism," "psychical research," &c., are conversant. In modern philosophic parlance the position is that the "occult," like everything else that lays claim to "truth," must submit to a "pragmatic" test. In other words, its being "true" must make a difference, must express itself in practical consequences, must be revealed in overt acts. For with the doubtful exception of a few metaphysical dogmas which have always been too abstruse and obscure to be really functional, and so have never really been believed, everything that has hitherto been accepted as true has been so accepted because, directly or indirectly, it has proved useful for the satisfaction of some wide human interest. Why, then, one asks, should the "occult" be exempted from the operation of this principle ? If it is "true," this can be most convincingly shown by rendering it useful, and if it cannot be rendered useful, it is certain that its claim to " truth " will continue to be disregarded.

Now the coarsest and most obvious form in which this practical test can be applied is the commercial. Commercialism is a most potent and almost universal human interest. It is futile to dispute the value of what finds a ready market, however much one may personally dislike it. " Truths " which can be sold and can find buyers have to be reckoned with. " Truths " which cannot be brought, however indirectly, into relation with practical life, are illusions. Nay, even " truths " for which no wide demand can be aroused are always more or less precarious. They have to be endowed and protected, and even so are always in danger of disestablishment and disendowment. And because they do not percolate into the mass of humanity, the restriction of their sphere of influence is *practically* a detraction from their reality. If, therefore, a subject has a commercial side to it, and if by drawing attention to this we can promote its development, why should we allow a false delicacy to bar its progress ? When the Emperor Vespasian was reproached with laying a tax on manure in his efforts to restore the finances of the empire, he is said to have flaunted a coin in his critic's face and to have asked him *whether it smelt.* Similarly I would like to impress on all who are really interested in extending the boundaries of knowledge in the direction of the " occult," that a good sound efficient fact does not smell the worse, whatever its *provenance,* and that the odour of a serviceable commercialism may even form a salutary antiseptic to the savour of fraud and illusion of which the whole realm of the " occult " has been redolent too long. And so I venture to conclude with the hope that this Review will not leave out of sight this practical aspect of the matter, and will never hesitate " to try the spirits " whether indeed they be of Mammon !

OCCULTISM IN FRANCE
By G. FABIUS DE CHAMPVILLE

THE position of the student of occult science becomes increasingly difficult from certain points of view, whilst, on the other hand, it is considerably simplified by the fact of modern science having elected to resume the study of old-world concepts.

Occultism no longer hides itself in the obscurity of the apothecary's shop, in the cave of the sorceress, or the Satanic cauldron of the alchemist. It is rather in the laboratory of the experimental chemist, of the skilful physician, of the learned bacteriologist, that this *ensemble* of unrecognised forces and unknown laws seems now to be taking refuge.

Since the experiments of Dr. Loddo in the fluorescence of the vital fluid, radio-activity has taken such a position in orthodox science that there seems every likelihood of the theories of occult students and the discoveries of initiates and adepts becoming an integral part of an up-to-date scientific equipment in the not far distant future.

Orthodox science, to which Pasteur did not subscribe, after having denied through successive centuries all those principles which we occultists sought to inculcate, all those forces which it was our wish to submit to it in their more engaging aspects, must needs at the present time admit the undeniable phenomena and the incontrovertible properties of matter for which we have contended. It is the triumph of determination and perseverance, of modest work which only looks for the good of humanity as its reward and the gradual attainment by man of spiritual powers. We see, in effect, that the labours of the occultists are like the flame of the wax taper which Raniero the Florentine carried alight from Jerusalem to Florence, of which we read in the Swedish novelist Selma Lagerloef's " Legends of Christ."

The efforts of these indefatigable workers who despoiled nature of her secrets are as an unbroken chain between the divine spark—stolen from the very first—which will kindle the giant torch appointed for the enlightenment of the world and for the opening of the eyes of the most simple-minded of mankind. And the analogy is not lost if we compare the wax taper which must be kept alight at all costs whilst everything conspires to extinguish it—peoples, elements, circumstances, ignorance, malignity —with the persevering labours of the occultists. The same task, the same obstacles are there.

But to-day in the laboratory of the chemist, in the study of the physicist and of the doctor, the theories propounded by Paracelsus, Maxwell and Van Helmont are daily finding confirmation. Our theories are no longer laughed at, they are applied. So we see nowadays the treatment by red, blue and violet rays entering into the domain of the practical.

Close upon a year ago—and it is with satisfaction that we turn to the evidence—the Academy voluntarily recorded that certain light rays were possessed of noxious or healing properties. Chemistry had already borrowed from alchemy the theory of the antipathy of light to certain fluids which were transformed under the influence of the solar rays, and without doing alchemy justice, was forced to admit that there were certain rays of the spectrum productive of a chemical action which had been scientifically observed.

The discovery of the N-rays by the doctors has been accepted by the *savants* quite recently, but this acceptance, it is thought, confers too high an honour upon those who, more than fifteen years ago, described this simple radio-activity of the human body, which, in certain cases, may be compared to the radio-activity of radium, palladium and uranium. As, however, their precursors had not then solicited the endorsement of the Academy of Medicine, in order to avoid admitting that they had been anticipated in this discovery, they expressed doubts as to the reality of the rays of M. Charpentier and M. Blondlot of Nancy. In this matter they have been somewhat unfortunate, for the proof of the occult theories, which have been scientifically established for some twenty years, is conveyed as an explicit fact in the following note from an account of the *seance* of Monday, December 5, 1904 :

"M. le docteur Albert Robin is about to open up some unexpected horizons in the domain of therapeutics. He yesterday developed before the Academy the results of researches he had been pursuing in collaboration with M. Bardet on the action of infinitesimal doses of metallic bodies upon the human organism. On hypodermically injecting solutions containing about one ten-thousandth of a gramme (about gr. .0015432) of a metal such as palladium, platinum, gold or silver, considerable chemical effects were observed, analogous to those obtained from the diastase of yeast. Thus it is observed that there is an increase of tension in the blood, a modification of the component elements of the blood, and a notable diminution of the white corpuscles. The urine products are also greatly increased. It appears that these metallic ferments do not act merely on account of their being gold, silver, or some other metal, but rather on account of their being in *a radiant state*."

We were justified, then, in our theory that one characteristic of the properties of the vital fluid emanating from the human body was due to the action of metals in infinitesimal dispersion in the blood.

During the past few months magnetism has continued to make progress, and every instance of a therapeutic nature adds more to the sum total of felicitous results. At the " Ecole Pratique de Magnetisme," the well-known school of instruction under the auspices of the University, we have all the recognised grades and diplomas. Recently a pupil who had formerly qualified as magnetiser and masseur, after two years of strenuous work, presented himself for the diploma of professor. There is a curriculum here as complete and severe as that of the Sorbonne. This goes to show that the rational study of those sciences which at one time were stigmatised as diabolical is now being developed under the favourable recognition of professed science. This is a considerable step in advance, and Mesmer, who was so badly received at the hands of the Academicians, would note a remarkable change since his day. We may state, further, that every week at the surgery the sick who have been abandoned by the doctors—poor creatures reduced to despair—come, are treated and go away again, some relieved and full of hope, others entirely cured. Will-power, and the magnetic fluid on the one hand, and faith on the other, accomplish these results.

Let us not forget that the will-power and the fluid with which we are endowed, together constitute the basis of all magic. By these two means and a knowledge of natural laws, we may utilise these little understood forces and bring about results conducive to the individual and general welfare. Schopenhauer, pessimist though he was, admirably understood the part played by the will, and in closely studying his philosophy as one studies likewise the acts of the thaumaturgists, the sorcerers, the magicians and the enchanters, one comes to understand how, through magnetism, man may acquire, little by little, some share, however infinitesimal, in the Divine Omnipotence.

Among the opponents of magnetism in the domain of hypnotism, we may equally discern conscientious effort, but it is worthy of remark that, as regards therapeutics, it is particularly by the use of purely magnetical means, aided by suggestion, that the hypnotist is able to effect his cures. At all times the one essential thing is the clear and definite employment of the attributes of the human being—conscious of himself, of his forces, of his capabilities and the extent of his powers. And as a matter of pure science we may repeat that this occult basis leads us back again to our theory of radio-activity pure and simple. In this connection we may recall the definition of a celebrated occultist :

" There are two emanations and two atmospheres, the one physical and the other hyper-physical, the one gaseous and the other ethereal. They interpenetrate and enfold us upon all sides. The former acts upon our bodies, the latter on our souls. The one is a wave of sensation and the other a wave of emotion. To will is an immaterial act, but the volition operates by means of a plastic medium which is called ether in space, astral fluid on the earth, and nervous fluid in the human body. At the command of the will the nervous fluid coagulates and freely moulds the astral fluid, which becomes in its turn the hand that cures, the sword that strikes, the force that blinds Elymas or translates Elijah to Heaven."

The will sends out radiant emanations. We do not imply in this statement that the will possesses equal force with radium, but we cannot, for all that, dispute its superiority as to quality. Eliphas Levi has clearly defined those phenomena which the discovery of radium enables us to realise. He says :

" The substance which Hermes calls the Great Talisman we call Light in its effect as radiance. It is at the same time both substance and motion. It is at once a continuous fluid and a perpetual vibration. In space it is called Ether ; in the stars, the Astral Light ; in organic bodies, the Magnetic Fluid ; and in man, the Plastic Medium or Fluidic Body."

In view of the practical realisation of the statements of the occultists, theirs is fair ground for satisfaction. Science slowly tears aside the veil which hides the Unknown from our eyes, the mists of time are cleared away, and we are proud to behold the formulæ of an almost execrated prescience becoming realised in the laboratories and studies of our *savants*.

M. Berthelot, with his theory of atoms, maintains the march of progress towards the realisation of every promise of occultism.

In spiritism we have nothing to record that is altogether fresh. The reviews continue their teachings and relate many instances of the externalisation of thought. We shall again revert to this matter, for it is one of the manifestations of the marvellous which is truly surprising, but not by any means inexplicable. M. Blondlot of Nancy claims to have actually seen the radiations of his own brain, to have seen himself thinking ! Often enough our magnetised subjects affirm the same thing, and inasmuch as they indicate with singular precision the preoccupying idea, expressed in a radiation of greater force or of a different colour, we are disposed to believe MM. Charpentier and Blondlot. Further, these gentlemen have been able to indicate at will the muscular and nervous radiations, and by means of a screen have also determined their colours.

In the alchemical field a small treatise has made its appearance, but we are not yet in a position to review it, having no copy yet to hand. It is a contribution to the evidences of alchemy by M. Abel Haatan.

In the literature of philosophy we should call attention to a work of exceptional merit entitled, " La Personalité Humaine, sa Survivance et ses Manifestations" (published by M. Alcan of Paris). It is an excellent translation from the English work by Mr. F. W. H. Myers, the late well-known psychologist. We have no need to dwell upon it in this place, for your own Society for Psychical Research is far in advance of anything of a like nature which has been attempted in France along these lines.

THE NEW GOD

By CULTOR VERITATIS

" They chose new gods."- Judges v. 8.

THERE has been a bloodless revolution in the kingdom of heaven. Silently but no less surely the Puritan Divinity has evacuated the celestial throne and made way for a Deity of a more facile temperament.

So it was in Sicily in the days of Robert, brother of Pope Urbane. Unmarked and unnoted the angel of the Lord took up the administration of the island realm. Disguised in the semblance of the king the keen eyes of the courtiers detected in him nothing unusual. Only in the effects of his beneficent rule was there any evidence that a change had taken place. Only in the abnormally bounteous harvests and in the perennial buoyancy of the Stock Exchange was there ground for suspicion that the reins of government were in other than mortal hands.

Neither did we note when the transfer of power took place in the Eternal Realms. No newspaper boys proclaimed it in strident tones through the public thoroughfares. There were no cries of "Le Dieu est mort, vive le Dieu" to awaken our sleeping spirits to the altered outlook. Only by-and-bye we noted that the yoke of the kingdom of heaven weighed upon our shoulders less heavily. Only we observed that the demands made upon us by its officials on earth were less exacting, that the dues were collected less rigorously. Only in the relaxation of the fetters with which the human intellect lay bound, did we realise that, unsuspected by us at the time, an event had occurred in heaven fraught with the most momentous consequences for the children of men.

There was nothing in common between the easy opportunism of the new reign and the stern orthodoxy of its predecessor. The "fiend with names divine" that haunted the puritan's nightmare had gone for ever. In his stead reigned the new God, of whom his worshippers might reflect in the consoling words of the old Persian poet that

He's a good fellow and 'twill all be well.

There never was an age more tenacious of the name of Christian than our own or more indifferent to the main dogmas of

Christianity. There never was an age with a greater passion for critical analysis or a sublimer faith in vague generalities.

We reject piecemeal the very basis of our belief, only to reassert it comfortably enshrined in the ambiguous phrases of the philanthropist or metamorphosed by the allegorical interpretations of the Christian mystic.

This change in our attitude towards religion, carefully veiled though it be by the retention of old names that have lost their meaning, is the measure of a revolution in the mode of thought of man which is in process of transforming all departments of our mental activity.   In attempting to shut our eyes to its import we are only darkening counsel and giving rise to needless misconceptions through fear of calling things by their real names. The medicine is changed. The label on the bottle remains as before.

This unwillingness to look facts in the face, disguise it how we may, is undoubted evidence of that loss of mental and moral virility which is so constantly associated with periods of intellectual change and transition.

The dangers with which we are threatened to-day are not those which confronted our fathers. They were in danger of believing in absurdities through sheer force of habit : we are in danger of believing in shadows. They were menaced by dogma : we are menaced by our own open-mindedness. Their danger lay in the strength of their convictions : ours in the fact that we have no genuine convictions at all. Nothing could penetrate the brazen cloak of their obdurate prejudices : we are receptive mediums for every passing wind of opinion. We have no original thoughts, no ideas to give us individuality, but every suggestion that is floating in the air finds a ready harbourage in our brains. We have ransacked the centuries in search of the opinions, the religions, the principles, the arts of our forefathers. Ours is the great age of revivalism. We are all bent on making the past live again. What matters it what it be ? The spirit of the architecture of the past, the spirit of a smouldering Roman Catholicism brought back to life, the spirit of the East, mystic and measureless, the spirit of mediæval Italy, the spirit of early Christianity and early Christian socialism, we would fain revive them all—anything and everything that might give a spurious life to the dead present. We are never weary of harking back, never weary of plundering our forefathers' fields of their rich harvests, never troubling to plant our own for future generations to reap. It is not our forefathers who are dead, it is we. Like Hannibal's soldiers after crossing the Alps, we may well be described as "imagines immo umbræ hominum." Lacking in purpose, in intensity, in sincerity, in all that goes to make up character, we are but the vehicles for the opinions of others, the actors of other men's parts. True, we live in an age of mechanical ingenuity and political experiment, but is this sufficient compensation for our lack of individuality ? Is this sufficient atonement, when we reflect that we have nothing left that we can call our own, if it be not the smoke of our manufactories and the stupendous complexity of our social life ?

We have sapped the foundations of the faiths of our forefathers, but the whole atmosphere of our thought and feeling is steeped in the glamour of the sunset glow of dead or dying creeds. We still cling tenaciously to the corpses of our dead faiths, to the forms and ceremonies which were once animated by a living and life-giving belief. What would the zealot of the past find left of his dogmas if he cross-examined us on our articles of faith ? How much that was solid ground and not shifting sand ? He would find not Christianity at all, but aspirations after high ideals ; not faith, but philanthropy ; not the acceptance of what our fathers held to be deep religious truths, but a love of old forms and ceremonies and a tenacious conservatism. He would detect an infinite capacity for explaining away the essentials of Christianity and, to parody the poet's phrase,

> Religion slowly watered down
> From sentiment to sentiment.

There is so much that is good (they tell us nowadays) in all the religious systems of the world; there is so much that is accidental in the particular form that our or our neighbour's religion may happen to take that it would really be impertinent in us to say definitely that ours is better than anybody else's. We are freely assured that they are all equally true, but that this truth expresses itself to divers national temperaments in divers and various ways. And it adds a sense of comfort to our devotions to reflect that everybody has thought and has meant the same as we do all along, and that it is only their way of putting it that has been somewhat different. We are told that names are quite immaterial, and that what we mean by Christ the Buddhist means by Buddha ; and we feel that all religions are the expression of the realisation that there is something mysterious beyond us and above us after which we are all yearning.

This is what makes us so cosmopolitan in our appreciation and so universal in our receptivity, for we have learnt to recognise the Truth of Falsehood and the Falsehood of Truth and to see (doubtless as through a glass darkly) that alike in Truth and in Falsehood, Falsehood and Truth are about evenly divided.

We feel that the golden age of Theology is at hand when the lion will lie down with the lamb, the Roman Catholic and the Protestant and the Buddhist together, and we cannot help thinking how nice this will be.

Perhaps, however, we are congratulating ourselves somewhat prematurely, for it does not require a very shrewd eye to appreciate the fact that the majority of the dogmas of Christianity occupy a position in religion to-day analogous to that of the Turk at Constantinople. They are in as caretakers, and liable to receive notice to quit at any moment. Even the more advanced of the clergy admit this from their pulpits. The only difficulty is that we do not know what to put in their place. Can we suppose that this difficulty is capable of solution ? Most people to-day would answer " No." It may be, however, that a later generation, for whom psychical societies will not have worked in vain, will be able to substitute something more credible, more authoritative in tone, for the worn-out dogmas of the past. It may be that evidence will be forthcoming which will establish on the impregnable rock—not of the Holy Scriptures, but of Science—such facts as shall constitute for us a sure and certain hope in that which " eye hath not seen, neither hath ear heard, neither hath it entered into the heart of man to conceive." It may be that scientific investigation will point the way to a truer conception of the essence of religion, and that through this purer channel rather than through disputing over old manuscripts of doubtful authenticity we shall learn to realise the existence of living truths, deep and mystical, the evidence for which among us, above us, beneath us, and around us is the breath of the universal Spirit of Life transforming itself into innumerable forms of beauty or of dread, permeating every pore of earth and air, ever ready when least suspected to spring forth into some new shape of consciousness from its chrysalis sleep—life unconquerable, immortal, protean !

It may be we shall at length recognise that at the source of all religions and all superstitions of all time, as an explanation and clue to every beginning of worship or of faith, there lay the faint suspicion of a consciousness of the supreme significance of this mystery which religion after religion has admitted, caricatured, and forgotten in turn.

Meanwhile, there are and must remain many among us who live in an atmosphere of permanent regret for lost religious ideals. These people, whose own soundness of judgment is to them a source of perpetual sorrow, turn upon the profane scientist not with the righteous indignation of the orthodox against the enemies of religious truth, but with the petulant temper of one who has tried to nurse an illusion into reality, and is confronted by Science with its brutal facts just when he begins to think that he has almost succeeded. There is no compensation to be obtained in our courts of law for injury done to cherished illusions, however irretrievable it may be, and the victim of Science not unnaturally thinks himself aggrieved by what he puts down as so much pure loss instead of being grateful to her for saving him from himself. But the edict has gone forth, " Take from him even that which he seemeth to have," and the scientific police act up to their instructions. And rightly. For our own judgment will be falsified and our own method of living will be distorted and rendered untrue should we base it upon an admittedly false assumption leading in practice to an untenable position and to actions whose only justification is a fiction of fancy.

Whatever opinions we may hold, we cannot live truly if we are afraid to look facts in the face, if we are afraid to recognise reality and prefer to nurture our illusions even when we know them to be unreal.

Surely the time is past for longing after lost ideals and worshipping at the shrines of deities in whose power to aid we have no longer faith. Surely we can better occupy ourselves with the stern facts of to-day than with the glowing fictions of yesterday. To abandon the beliefs of our childhood is not necessarily to abandon faith in a world unseen which may be as scientifically true and as scientifically provable as that which meets our material vision. Agnosticism cannot place a limit to our knowledge, and the last word of Science, with all deference to Dr. Haeckel, was not spoken in the last century.

THE LIFE OF THE MYSTIC
By A. E. WAITE

THERE are certain conventional terms which, on the one hand, do not accurately represent the construction placed upon them along a given line, but that construction has been accepted so long and so generally that the defect in the application may be regarded as partially effaced ; and, on the other hand, there are also conventional terms between which a distinction has come into existence, although it is not justified by their primary significance. As regards the first class, the very general use of the term " occult movement " may be taken as an example. It is inexact after two manners : in involves at once too much and too little— too much, because it has served to represent a good deal that is not at all of the occult order ; and too little, because a slight change in the point of view would bring within the range of its meaning many things which nobody who now uses it would think of including therein. The doings of more than one great secret political organisation might, in the full sense of the words, require to be classed as part of the occult movement, though no one will need to be informed that the latter is not political ; while certain events which have occurred and are occurring in the open day, and have all along challenged the verdict of public opinion, cannot strictly be included in occultism, as they betray none of its external characteristics. I refer to the phenomena of animal magnetism, hypnotism, spiritualism and all that which is included in the field of psychical research. In respect of the second class, a very clear differentiation now exists between the terms " occult " and " mystic," and it is one also which it is necessary to recognise, though, fundamentally speaking, the two words are identical, differing only in the fact that one of them is of Latin and the other of Greek origin. By the occultist we have come to understand the disciple of one or all of the secret sciences ; the student, that is to say, of alchemy, astrology, the forms and methods of divination, and of the mysteries which used to be included under the generic description of magic. The mystic is, at the first attempt, perhaps more difficult to describe, except in the terminology of some particular school of thought ; he has no concern as such with the study of the secret sciences ; he does not work on materials or investigate forces which exist outside himself ; but he endeavours, by a certain training and the application of a defined rule of life to re-establish correspondence with the divine nature from which, in his belief, he originated, and to which his return is only a question of time, or what is commonly understood as evolution. The distinction between the occultist and the mystic, however much the representative of physical science at the present day might be disposed to resent the imputation, is therefore, loosely speaking, and at least from one point of view, the distinction between the man of science and the man of introspection. The statement, as we shall see, is not exhaustive, and it is not indeed descriptive. It may be said more fully, in the words of the late Edward Maitland, that the occultist is concerned with " transcendental physics, and is of the intellectual, belonging to science," while the mystic " deals with transcendental metaphysics, and is of the spiritual, belonging to religion." Expressed in modern terms, this is really the doctrine of Plotinus, which recognises " the subsistence of another intellect, different from that which reasons, and which is denominated rational." Thus, on the one hand, there are the phenomena of the transcendental produced on the external plane, capable of verification and analysis, up to a certain point ; and, on the other, there is the transcendental life. " That which is without corresponds with that which is within," says the most famous Hermetic maxim ; indeed the connection suggested is almost that of the circumference with the centre ; and if there is a secret of the soul expressed by the term mysticism, the phenomena of the soul manifesting on the external plane must be regarded as important; but these are the domain of occultism. The importance must, of course, differ as the phenomena fall into higher and lower classes ; the divinations of geomancy carry an appearance of triviality, while the design of ceremonial magic to establish communication with higher orders of extra-mundane intelligence wears a momentous aspect; but both are the exercise of seership, and this gift, as a testimony of the soul and her powers, is never trivial.

Assuming therefore a relationship subsisting between occult practice and the transcendental life of the soul, it seems worth while to contrast for a moment the work of the mystic with that of the disciple of occult science, so as to realise as accurately as possible the points of correspondence and distinction between Ruysbroeck, St. John of the Cross and Saint-Martin, as types of the mystic school, and Arnoldus de Villanova and Martines de Pasqually, as representing the school of occult science. The examples of such a contrast must naturally be sought in the past, because, although occult science is pursued at the present day, and by some ardently, it can scarcely be said to have votaries like those who were of old. The inquiry belongs also to the past in respect of the mystic, for, to speak plainly, the saint belongs to the past. So far as the life of the outside world is concerned, there is little opportunity amidst mundane distractions for the whole-hearted labours of the other centuries. The desire of the house is indeed among us, but the zeal of it is scarcely here, not, at least, in the sense of the past.

The distinction in question is more than that which is made between the man of action and the man of reflection ; it is not that which we have come to regard as differentiating the man of science from the philosopher. There are many instances of synthetic occult philosophers—among them Cornelius Agrippa and Robert Fludd—who neither divined nor evoked—who were not alchemists, astrologers or theurgists—but rather interpreters and harmonisers ; and yet these men were not mystics in the proper sense of the term. Nor is the distinction quite that which constitutes the essential difference between the saint and the specialist, though the occult student of the past was in most cases a specialist who was faithful to his particular branch. The activity and the strenuousness of the life was often greater with the mystic than in the case of the man who was dedicated to some particular division of occult knowledge, though alchemist and astrologer were both laborious men—men whose patience imbued them with something of the spirit which governs modern scientific research. The ground of the contrast is in the purpose which actuated the two schools of experience. The crucible in which metals are transmuted, on the assumption of alchemy, is still a crucible and the converted metal is still a metal ; so also the astrologer may trace the occult and imponderable influences of the stars, but the stars are material bodies. The practical work of the mystic concerned, on the contrary, the soul's union with God, for, to state it briefly, this, and this only, is the end of mysticism. It is no study of psychic forces, nor, except incidentally, is it the story of the soul and her development, such as would be involved in the doctrine of reincarnation. It is essentially a religious experiment and is the one ultimate and real experiment designed by true religion. It is for this reason that in citing examples of mystics, I have chosen two men who were eminent for sanctity in the annals of the Christian Church, for we are concerned only with the West ; while the third, though technically out of sympathy, essentially belonged to the Church. I must not, therefore, shrink from saying that the alternative name of the mystic is that of the saint when he has attained the end of his experiment. There are also other terms by which we may describe the occultist, but they refer to the science which he followed.

The life of the mystic was then in a peculiar sense the life of sanctity. It was not, of course, his exclusive vocation ; if we are to accept the occult sciences at their own valuation, more than one of them exacted, and that not merely by implication, something more than the God-fearing, clean-living spirit, which is so desirable even in the ordinary business man. He who was in search of transmutation was counselled, in the first instance, to convert himself, and the device on the wall of his laboratory was *Labora* but also *Ora*. The astrologer, who calculated the influences of the stars on man, was taught that, in the last resource, there was a law of grace by which the stars were ruled. Even the conventional magician, he who called and controlled spirits, knew that the first condition of success in his curious art was to be superior to the weakness of the inconstant creatures whose dwelling is amidst the flux of the elements.

I have said that, in most cases, the occult student was, after his manner, a specialist—he was devoted to his particular branch. Deep down in the heart of the alchemist there may have been frequently the belief that certain times and seasons were more favourable than others for his work, and that the concealed materials which he thought of symbolically as the Sun and Moon, as Mercury, Venus or Mars, were not wholly independent of star and planet in the sky ; and hence no doubt he knew enough of elementary astrology to avoid afflicted aspects and malign influences. But, outside this, the alchemist was not an astrologer, and to be wise in the lore of the stars was an ambition that was sufficient for one life, without meddling in the experiments of alchemy. On the other hand, the mystic, in common with all the members of his community, having only one object in view, and one method of pursuing it—by the inward way of contemplation—had nothing to differentiate and could not therefore specialise.

Again, occult science justifies itself as the transmission of a

secret knowledge from the past, and the books which represent
the several branches of this knowledge bear upon them the outward marks that they are among the modes of this transmission,
without which it is certain that there would be no secret sciences.
The occult student was, therefore, an initiate in the conventional
sense of the term—he was taught, even in astrology. There were
schools of kabalism, schools of alchemy, schools of magic, in
which the mystery of certain knowledge was imparted from adept
to neophyte, from master to pupil. It is over this question of
corporate union that we have at once an analogy and a distinction between the mystic and the occultist. The former, as we find
him in the West, may in a sense be called an initiate because he
was trained in the rule of the Church ; but the historical traces
of secret association for mystic objects during the Christian
centuries are very slight, whereas the traces of occult association
are exceedingly strong. The mysteries of pre-Christian times
were no doubt schools of mystic experience. Plato and Plotinus
were assuredly mystics who were initiated in these schools.
Unfortunately the nature of this experience has come down to
us, for the most part, in a fragmentary and veiled manner. But,
outside exoteric writings, it has in my belief come down, and it
is possible to reconstruct it, at least intellectually and specula-
tively, for it is embedded in the symbolic modes of advancement
practised by certain secret societies which now exist among us.
A transmission of mystic knowledge has therefore taken place
from the past, but the evidence is of an exceedingly complex
nature and cannot be explained here. Nor is it necessary to our
purpose, for western mysticism is almost exclusively the gift of
the Church to the West, and the experiment of Christian mysticism, without any veils or evasions, is written at large in the
literature of the Church. It may call to be re-expressed for our
present requirements in less restricted language, but there is not
really any need to go further. " The Ascent of Mount Carmel,"
" The Adornment of the Spiritual Marriage," and " The Castle of
the Inward Man," contain the root-matter of the whole process.
I have also found it well and exhaustively described in obscure
little French books which might appear at first sight to be simply
devotional manuals for the use of schools and seminaries. I have
found it in books equally obscure which a few decades ago would
have been termed Protestant. There is the same independent
unanimity of experience and purpose through all which the
alchemists have claimed for their own literature, and I have no

personal doubt that the true mystics of all times and countries constitute an unincorporated fellowship communicating continually together in the higher consciousness. They do not differ essentially in the East or the West, in Plotinus or in Gratry.

In its elementary presentation, the life of the mystic consists primarily in the detachment of the will from its normal condition of immersion in material things and in its redirection towards the goodwill which abides at the centre. This centre, according to the mystics, is everywhere and is hence, in a certain sense, to be found in all ; but it is sought most readily, by contemplation, as at the centre of the man himself, and this is the quest and finding of the soul. If there is not an open door—an entrance to the closed palace—within us, we are never likely to find it without us. The rest of the experiences are those of the life of sanctity leading to such a ground of divine union as is possible to humanity in this life.

In the distinction—analogical, as already said—which I have here sought to establish, there lies the true way to study the lives of the mystics and of those who graduated in the schools of occult science. The object of that study, and of all commentary arising out of such lives, is to lead those, and there are thousands, who are so constituted as to desire the light of mysticism, to an intellectual realisation of that light. The life of the mystic belongs to the divine degree, and it would be difficult to say that it is attainable in the life of the world ; but some of its joys and consolations—as indeed its trials and searchings—are not outside our daily ways. Apart from all the heroisms, and in the outer courts only of the greater ecstasies, there are many who would set their face towards Jerusalem if their feet were put upon the way—and would thus turn again home.

ANCIENT BELIEFS AND MODERN NOTIONS

By WALTER GORN OLD

I. STELLAR INFLUENCE IN HUMAN LIFE

IN the course of the series of articles in which I am about to engage it is proposed to show the existence, at a very early date in human history, of an ancient science based upon astronomical knowledge and pursued by empirical methods into the domain of what—for want of a more exact term—may be called the "occult." It will be shown, further, that this gnosis was anciently applied to principles of government and civil administration ; and that the neglect of this gnosis was followed, as a matter of fact, by the collapse of those dynasties and the disorganisation of those communities which had moulded their principles upon it.

To reach back to the earliest historical times of which we have authentic record it is necessary to refer to the Far East, where, some forty-two centuries ago, there existed a vast multitude of people known as the black-haired people of Hwa, the progenitors of the modern Chinese. These people of the Yellow Empire, under the government of a patriarchal dynasty, inhabited that territory comprised between the main streams of the Yang-tze-kiang and the Hwang-ho, known as the Chung-kwo or Middle Kingdom. We first come upon these people through "The Shu-king" * (The Historical Classic) in the days of the Emperor Yaou (B.C. 2356). Tradition does not extend further back than some seven hundred years before this date, when Fuh-hi, the "Adam" of the Mongolian race, is said to have brought fire from heaven to illumine and guide mankind in much the same manner as did Prometheus in the Greek mythos. Fuh-hi and his spouse Niu-wo are sometimes spoken of as the spiritual progenitors of the race of Celestial kings.

Putting tradition aside we may take up the record where it presents marks of authenticity, and in the very earliest pages of the "Shu-king," a history which is handed down to us on the

* "The Shu-king." London : The T.P.S., 161 New Bond Street, W.

authority of the great historian Confucius, we find abundant
evidence of an already developed civilisation, a wide display of
industrial arts, an extensive commerce, a more or less complete
political organisation, and a considerable degree of scientific
knowledge. Hieroglyphic writing was in use, and records
appear to have been kept with care and precision. There were
statute and civil laws, together with a penal code ; while on the
one hand the Ministers of Agriculture, of Public Instruction, of
Public Works, and others, acting under the direction of a Prime
Minister, dispensed the affairs of government ; literature and
science, on the other hand, were pursued by a considerable body
of men under the protection and patronage of hereditary earls,
marquises, viscounts, and barons. A religious system had already
been adopted, wherein the spirits or manes of the departed formed
the channel of communication between the Supreme Ruler
(Shang-ti) and embodied man.

Permeating the whole of this civil, political and religious
structure we find an authorised use and practice of what are
now popularly known as the Occult Sciences. In pursuit of the
main object of this essay, it will be convenient to deal in the
first place with the traditions of a scientific empiricism, and
afterwards with other phases of belief and practice which form
the superstructure of this ancient body of teaching. I shall
show in the course of this study that both tradition and practice
have survived until the present day, and are now, under modified
forms, extensively studied and believed in. In this I shall give
the foremost place to the ancient science of Astrology, as being
at the root of all other aspects of occult tradition, and finding
reflection in every craft and gnosis which at any time have
constituted a doctrine of human thought and belief.

The Chinese record, then, refers to the days of Chuen-hio,
who, about the year B.C. 2448, reformed the calendar, and fixed
the beginnings of the four seasons by reference to the sun's
progress among the constellations. These latter were divided by
him into twenty-eight asterisms by the mean daily elongation of
the moon, and then comprised in four quarters of seven asterisms
each, called respectively the Red Bird, the Azure Dragon, the
Black Warrior, and the White Tiger. All this was done with a
view to the proper government of the people, and Ministers were
appointed to dispose agricultural and other work in accord with
the celestial dispositions, the increase and decrease of the
moon, and the aspects of the heavenly bodies. The same con-

siderations marked the regulation of all religious and State ceremonies.

Thus we read in the "Shu-king" that the Emperor Yaou commanded Hi and Ho (the astronomical observer and recorder) to "determine and portray the courses of the sun, moon and stars among the asterisms, and duly to inform the people concerning the seasons." * These, with their juniors, were appointed to observe whether, at the commencement of the seasons, the culminating star at sunset was in agreement with the record of Chuen-hio, and accordingly to regulate the various labours of the people and the functions of the mandarins. The Emperor further instructed the astronomers that the difference between the lunar and solar years amounted to just seven moons in nineteen years, for the regulation of which he prescribed the intercalation of seven months in the course of that period, at the end of which the months would again begin on the same days and coincide with the conjunctions of the sun and moon. This statement is in itself sufficient evidence of the existence, even in the days of Yaou, of a body of traditional knowledge and astronomical learning to which succeeding rulers had access.

The three orders of "lights" mentioned in the history are *jih* (the sun), *yue* (the moon), and the *wuh-sing*, or five planets. Collectively they are referred to as the *ki-cheng* or "seven controllers."

On the accession of Shun to the throne vacated by Yaou one hundred years later, the monarch is reported to have " examined the pearl-studded sphere and the jewelled scale in order to verify the positions of the seven controllers." The pearl-studded sphere was a hemispherical plan set with pearl studs in imitation of the various constellations in the visible heavens, which could be consulted at night as well as by day. The jewelled scale was a tube mounted upon a quadrant similar to the sextant of to-day, and was employed in finding the altitudes and declinations of the celestial bodies. Thus they traced the course of the sun, moon, and planets among the constellations, making all these observations for the purpose of controlling the various industries and the several functions of the State. It is affirmed that the sun was related to the male principle in nature (*yang*) and the moon to the female principle (*yin*); the sun governed life and time while the moon controlled work and place. The planets ruled over the *wuh-hing*, or five commodities, earth, wood, metal, fire,

* "Shu-king," Book I. sec. ɪ.

and water. Saturn ruled over earth, Jupiter over wood, Venus over metal, Mars over fire, and Mercury over water. They called the planets by these names : *tu-sing*, the earth-star ; *wu-sing*, the wood-star ; *kin-sing*, the metal-star; *ho-sing*, the fire-star ; and *shui-sing*, the water-star. By this "ruling over" the five useful things is to be understood a certain natural correspondence presumed to exist between the things of the greater world, or macrocosm, and those of the lesser world, or microcosm. It is the doctrine of correspondence, thus referred to in the classic :

"The heavens are the cause of action and men are only the agents. The celestial disposition of things is the law by which to regulate our five statutes and to establish the five standards of relationship. There is a correspondence between the higher and lower worlds."

The five relationships were those which existed between parents and their children, rulers and their subjects, masters and their servants, husbands and their wives, friends and their associates. There were also five degrees of rank, represented by the five sceptres, namely, dukes, marquises, earls, viscounts, and barons. All these groups of fives correspond to the five planets. The Emperor was represented by the sun and the populace by the moon. The establishing of government was, therefore, "after the pattern of things in the heavens," as St. Paul observed concerning some Jewish institutions.

This system of correspondence between mundane and celestial things is still further developed in the Great Plan of Tao, which was handed down as a model of government from one Emperor to another. It is also called the Eightfold Path of Imperial Perfections. It was inscribed on the back of the Great Tortoise, which, on account of its longevity and amphibious nature, was a most suitable depository of permanent records and plans. The plan was lost during the period of the great floods which began in the year B.C. 2348—in strict agreement with the Hebrew account of the Noachian deluge—but was afterwards found when the great administrator, Ta-yu, undertook the work of draining the land and embanking the rivers. Having been found in the Lo River, it came to be known as the Lo Book, and is incorporated in the book of divinations known as the "Yih-king," or Book of Changes, which is one of the five classics of China, and of which the great Confucius said that if he lived to one hundred years he would spend fifty of them in the study of the "Yih-king."

I shall have occasion in another place to speak more fully of this remarkable work. But as regards its bearing on the astrological idea with which we are now concerned, it is said that the king corresponds to the year, the nobility to the months, and the officials to the days. In other words, the king is the sun, which determines the year ; the nobility are denoted by the moon, the chronocrator of the month ; and the planets, which give their names to the days, are the officials. The people, it is said, are indicated by the stars, among which these bodies move as they pursue their appointed orbits. In this connection it should be observed that the nobility and the people are in a sense equally denoted by the moon, inasmuch as, in those days, the nobility were the representatives and protectors of the people and had common duties among them.

Very early in the history we find much regard paid to the phenomena of eclipses, especially those of the sun. The earliest record is in the year B.C. 2154. I have verified this eclipse by retrogressive calculation, and find that it took place in the morning of October 12 (O.S.) in the constellation Fang, *i.e.,* Scorpio of our zodiac. The text says that it occurred in the hour "shin," *i.e.,* between six and eight in the morning. My own calculation brings it out at 7.34 A.M. ("Shu-king," p. 73). At that time the hereditary Hi and Ho, who represented the theory and practice of astronomy, were neglectful of their duties and failed to give warning of this eclipse, so that of a sudden the Imperial City was thrown into confusion. The penalty attaching to this neglect of official duties was death, so that it may be inferred that considerable accuracy of prediction was attained by Chinese astronomers over forty centuries ago. The Chinese early recognised the scientific importance of eclipses and made observation of the effects which followed them and which they were held to portend. Thus they had prescience of the occurrence of insurrections, earthquakes, floods, droughts, destruction of crops and political changes. They argued from physical causes to moral effects, and from moral causes to physical effects, and held a rational astrology as an essential part of their system of government. The princes made particular study of the celestial laws, we are told, and attained to " clear illumination." ("Shu-king," Book I. sec. 4).

The Indian record does not present the same degree of authenticity as is to be found in the Chinese history, but their sacred writings extol the names of such men as the Rishis (sages),

Narada, Garga, Paràshara, and Varaha Mihira. The former flourished as one of the seven spiritual progenitors of the Aryan race in the early days of the *Kaliyuga* or Dark Age, which began in the year B.C. 3102. Mihira lived about the fifth century of the present era. Like the Chinese, they have their sixty-year cycle, and also divide their zodiac in the same manner, into twelve signs comprising twenty-eight constellations, and like the Chinese they begin their months at the New Moon. In their astrological system they employ the same factors, the sun, moon, and five planets, taking account also of the position of the moon's nodes, which they call Rahu and Ketu, the dragon's head and tail. This introduction of the dragon into what is otherwise an universal system strongly suggests a Mongolian tradition. The important part which this system of celestial observances occupies in the daily life and national ceremonies of the Hindus is clearly set forth in the Institutes of Manu, upon which every Brahmin models his life from first to last. This ancient book, which is ascribed to the Manu or Grand Patriarch of the Aryan race, is in many respects akin to the Levitical Book of the Pentateuch. It wholly concerns the duties (*dharma*) of the Four Castes. There are observances which depend on the moon's changes, and others which are regulated by the moon's passage through the constellations, while others again are related to the beginnings of the solar months and periods of eclipse. In the Brihat Jàtaka, Mihira delivers the whole of the traditional knowledge concerning nativities, while in the Brihat Samhità he displays the system of State astrology which has regard to the various departments of civil, religious, and political life. At this day there are scores of Jyoshis (astrologers), good, bad, and indifferent, and many of the Ràjas and Zemindars have their Court astrologers, some of whom are capable and learned exponents of jyotish shàstra.

That astronomy, as a means to astrology, was very anciently studied by the Hindus we learn on the authority of Mihira, who called attention to the precession of the equinoxes in these words :

" At present the summer solstice is in the first point of Kàtakam (Cancer), and the winter solstice in Makaram (Capricorn), but at one time the summer solstice was in the middle of Aslesha, according to former shàstras."

In this passage Mihira is referring to writings which recorded observations made over three thousand years before his time, that is, about B.C. 2600, and as it is quite exceptional for an exclusive Brahmin to quote any other writings than those of Aryan authority, we may credit the Hindus with this ancient observation.

Passing on to the Hebrew record, we find in the earliest passages of the Scriptures a statement that the celestial bodies were made "for signs and for seasons, for days and years, together with the stars." This othic attribute of the moving bodies of the visible heavens imports nothing else than that they were portents of things to come. Their use as chronocrators or time-makers is separately referred to in the words : "*And* for seasons, for days and for years." The word *shemayim* (translated " heavens ") means literally the disposers or controllers, making of the celestial bodies to which this term is applied nothing less than causative agents under the Divine Will. And that this was the current belief in regard to them we learn from the exultation of Deborah, who sings : "They fought from Heaven. The stars in their courses fought against Sisera ! "

(To be continued.)

THE PRESENT ASPECT OF THE CONFLICT BETWEEN SCIENTIFIC AND RELIGIOUS THOUGHT

By W. L. WILMSHURST

> . . . And He made of one every nation of men, . . .
> having determined their appointed seasons, . . . that
> they should seek God if haply they might feel after
> Him and find Him,—though He is not far from each
> one of us. St. Paul.

> So much more near than I had known,
> So much more great than I had guessed ;
> An' me like all the rest,—alone,
> But reachin' out to all the rest. Kipling.

I. THE PARTING OF THE WAYS

IN 1893 the present Prime Minister, speaking at a Royal Society dinner, used these words : " My friend Lord Kelvin has often talked to me of the future of Science. He has·told me that to the man of science of to-day it appears as if we were trembling on the brink of some great scientific discovery which should give us a new view of the forces of Nature among which and in the midst of which we move." This peep into the private reflections of the greatest scientific mind since Sir Isaac Newton was a matter of much more than ordinary interest. As a Frenchman would say, it "gave one furiously to think." To the observant watcher of events the announcement was in the first place exciting, for it implied that at the end of a century, the richest upon record in the discovery of the processes of Nature, the foremost scientific genius of our time, who had lived through the longer part of that astonishing period, who from the pinnacle of his own great intellectual eminence had watched the gradual unfolding of the secret volume, and had himself, in ample measure, contributed both to the discoveries and to the practical application of some of the newly acquired knowledge to the service of his fellow men, seemed to regard these inestimable gains as but the prelude to a revelation in comparison with which they would pale into insignificance. And in the second place it was disquieting ; for past experience has taught us that any great revolution in the point of view from which we must look out upon the universe is liable to produce considerable reaction upon religious faith, and there is trouble until we grow used to the altered conditions. Old ideas become upset ; cherished preconceptions are dislocated ; new demonstrations of science not squaring with ancient beliefs play havoc with both the private and the public conscience ; scientific theory falls foul of religious dogma ; and, our minds being probably made up and our convictions settled upon the deeper things of life, either we have to put up with an intellectual plant more or less old-fashioned, trusting that it will last out during our time, or else at some mental cost and pain throw it into the scrap-heap of worn-out ideas and formulate our views afresh.

Take an illustration. Imagine the outlook upon the world of a Christian man 400 years ago. For him no principle was more settled, sure and irrefragable than that the earth was the centre and chief fact of the Universe, that it was immovable, that it was flat, and that the sun and all the stars had been fashioned for the exclusive performance of certain functions for the convenience of man. For him the Scriptures contained the sum of all knowledge and the authority of the Church discouraged any independent investigation of Nature. If by chance a passing interest was taken in some physical question, it was settled by a reference to the Bible or patristic literature, not by an appeal to phenomena. So great was the preference given to sacred over profane learning that Christianity had been in existence 1500 years without producing a single man of science in the ordinary acceptation of that term. Suddenly there came announcements tending to shake established ideas to the roots, and then began the conflict between scientific and religious thought which has waxed fiercer and fiercer until our own day. To begin with, Ptolemy's old geographical scheme of the world with which men had been content for more than a dozen stay-at-home centuries, was shattered into bits by the prows of the tiny vessels with which Columbus lighted on his New World, by the doubling of the Cape of Good Hope and the opening of a sea route to the east by De Gama, and by the triumphant circumnavigation of the globe from west to east by Magellan. When the *San Vittoria* dropped anchor near Seville in 1522 after her three years voyage the theological doctrine of the flatness of the earth was irretrievably overthrown. The scientific reasoning of three sailors had in twenty years upset the faith of fifteen centuries in regard to the form and size of the earth. In another twenty years a still more momentous announcement was forthcoming respecting its position with regard to the sun and the planetary bodies. Copernicus amid the denunciations of the Church propounded the heliocentric theory. He showed that the earth is a mere point in the heavens, revolving round the sun which itself with its concomitant planets is wheeling at inconceivable speed, through ghastly vacuities of space, among other sidereal systems compared with some of which ours is a trifle. Then indeed were the vials of orthodox wrath opened. What happened is a familiar story. Time has withered most of the romance out of it, but the imagination will always interest itself in contemplating the history of the days when natural science first ran at full tilt against religious authority. It is almost impossible now to realise the dismay, the disquietude and the anxiety with which such a proposition must have been listened to 400 years ago. We, living in an age of discovery, instead of being lost in wonder at new disclosures, have almost lost our wonder altogether, and can hardly realise the effect that must have been produced upon a thinking mind four centuries ago by scientific revelations which displaced all previous ideas of man's place in the Universe; affected, apparently, the relationship between him and his Maker, and plied him with many obstinate and pitiless questionings. To dethrone the earth from her central dominating position, to give her many equals and not a few superiors, seemed to diminish her claims upon the divine regard. If each of the countless myriads of stars was a sun, surrounded by revolving globes peopled with responsible beings like ourselves ; if we had fallen so easily and had been redeemed at so stupendous a price as the death of the Son of God, how was it with them ? Of them were there none who had fallen or might fall like us ? Where, then, for them could a Saviour be found ? Thus was cast the first shadow of doubt and scepticism upon the pages of Holy Writ wherein were contained not only the law and the gospel to guide man's faith and morals, but also, as was supposed, whatsoever things were true and worthy to be believed in matters of natural science.

The establishment of the heliocentric theory, then, was the first great achievement won by natural science at the expense of theological teaching. Propounded by Copernicus it came to be established by the astronomical researches of Galileo, Tycho Brahe, and Kepler. The Church fought against the heresy with all the furious vengeance of the Inquisition and the Index. It imprisoned

Galileo ; it murdered Bruno. The truth it could not kill. Then, fortunately for every one, occurred the Reformation, securing comparative liberty of thought and weakening many of the old ecclesiastical bonds. Under its liberal influence occurred the next great epoch not only in European science but in the intellectual development of man. Newton,

<blockquote>
with his prism and silent face
Voyaging through strange seas of thought alone,
</blockquote>

presented the world with the " Principia," confirming the pronouncements of his astronomical predecessors, and establishing the theory of gravitation. The "Principia" established for the first time the presence of the operation of law in the physical universe. It not only accepted the heliocentric theory but showed it to be a mathematical necessity, and demonstrated the impossibility of things being other than they are ; that the solar and starry systems are not, as ecclesiastical authority alleged, brought into existence by arbitrary fiats and controlled by periodical providential interventions, but are under the government of irreversible law—of law that is the issue of mathematical necessity. The outcome of Newton's teaching was the development of the nebular hypothesis of Laplace which explains, upon the basis of the perpetual operation of law, the genesis, progress and decay of the members of the sidereal systems. Upon this hypothesis is based the whole fabric of modern astronomy. It stands in direct conflict with all that ecclesiastical authority held true as to the creation of the earth. In the light of it the literal construction of the first chapter of Genesis, which theretofore had been the sole explanation of the creation of the world, led to palpable untruth. In the place of the creative fiat of the Deity, bidding this world and starry firmament suddenly to be, it disclosed that going on through illimitable space was a mechanical process by which nebulous gaseous mists coalesce into vast masses of matter at a temperature of incandescence ; that cooling and radiation are necessary incidents ; that the nebulæ break up into fragmentary planets with a decline of heat and form themselves into organised solar systems, such as that of which we form a part, and that they eventually lose heat, decay, and become destroyed. So far had astronomical science come into conflict with the Scriptural cosmogony. But other sciences came forward to reinforce the conclusions of astronomy. Geology and palæontology furnished evidence of the far greater antiquity of the earth and of man than

Scripturalists taught ; biology accounted for the development of organic life of every type by a far different method than that of special creation offered by the Bible. The doctrine of the fall of man, which was the very bedrock of the Christian scheme of salvation, was met point blank by evidence of the rise of man from sources much humbler than his present state. The converging testimony of a score of distinct departments of knowledge pointed to a principle underlying all organic and inorganic nature—the principle of evolution. There are *lacunæ* in the chain of knowledge, the most conspicuous being the gap, yet to be bridged, between inorganic matter and living organisms. But the cumulative evidence in favour of the evolutionary process from the lowest form of matter to matter charged with and exhibiting the highest functionings of mind is well-nigh irresistible.* From the nebula to the gaseous sun, from the sun to the separated planet, from the molten planetary mass to the vaporous and solidifying stages, from the decomposition and re-arrangement of particles of inorganic matter to the germination of rudimentary life, from the simple organism to the complex, from the brute to man, from barbaric man to civilised and social man, from the homogeneous to the heterogeneous in every department and phase of existence ; such was found to be the process of creation.

> From harmony to harmony this universal world began,
>   When Nature underneath a heap of jarring atoms lay . . .
> Then cold and hot and moist and dry in order to their stations leaped. . . .
>   From harmony to harmony, this universal world began ;
>   Through all the compass of the notes it ran,
>   The diapason closing full in Man.

Thus did the muse of Dryden anticipate the conclusions of modern Science.

To sum up ; the teeming discoveries of modern natural science have resulted in the formulation of three fundamental principles

---

* " Already in Germany have inorganic and artificial substances been found to crawl about on glass slides under the action of surface-tension or capillarity, with an appearance which is said to have deceived even a biologist into hastily pronouncing them living amœbæ. Life in its ultimate element and on its material side is such a simple thing ; it is but a slight extension of known chemical and physical forces. . . . I apprehend there is not a biologist but believes (perhaps quite erroneously) that sooner or later the discovery will be made and that a cell having all the essential functions of life will be constructed out of inorganic material."—Sir O. Lodge, " Hibbert Journal," 1902, p. 59.

which, so far as can be seen, must be rooted for ever as cardinal concepts in our apprehension of the Universe ; principles to which all ecclesiastical teaching, whatever else it may inculcate, must henceforth conform.   They are these :

(1) The presence of Law, operating in a diversity of ways, but persistently, not sporadically, throughout the Universe.*

(2) Creation by means of Evolution, a perennial process operating *nunc, semper et ubique* by means of gradual development and selection ; as opposed to creation by arbitrary fiat and instantaneous manifestation.

(3) The existence of the Ether, a tenuous fluid embracing the whole Universe and uniting its parts into (so to speak) solidity ; saturating its minutest atomic constituents, making our world brother to the remotest stars and one with interstellar space ; (a sublime conception which, by demonstrating the earth's relation to the All, invalidates the idea of its comparative insignificance when measured by the scale of cosmic vastness).

The crowning achievement of the nineteenth century is to have ascertained and formulated these fundamental principles of the objective Universe.   And now at the end of it, with this tremendous addition to our stock of knowledge, and after we have been obliged to reformulate our ideas upon the majority of matters, we are told in " bated breath and whispering humbleness " by the most eminent of our scientists that after all we are trembling on the brink of some further great discovery that shall give us a new view of the forces of Nature !   What will that discovery reveal ?   Past experience tells us it will disclose something lying very close to us, sealed from us only by our ignorance or the undeveloped state of our faculties ; that it will be some important factor in the mechanism of the Universe of which we are at present unconscious, but which all the time is

> So much more near than we have known,
> So much more great than we have guessed.

It is too early to say with any definiteness what it will be found to be ; but as we scan the scientific horizon and watch the accumulating portents of the times, as we piece together fragments of new knowledge that are coming out of the laboratories, and study the deductions that speculative thought is drawing from that new knowledge, it is possible to venture upon, at all

* Compare 1 Cor. xii. 5–6.

events, some provisional forecast. And what will be the effect of the new disclosure upon religious thought and belief ? Will it tend, as the increase of scientific knowledge has hitherto done, to the further disintegration of ideals of faith ? Or will it tend to restore and strengthen them ? These are questions upon which I hope to throw a little light before the conclusion of this essay. For the present it is advisable to go back a little and see how the conflict has developed and what issues are at stake.

(To be continued.)